METHODS in
MICROBIOLOGY

METHODS in MICROBIOLOGY

Edited by

J. R. NORRIS
Borden Microbiological Laboratory,
Shell Research Limited,
Sittingbourne, Kent, England

D. W. RIBBONS
Department of Biochemistry,
University of Miami School of Medicine,
and Howard Hughes Medical Institute,
Miami, Florida, U.S.A.

Volume 8

 1973

ACADEMIC PRESS
London and New York

A subsidiary of Harcourt Brace Jovanovich, Publishers

ACADEMIC PRESS INC. (LONDON) LTD
24–28 Oval Road
London NW1

U.S. Edition published by
ACADEMIC PRESS INC.
111 Fifth Avenue
New York, New York 10003

Library of Congress Catalog Card Number: 68–57745
ISBN: 0–12–521508–8

PRINTED IN GREAT BRITAIN BY
ADLARD AND SON LIMITED
DORKING, SURREY

LIST OF CONTRIBUTORS

M. C. Allwood, *Department of Pharmacy, University of Manchester, Manchester, England*

F. L. Baker, *Northern Regional Research Laboratory, Peoria, Illinois, U.S.A.*

L. A. Bulla, *Northern Regional Research Laboratory, Peoria, Illinois, U.S.A.*

E. Canale-Parola, *Department of Microbiology, University of Massachusetts,* Amherst, Massachusetts, U.S.A.

O. Felsenfeld, *Department of Tropical Medicine and Parasitology, Tulane University School of Public Health and Tropical Medicine, New Orleans, and Tulane University Delta Regional Primate Research Centre, Covington, Louisiana, U.S.A.*

C. W. Hesseltine, *Northern Regional Research Laboratory, Peoria, Illinois, U.S.A.*

A. Morris, *Welsh School of Pharmacy, University of Wales Institute of Science and Technology, Cathays Park, Cardiff, Wales*

A. D. Russell, *Bacterial Chemotherapy Unit, Glaxo Research Laboratories, Greenford, Middlesex, England*

G. St. Julian, *Northern Regional Research Laboratory, Peoria, Illinois, U.S.A.*

H. H. Topiwala, *Shell Research Limited, Borden Microbiological Laboratory, Sittingbourne, Kent, England*

P. J. Wyatt, *Science Spectrum Incorporated, P.O. Box 3003, Santa Barbara, California 93106, U.S.A.*

ACKNOWLEDGMENTS

For permission to reproduce, in whole or in part, certain figures and diagrams we are grateful to the following—

Science Spectrum Incorporated, Santa Barbara, California, U.S.A.

Detailed acknowledgments are given in the legends to figures.

PREFACE

With the publication of Volume 7 the initial Series of "Methods in Microbiology" was completed. As work on the Series progressed, we were encouraged by receiving several suggestions for further topics and offers of contributions over and above the areas covered in the planned Volumes, and we decided to put some of these together to form a single continuation Volume.

Inevitably the topics are diverse and there is no connecting theme for Volume 8. Nevertheless, we have continued with our policy of treating subjects which are not adequately detailed elsewhere in the literature, or which represent technical developments at the advancing forefront of microbiology—attractive by virtue of their evident potential rather than by their established value in the armoury of the research worker.

As with earlier Volumes, we have allowed individual contributors largely to determine the nature of their presentations. In some areas it is clearly appropriate and valuable to present detailed operating instructions; in others a more general orientation with adequate references to technical methods is more useful. As with earlier Volumes we are grateful for the friendly co-operation we have received from authors during the preparation of Volume 8. We have no firm plans for continuing the Series but will re-assess the situation periodically to see whether advances in technique and methodology suggest that the production of a further Volume would be useful.

J. R. NORRIS

D. W. RIBBONS

March, 1973

CONTENTS

LIST OF CONTRIBUTORS v

ACKNOWLEDGMENTS vi

PREFACE vii

Chapter I. Scanning Electron Microscopy—L. A. BULLA, JR.,
G. ST. JULIAN, C. W. HESSELTINE AND F. L. BAKER . . 1

Chapter II. Mathematical Models in Microbiology—H. H.
TOPIWALA 35

Chapter III. Isolation, Growth and Maintenance of Anaerobic
Free-living Spirochetes—E. CANALE-PAROLA 61

Chapter IV. Borrelia—O. FELSENFELD 75

Chapter V. Methods for Assessing Damage to Bacteria Induced by
Chemical and Physical Agents—A. D. RUSSELL, A. MORRIS AND
M. C. ALLWOOD 95

Chapter VI. Different Light Scattering Techniques for Microbiology—P. J. WYATT 183

AUTHOR INDEX 265

SUBJECT INDEX 275

CONTENTS OF PUBLISHED VOLUMES

Volume 1

E. C. ELLIOTT AND D. L. GEORGALA. Sources, Handling and Storage of Media and Equipment

R. BROOKES. Properties of Materials Suitable for the Cultivation and Handling of Micro-organisms

G. SYKES. Methods and Equipment for Sterilization of Laboratory Apparatus and Media

R. ELSWORTH. Treatment of Process Air for Deep Culture

J. J. McDADE, G. B. PHILLIPS, H. D. SIVINSKI AND W. J. WHITFIELD. Principles and Applications of Laminar-flow Devices

H. M. DARLOW. Safety in the Microbiological Laboratory

J. G. MULVANY. Membrane Filter Techniques in Microbiology

C. T. CALAM. The Culture of Micro-organisms in Liquid Medium

CHARLES E. HELMSTETTER. Methods for Studying the Microbial Division Cycle

LOUIS B. QUESNEL. Methods of Microculture

R. C. CODNER. Solid and Solidified Growth Media in Microbiology

K. I. JOHNSTONE. The Isolation and Cultivation of Single Organisms

N. BLAKEBROUGH. Design of Laboratory Fermenters

K. SARGEANT. The Deep Culture of Bacteriophage

M. F. MALLETTE. Evaluation of Growth by Physical and Chemical Means

C. T. CALAM. The Evaluation of Mycelial Growth

H. E. KUBITSCHEK. Counting and Sizing Micro-organisms with the Coulter Counter

J. R. POSTGATE. Viable Counts and Viability

A. H. STOUTHAMER. Determination and Significance of Molar Growth Yields

Volume 2

D. G. MacLENNAN. Principles of Automatic Measurement and Control of Fermentation Growth Parameters

J. W. PATCHING AND A. H. ROSE. The Effects and Control of Temperature

A. L. S. MUNRO. Measurement and Control of pH Values

H.-E. JACOB. Redox Potential

D. E. BROWN. Aeration in the Submerged Culture of Micro-organisms

D. FREEDMAN. The Shaker in Bioengineering

J. BRYANT. Anti-foam Agents

N. G. CARR. Production and Measurement of Photosynthetically Usable Light

R. ELSWORTH. The Measurement of Oxygen Absorption and Carbon Dioxide Evolution in Stirred Deep Cultures

G. A. PLATON. Flow Measurement and Control

RICHARD Y. MORITA. Application of Hydrostatic Pressure to Microbial Cultures

D. W. TEMPEST. The Continuous Cultivation of Micro-organisms: 1. Theory of the Chemostat

C. G. T. EVANS, D. HERBERT AND D. W. TEMPEST. The Continuous Cultivation of Micro-organisms: 2. Construction of a Chemostat

xi

J. Řičica. Multi-stage Systems
R. J. Munson. Turbidostats
R. O. Thomson and W. H. Foster. Harvesting and Clarification of Cultures—
Storage of Harvest

Volume 3A

S. P. Lapage, Jean E. Shelton and T. G. Mitchell. Media for the Maintenance
and Preservation of Bacteria
S. P. Lapage, Jean E. Shelton, T. G. Mitchell and A. R. Mackenzie. Culture
Collections and the Preservation of Bacteria
E. Y. Bridson and A. Brecker. Design and Formulation of Microbial Culture
Media
D. W. Ribbons. Quantitative Relationships Between Growth Media Constituents
and Cellular Yields and Composition
H. Veldkamp. Enrichment Cultures of Prokaryotic Organisms
David A. Hopwood. The Isolation of Mutants
C. T. Calam. Improvement of Micro-organisms by Mutation, Hybridization and
Selection

Volume 3B

Vera G. Collins. Isolation, Cultivation and Maintenance of Autotrophs
N. G. Carr. Growth of Phototrophic Bacteria and Blue-Green Algae
A. T. Willis. Techniques for the Study of Anaerobic, Spore-forming Bacteria
R. E. Hungate. A Roll Tube Method for Cultivation of Strict Anaerobes
P. N. Hobson. Rumen Bacteria
Ella M. Barnes. Methods for the Gram-negative Non-sporing Anaerobes
T. D. Brock and A. H. Rose. Psychrophiles and Thermophiles
N. E. Gibbons. Isolation, Growth and Requirements of Halophilic Bacteria
John E. Peterson. Isolation, Cultivation and Maintenance of the Myxobacteria
R. J. Fallon and P. Whittlestone. Isolation, Cultivation and Maintenance of
Mycoplasmas
M. R. Droop. Algae
Eve Billing. Isolation, Growth and Preservation of Bacteriophages

Volume 4

C. Booth. Introduction to General Methods
C. Booth. Fungal Culture Media
D. M. Dring. Techniques for Microscopic Preparation
Agnes H. S. Onions. Preservation of Fungi
F. W. Beech and R. R. Davenport. Isolation, Purification and Maintenance of
Yeasts
Miss G. M. Waterhouse. Phycomycetes
E. Punithalingham. Basidiomycetes: Heterobasidiomycetidae
Roy Watling. Basidiomycetes: Homobasidiomycetidae
M. J. Carlile. Myxomycetes and other Slime Moulds
D. H. S. Richardson. Lichens

S. T. WILLIAMS AND T. CROSS. Actinomycetes

E. B. GARETH JONES. Aquatic Fungi

R. R. DAVIES. Air Sampling for Fungi, Pollens and Bacteria

GEORGE L. BARRON. Soil Fungi

PHYLLIS M. STOCKDALE. Fungi Pathogenic for Man and Animals: 1. Diseases of the Keratinized Tissues

HELEN R. BUCKLEY. Fungi Pathogenic for Man and Animals: 2. The Subcutaneous and Deep-seated Mycoses

J. L. JINKS AND J. CROFT. Methods Used for Genetical Studies in Mycology

R. L. LUCAS. Autoradiographic Techniques in Mycology

T. F. PREECE. Fluorescent Techniques in Mycology

G. N. GREENHALGH AND L. V. EVANS. Electron Microscopy

ROY WATLING. Chemical Tests in Agaricology

T. F. PREECE. Immunological Techniques in Mycology

CHARLES M. LEACH. A Practical Guide to the Effects of Visible and Ultraviolet Light on Fungi

JULIO R. VILLANUEVA AND ISABEL GARCIA ACHA. Production and Use of Fungal Protoplasts

Volume 5A

L. B. QUESNEL. Microscopy and Micrometry

J. R. NORRIS AND HELEN SWAIN. Staining Bacteria

A. M. PATON AND SUSAN M. JONES. Techniques Involving Optical Brightening Agents

T. IINO AND M. ENOMOTO. Motility

R. W. SMITH AND H. KOFFLER. Production and Isolation of Flagella

C. L. OAKLEY. Antigen-antibody Reactions in Microbiology

P. D. WALKER, IRENE BATTY AND R. O. THOMSON. The Localization of Bacterial Antigens by the use of the Fluorescent and Ferritin Labelled Antibody Techniques

IRENE BATTY. Toxin-antitoxin Assay

W. H. KINGHAM. Techniques for Handling Animals

J. DE LEY. The Determination of the Molecular Weight of DNA Per Bacterial Nucleoid

J. DE LEY. Hybridization of DNA

J. E. M. MIDGLEY. Hybridization of Microbial RNA and DNA

ELIZABETH WORK. Cell Walls

Volume 5B

D. E. HUGHES, J. W. T. WIMPENNY AND D. LLOYD. The Disintegration of Micro-organisms

J. SYKES. Centrifugal Techniques for the Isolation and Characterization of Sub-Cellular Components from Bacteria

D. HERBERT, P. J. PHIPPS AND R. E. STRANGE. Chemical Analysis of Microbial Cells

I. W. SUTHERLAND AND J. F. WILKINSON. Chemical Extraction Methods of Microbial Cells

PER-ÅKE ALBERTSSON. Biphasic Separation of Microbial Particles

MITSUHIRO NOZAKI AND OSAMU HAYAISHI. Separation and Purification of Proteins
J. R. SARGENT. Zone Electrophoresis for the Separation of Microbial Cell Components
K. HANNIG. Free-flow Electrophoresis
W. MANSON. Preparative Zonal Electrophoresis
K. E. COOKSEY. Disc Electrophoresis
O. VESTERBERG. Isoelectric Focusing and Separation of Proteins
F. J. MOSS, PAMELA A. D. RICKARD AND G. H. ROPER. Reflectance Spectrophotometry
W. D. SKIDMORE AND E. L. DUGGAN. Base Composition of Nucleic Acids

Volume 6A

A. J. HOLDING AND J. G. COLLEE. Routine Biochemical Tests
K. KERSTERS AND J. DE LEY. Enzymic Tests with Resting Cells and Cell-free Extracts
E. A. DAWES, D. J. McGILL AND M. MIDGLEY. Analysis of Fermentation Products
S. DAGLEY AND P. J. CHAPMAN. Evaluation of Methods to Determine Metabolic Pathways
PATRICIA H. CLARKE. Methods for Studying Enzyme Regulation
G. W. GOULD. Methods for Studying Bacterial Spores
W. HEINEN. Inhibitors of Electron Transport and Oxidative Phosphorylation
ELIZABETH WORK. Some Applications and Uses of Metabolite Analogues in Microbiology
W. A. WOOD. Assay of Enzymes Representative of Metabolic Pathways
H. C. REEVES, R. RABIN, W. S. WEGENER AND S. J. AJL. Assays of Enzymes of the Tricarboxylic Acid and Glyoxylate Cycles
D. T. GIBSON. Assay of Enzymes of Aromatic Metabolism
MICHAEL C. SCRUTTON. Assay of Enzymes of CO_2 Metabolism

Volume 6B

J. L. PEEL. The Use of Electron Acceptors, Donors and Carriers
R. B. BEECHEY AND D. W. RIBBONS. Oxygen Electrode Measurements
D. G. NICHOLLS AND P. B. GARLAND. Electrode Measurements of Carbon Dioxide
G. W. CROSBIE. Ionization Methods of Counting Radio-Isotopes
J. H. HASH. Liquid Scintillation Counting in Microbiology
J. R. QUAYLE. The Use of Isotopes in Tracing Metabolic Pathways
C. H. WANG. Radiorespirometric Methods
N. R. EATON. Pulse Labelling of Micro-organisms
M. J. ALLEN. Cellular Electrophysiology
W. W. FORREST. Microcalorimetry
J. MARTEN. Automatic and Continuous Assessment of Fermentation Parameters
A. FERRARI AND J. MARTEN. Automated Microbiological Assay
J. R. POSTGATE. The Acetylene Reduction Test for Nitrogen Fixation

Volume 7A

G. C. WARE. Computer Use in Microbiology
P. H. A. SNEATH. Computer Taxonomy

H. F. DAMMERS. Data Handling and Information Retrieval by Computer

M. ROBERTS AND C. B. C. BOYCE. Principles of Biological Assay

D. KAY. Methods for Studying the Infectious Properties and Multiplication of Bacteriophage

D. KAY. Methods for the Determination of the Chemical and Physical Structure of Bacteriophages

ANNA MAYR-HARTING, A. J. HEDGES AND R. C. W. BERKELEY. Methods for Studying Bacteriocins

W. R. MAXTED. Specific Procedures and Requirements for the Isolation, Growth and Maintenance of the L-Phase of Some Microbial Groups

Volume 7B

M. T. PARKER. Phage-Typing of *Staphylococcus aureus*

D. A. HOPWOOD. Genetic Analysis in Micro-organisms

J. MEYRATH AND GERDA SUCHANEK. Inoculation Techniques—Effects Due to Quality and Quantity of Inoculum

D. F. SPOONER AND G. SYKES. Laboratory Assessment of Antibacterial Activity

L. B. QUESNEL. Photomicrography and Macrophotography

CHAPTER I

Scanning Electron Microscopy

LEE A. BULLA, JR., GRANT ST. JULIAN,
CLIFFORD W. HESSELTINE, AND FREDERICK L. BAKER

Northern Regional Research Laboratory, Peoria, Illinois, U.S.A.

I.	Introduction	1
II.	The Scanning Electron Microscope	2
	A. Imaging system	2
	B. Electron-optical column	4
	C. Vacuum system	7
	D. Mechanisms of contrast formation and signal detection	7
	E. Visual and record display	11
	F. Lens aberrations	12
	G. Magnification, resolution, and depth of focus	13
III.	Specimen Preparation	13
	A. Sample washing	14
	B. Fixation and dehydration	14
	C. Critical point drying and freeze-drying	14
	D. Specimen mounting	15
	E. Specimen surface coating	17
IV.	Applications	18
	A. Bacterial spore morphology	18
	B. Bacterial colony morphology	20
	C. Systematics	20
	D. Spore germination and outgrowth	25
V.	Ancillary Techniques	28
	A. Scanning transmission electron microscopy	28
	B. Three-dimensional analysis	28
	C. Y-modulation	29
	D. Ion etching	29
	E. Low voltage operation	30
VI.	Conclusion	30
VII.	Some Scanning Electron Microscope Manufacturers	31
	References	31

I. INTRODUCTION

The concept of scanning electron microscopy dates back to that of conventional transmission electron microscopy. The initial patent application for a scanning electron microscope was made in 1927 (Stintzing, 1929),

2

but the first instrument was not built until 1938 (Von Ardenne, 1938). Shortly thereafter though, several instruments were constructed for experimental use. Only a few scanning electron micrographs appeared in the literature (Zworykin *et al.*, 1942). During the middle to late forties, emphasis was placed on instrumental development; and as a result of the concerted efforts of Oatley *et al.* (1965) in England, the first commercial instrument was produced. Now there is available a variety of commercial designs.

The scanning electron microscope has several features that render it advantageous for various kinds of microscopic observation. Information can be obtained from different electron beam-induced signals that include (1) secondary electrons, (2) back-scattered electrons, (3) X-rays, (4) visible light or infrared energy, and (5) currents from semiconductors. Thus, it is possible to gather information on the chemical composition and electrical properties of biological materials as well as interaction of such materials with specific stains. The scanning electron microscope affords image production comparable to light, ultraviolet, fluorescence, and X-ray microscopes. Furthermore, it has great depth of focus and produces images with three-dimensional quality. Specimen preparation usually is reduced to a minimum and, sometimes, requires no chemical fixation or physical pretreatment. Consequently, biological material can be viewed directly as it actually is, only magnified.

This Chapter is intended to provide a better insight into the usefulness of the scanning electron microscope, to summarize the principles of scanning electron microscopy; to describe briefly the methods for specimen preparation; and to outline some applications in microbiology. For a comprehensive treatise on the theory and principles of scanning electron microscopy, the reader is referred to the text by Thornton (1968). Other theoretical considerations of microscopy were presented earlier (see Quesnel, this Series, Volume 5A) as were methods of specimen preparation for electron microscopy (see Greenhalgh and Evans, this Series, Volume 4).

II. THE SCANNING ELECTRON MICROSCOPE

A. Imaging system

A fundamental and unique characteristic of the scanning electron microscope is its imaging system. Fig. 1 compares the imaging system of a scanning microscope to those of optical and transmission electron microscopes. In a light microscope (Fig. 1a), the light beam passes through a transparent specimen, and the resulting image is magnified by glass lenses. An analogous situation exists in a transmission electron microscope

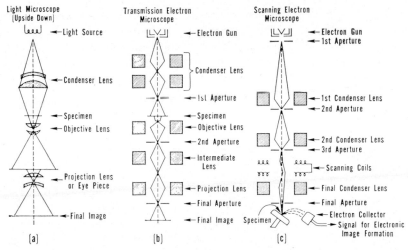

Fig. 1. Diagrammatic comparison of imaging systems in (a) optical microscope, (b) transmission electron microscope, and (c) scanning electron microscope.

(Fig. 1b) where the electrons likewise pass through the specimen and are focused by electron lenses to form an enlarged image on a fluorescent screen or a photographic plate. The image produced by light optics contains an abundance of information. Such aspects as chemical composition, localized interaction of biochemical stains, and general specimen shape can be determined. Of course, the major limitation of a light microscope is its low resolving power. In contrast, electron optics of a conventional transmission electron microscope provide high-resolution images. An inherent limitation of this system, however, is a restricted amount of image information content.

The scanning electron microscope has a quite different imaging system (Fig. 1c) that depends upon electron beam radiation for localization and upon visible light energy for information gathering. Electrons are formed into a fine probe as a result of demagnification by condenser lenses. The probe is moved over the surface of a specimen in a rectangular or zigzag pattern by two pairs of scanning coils powered by a generator. At the same time, the generator current passes through scanning coils of a cathode ray tube to produce a magnified raster identical to that on the specimen. Electrons emitted from the specimen are collected and the resulting current is amplified for regulating brightness of the cathode ray tube. In this way, an enlarged picture of the specimen is viewed on the face of the cathode ray tube with point-by-point correspondence. Such a system provides both high-resolution images and a great deal of information about the image.

Three major components are responsible for image production and display: the electron-optical column, the vacuum system, and the signal detection and display system. A schematic representation of a scanning electron microscope with these components is presented in Fig. 2. Figure 3 is a photograph of a commercial unit showing the column and display system.

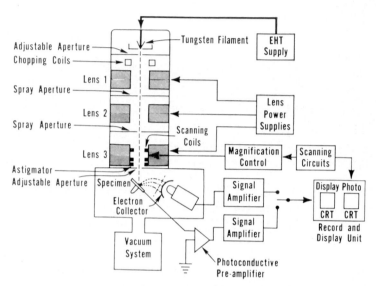

Fig. 2. Schematic diagram of a scanning electron microscope. CRT, cathode ray tube; EHT, electron gun-accelerating voltage.

B. Electron-optical column

The electron-optical system (see Fig. 2) is composed of an electron gun, two to four electron lenses, a set of apertures, an astigmator, and a set of beam modulating coils (chopping coils). Usually the electron gun is of triode design (Fig. 4) and produces a crossover of high-current density (Thornton, 1968). It contains a cathode consisting of a tungsten hairpin filament housed in a cylindrical shield with a circular aperture of about 2-mm diameter, and an annular cylindrical anode with a coaxial aperture. Electrons are boiled off the tungsten filament, heated by a high-voltage (EHT or electron gun-accelerating voltage) source, and passed through an aperture in the cylindrical shield that is negatively biased. The shield aids in controlling the electron source by forming a crossover point, or disc of least confusion, through which all electrons pass. By adjusting the bias voltage, the position of the crossover point can be regulated. The anode,

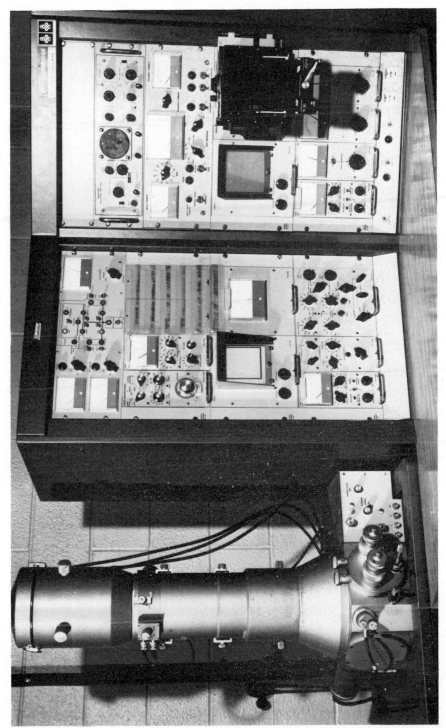

Fig. 3. Photograph of a "Stereoscan" scanning electron microscope (Mark 2A, Cambridge Scientific Instruments Ltd., Cambridge, England).

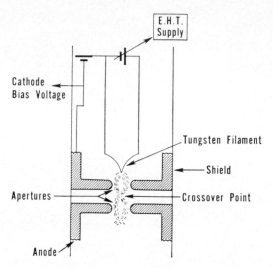

Fig. 4. Diagram of an electron source (electron gun) of a scanning electron microscope.

operated at earth potential, is responsible for the electron accelerating field.

The electron lenses are either magnetic or electrostatic and function to demagnify the diameter of the electron beam originating from the electron gun. The original 50-μm diameter of the electron beam is reduced by the magnetic lenses to 5 to 10 nm at the specimen surface. The diameter of the electron beam is referred to as spot size. In the final lens assembly are scanning coils which are responsible for deflecting the electron beam and creating a raster over the specimen. The scanning coils, as well as the cathode ray tubes, are conveniently powered by a single scan generator. Such an arrangement facilitates synchronized scanning of the electron beam and the cathode ray tubes.

One of the two kinds of apertures functions to define the angle that is subtended by the beam at the surface of a specimen; by altering the size of this aperture, the subtended angle can be varied. The second kind is called a spray aperture and helps reduce contamination of the lenses by collecting stray electrons. Occasionally additional apertures are used to control original spot size.

The principal function of an astigmator is to provide a variable asymmetric field. The design most utilized is one composed of four magnetic coils with variable current control and mechanical rotation. A description of such an astigmator and others is found in Thornton's text (1968).

The chopping coils modulate the electron beam and are usually located close to the electron source. The coils deflect the beam back and forth across an aperture and can be directed to turn the beam on and off repeatedly or to turn off the beam for extended periods. Chopping coils provide the instant beam turn-off (10 nsec or less) that is necessary for studying excitation decay in a specimen.

C. Vacuum system

The electron-optical column, as well as the specimen chamber that houses the specimen stage, must be kept under vacuum while the microscope is in operation. The specimen chamber can be isolated from the column while specimens are changed so that column vacuum pressure is maintained. A series of oil diffusion pumps (usually two) coupled to a rotary pump serves to evacuate the column and chamber. A vacuum pressure of less than 10^{-4} mm Hg is generally required before the EHT supply can be turned on. Protective devices, such as interlock circuits, are built into commercial models; control of the vacuum operation is either automatic or manual.

D. Mechanisms of contrast formation and signal detection

A variety of specimen data is obtainable with a scanning electron microscope because of the production of different electron beam-induced signals. As can be seen in Fig. 5, interaction of the electron beam with the

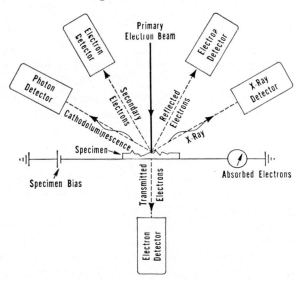

Fig. 5. Diagram of the electron products from interaction of the primary electron beam with a specimen.

specimen produces various effects, such as emission of secondary electrons, reflected electrons, X-rays, cathodoluminescence, and conduction (transmitted electrons).

As high-energy primary electrons strike and penetrate a specimen's surface, they lose their energy and give rise to secondary electrons. Some of the primary electrons are reflected (back-scattered) in the specimen and give rise to other secondary electrons, called back-scattered excited secondaries. The emitted secondary electrons are collected by a cylindrical metal shield covered at one end by copper gauze (Fig. 6). This detector

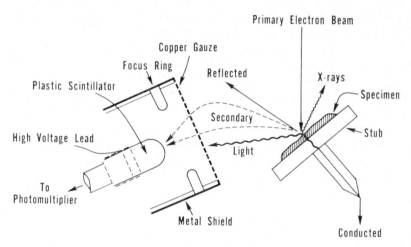

Fig. 6. Diagram of a secondary electron detector system (scintillator-photomultiplier combination) in the scanning electron microscope.

is biased positively (250 V) relative to the specimen. After passing through the gauze, the secondary electrons are accelerated toward a plastic scintillator that is coated with a thin film of aluminium. The aluminium layer also is positively biased (∼ 10 to 13 kV) and the electrons that strike the scintillator generate light energy which is transferred to a photomultiplier tube that converts the light into electronic signals. Arrangement of the detector and specimen within a specimen stage is pictured in Fig. 7.

Reflected primary electrons that strike the scintillator likewise are converted to electronic signals. A special system usually is required to detect primary electrons because they are not specifically attracted to the plastic scintillator. High-energy reflected electrons can be collected rather efficiently, however, without a special detector simply by removing the outer covering of the detector described above and maintaining its potential at the level of the scintillator.

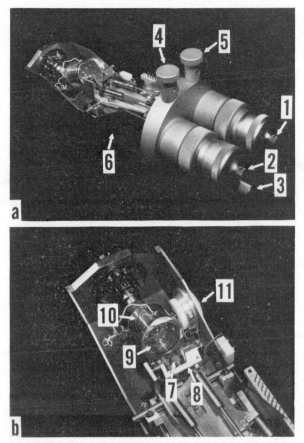

Fig. 7. Photographs of a scanning electron microscope specimen stage: (a) over-all view of the specimen stage; (1) X-shift; (2) Y-shift; (3) Z-shift; (4) tilt control; (5) rotation control; (6) stage base support; (b) closeup view of the electron detector system; (7) specimen stub containing sample; (8) focus stub; (9) collector wire gauze face; (10) collector body; (11) EHT connection.

Attraction of secondary electrons by the detector causes them to travel in curved lines. The detector has no such effect on reflected primary electrons; they travel in straight paths (Fig. 6). Because of the devious paths taken by the secondary electrons, information can be obtained from areas on the specimen surface that ordinarily are "invisible" or "hidden". A comparison of images from secondary electrons, reflected primary electrons, and light optics is depicted in Fig. 8. The image produced by secondaries (Fig. 8a) of a stack of three electron microscope grids reveals "hidden" detail from within the grid cluster. Less "hidden" detail is

Fig. 8. Photomicrograph of a stack of three transmission electron microscope grids tilted at 45°: (a) image produced from secondary electrons; (b) image of identical grids produced by primary electrons; (c) image produced by light optics.

afforded by the primary electron image in Fig. 8b. An important advantage of the scanning microscope, namely, its great depth of focus over a large area, is readily apparent from the clarity of the second and third grid layers in Fig. 8a. Thus, three-dimensional spatial information can be obtained from a two-dimensional image. The obvious lack of image depth from light optics can be seen in Fig. 8c.

A large portion of the secondary electrons never leave the material surface but become randomized throughout the specimen. A few of these secondaries recombine with the high-energy primary electrons and, consequently, generate radiant energy. Depending upon the nature of the recombination, photons are released with energy levels approximating those of X-rays, visible light, or near infrared energy. The spectrum of

X-rays produced is characteristic of the elements within a material and, consequently, analysis of such a spectrum provides information on the quantity and distribution of various elements. X-rays can be conveniently monitored by coupling to the scanning scope a crystal X-ray spectrometer. One of the best methods for detecting X-rays is by nondispersive means. Depending upon the kind of elemental analysis desired, either of two detectors can be used: a gas-flow proportional counter or a lithium-drifted silicon detector (Ogilvie, 1969).

Visible light or near infrared energy emitted from the specimen is referred to as cathodoluminescence. Cathodoluminescence is detected by photomultiplier tubes specifically designed for visible light and near infrared energy. The photomultipliers are placed at a greater distance from the specimen than the detectors for secondary and back-scattered electrons. Chemically stained biological materials can be examined by analysing the quanta of visible light and near infrared energy that emerges from them. However, the efficiency of production and collection of light quanta is so low that a minimum exposure time of at least 30 min is needed to obtain an acceptable photomicrograph (Hayes and Pease, 1968). A major problem with the luminescent mode is that the material bombarded does not luminesce sufficiently. Because most fluorescent stains now available are inadequate, the development of cathodoluminescent stains is necessary for this technique to become practicable.

Note in Fig. 6 that some of the electrons are not emitted from the specimen but are transmitted or conducted. By applying an external bias, these electron beam-induced currents (either short-circuit or charge-collection) and the voltage generated by such currents can be measured. The currents are then displayed by the cathode ray tube either as intensity modulation or as line scan. For proper conduction, the specimen must be mounted so as to provide proper electrical contact with the specimen stage. Essentially, the conductive mode enables measurement of an electric current generated by the primary electrons and depends upon the nature of the specimen and the bias voltage applied to the specimen stage. Although examination of material by this technique has not been very successful for microbiological studies, it does have potential for soft biological specimens.

E. Visual and record display

Usually two cathode ray tubes are present: one for visual display and another for record display. The cathode ray tube of the visual display unit is magnetically focused and operates at about 12·5 kV; resolution is in excess of 500 lines. It is composed of long-persistence, yellow-blue phosphor and in some cases is overlaid with a yellow filter to improve image contrast. The long-persistence phosphor produces a latent image for long-term visual observation. The record display unit also has a magnetically focused cathode ray tube that operates at about 12·5 kV. The phosphor is short-persistence blue; and resolution is about 800 lines. Latent images are undesirable for recording purposes and do not occur with short-persistence phosphor. A camera, e.g. Polaroid type or 35 mm, is attached to the record display unit. Appropriate controls in the scan generator regulate the scan rate per frame and per line for the visual and record cathode ray tubes. Also, raster size and position can be regulated. These controls are important for producing the kind of final image desired. Brightness of the tubes depends upon signals detected as the primary electron beam interacts with the specimen. Individual brightness and contrast controls are present on both cathode ray tubes. The arrangement of the manual controls allows the operator to regulate and select the desired properties of the image to be photographed. Quality of the photomicrograph depends upon the scan speed, brightness, and contrast of the cathode ray tube, and the kind of photographic film used. In combination, these factors determine film exposure time.

F. Lens aberrations

Several important aberrations in the scanning electron optical system affect the ultimate quality of image production and resolution. These disorders are spherical aberration, chromatic aberration, diffraction, and astigmatism. Spherical aberration results from deflection of those electrons that travel in close proximity to strong magnetic fields about the lens axes. It is an inherent function of both the electron beam voltage and the focusing field.

The cause of chromatic aberration is two-fold: instability of the cathode EHT and electron lens current, and inability to focus electrons in a finite point, i.e. formation of disc of least confusion. Diffraction is directly related to the wavelength of the imaging radiation and to the angle at which this radiation converges on the specimen. When spherical and chromatic aberrations are reduced to a minimum, diffraction becomes the limiting factor for resolution. Astigmatism due to asymmetry within the electron-optical column causes rapid deterioration of the final image. This defect may be the result of stray asymmetrical magnetic fields, built-in (designed) asymmetries, and contamination (foreign particles) on the apertures and lenses. Astigmatism can be corrected by superimposing an asymmetric magnetic field on the electron-optical column (see astigmator, Section II.B in this Chapter). Cleanliness of the column, particularly of the apertures that become contaminated easily, is important and cleaning should be routine.

G. Magnification, resolution, and depth of focus

The scanning microscope is capable of a very wide magnification range. Magnification from about × 20 to × 100,000 is common, although for biological preparations clear images are difficult to obtain above × 50,000. The magnification unit of a scanning scope usually consists of attenuators as well as current controls for the astigmator. An attenuator compensates automatically for magnification variation with accelerating voltage. Working magnification depends upon working distance, i.e. distance from the final aperture to the specimen.

Basically resolution depends upon two factors: final spot size and interaction of the electron beam with the specimen. In most commercial instruments, a final electron beam diameter of about 5 to 10 nm is attainable. As already pointed out, secondary electrons are formed upon primary electron bombardment of the specimen. Emission of secondary electrons occurs from within 5 to 10 nm of the original penetration, and this spreading of the secondaries also limits resolution. Considering these dimensions for final spot size and for spreading of the secondary electrons, a resolution of about 10 nm would be expected. However, because of other contributing factors in current commercial units such as signal-to-noise ratio and resolution of the cathode ray tubes and photographic plate, a resolution of 15 to 20 nm is maximum. Crewe (1971) has developed a research microscope with resolution capabilities of 0·5 nm and less.

Depth of focus as observed in the final specimen image corresponds to the cross-section of the electron beam which is defined by two points on either side of the principal focus. The tremendously large depth of focus in the scanning electron microscope (see Fig. 8) is determined by the diameter of the final aperture within the electron-optical column. As aperture size decreases, depth of focus increases. By selecting the appropriate aperture, maximum depth of focus can be obtained. Apertures range in diameter from 50 to 400 nm.

III. SPECIMEN PREPARATION

Artificial changes during preparation of microbial specimens for microscopic observation are not uncommon. To limit such artifacts the microscopist should have, at least, a general knowledge of the characteristic growth pattern and morphology of the micro-organism being examined. Temperature of incubation, nutrients, aeration, etc., affect cellular growth and morphology. Therefore, awareness of such factors is indispensable for proper selection of preparative methods and for evaluation of the final micrograph. Preparation of biological material for scanning electron microscopy includes a variety of methods. Often specialized techniques are necessary for different types and kinds of specimens. Generally speaking, the nature and kind of information desired dictate the method of preparation. Outlined below are some basic approaches to preparation of biological material which are applicable to micro-organisms.

A. Sample washing

Most samples must be washed free of nutrients and adhering material. Because cell washing techniques are well documented in the literature, suffice it to say that filtration, centrifugation, and liquid two-phase systems are adequate to clean cells for scanning electron microscopy (Bulla *et al.*, 1969; Sacks, 1969). The degree of cellular fragility determines the manner of washing.

B. Fixation and dehydration

The purpose of chemically fixing biological material is to preserve it in close to normal or living condition. The high vacuum necessary for operation of the scanning electron microscope causes delicate structures to collapse and fold. Therefore, it is important that such material be treated in some way to retain its normal form and shape. In certain instances, chemical fixation is not necessary to preserve the original shape and form of micro-organisms; but more frequently, some degree of chemical treatment is necessary. Fixation procedures have been discussed earlier (Pease, 1964) and, no attempt is made here to reiterate them. It is sufficient to note that the techniques already developed for light and transmission electron microscopy are suitable for scanning electron microscopy.

Following chemical fixation, the specimen can be dehydrated by passing it through graded concentrations of acetone or alcohol. For bacteria, dehydration in this fashion generally is not necessary. Simple air-drying after chemical fixation at room temperature or elevated temperatures under normal or slightly reduced atmospheric pressure may be sufficient.

C. Critical point drying and freeze-drying

Critical point drying is a process in which a wet specimen is rapidly dried without a liquid-gas phase boundary passing through it (Anderson, 1952). The entire procedure involves passing a specimen from water through an alcohol series to amyl acetate and then placing it in a chamber where liquid carbon dioxide is used to replace the amyl acetate. The chamber is evacuated and the temperature elevated to about 45 to 50°C at which point the liquid becomes gas without a phase boundary being formed. An advantage of critical point drying is that structural distortion is reduced to a minimum. Also, only relatively little time (about 1 h) is required for the operation.

Freeze-drying involves sublimation of rapidly frozen material in a high vacuum. A disadvantage in this technique is formation of ice crystals that may cause structural damage. Cryoprotective agents which reduce ice crystal formation may be added, but their low vapour pressure makes them inimical in a high-vacuum electron-optical column operated at room temperature. Small and Marszalek (1969) have used a chemical fixation-sublimation technique that preserves very well selected protozoa. Their process requires about 14 h. Detailed descriptions of several freeze-drying methods for scanning electron microscopy are offered by Boyde and Wood (1969).

Echlin *et al.* (1970) have described a procedure by which biological specimens can be observed at low temperatures (-140 to $-100°C$) within a scanning electron microscope. The specimen is first quench-frozen in liquid Freon 22 without ice crystal formation and then transferred to a temperature-controlled specimen chamber. Upon removal of water from the sample within the specimen chamber, the scanning operation is performed at an accelerating voltage of 20 kV and less. An advantage of this technique is the rapidity with which specimens can be examined after removal from their natural habitat.

D. Specimen mounting

Samples are placed on to a specimen stub and secured there either by natural adherence or by an adhesive material. The stub is circular in design (Fig. 9a) and is normally constructed of aluminium, although other

Fig. 9. Aluminium specimen stubs for scanning electron microscopy: (a) stub alone; (b) stub mounted with four strips of transparent double-coated tape; (c) stub mounted with glass square.

metals can be used. Adhesive materials like glue, paste, or double-coated adhesive tape are useful for anchoring specimens to the stub. In Fig. 9b can be seen a stub mounted with four strips of transparent double-coated adhesive tape. If necessary, additional mounting platforms can be placed on to the stub face. A glass square cut from a microscope slide has been placed on the stub face in Fig. 9c. It is best, if possible, to avoid the use of adhesives because they often contaminate the specimen, especially under high vacuum. Such contamination seems to hasten "blistering" of the specimen surface. Adhesives work well when not in direct contact with the specimen under observation, e.g. fungal spores on extended hyphae.

There are four basic procedures for mounting microbial specimens on a stub: (1) liquid transfer, (2) solid transfer, (3) stamping, and (4) undisturbed growth transfer. Liquid transfer is suitable for mounting cells that have been suspended in various liquid media such as water, buffer solutions, or fixative agents. The mounted suspension should be diluted so as to provide isolated cells on the stub and yet be representative of the total population. Commonly used tools for transferring suspended microorganisms include microsyringes, capillary pipettes, glass rods, and wire loops.

Solid transfer is the transportation of material from solid surfaces to the stub. It is useful for transferring mycelial mats, sporangiospores, colony sections, and the like from agar media. A microspatula, inoculating needle, or dissecting knife can be conveniently used to transfer solid material. Sometimes before mounting on the stub, the sample (e.g. bacteria) must be washed in liquid. However, certain fungi can be cleaned by irrigating them after they are mounted on the specimen stub.

Stamping simply involves carefully placing an inverted stub with or without an adhesive on to the surface of microbial growth. This technique is advantageous for observing the natural physical arrangement of cells grown on solid media.

A particularly useful procedure for examining undisturbed growth of bacteria has been developed by Afrikian, St. Julian, and Bulla (unpublished data). This technique involves growing bacteria on agar plates overlaid with sterilized dialysis membrane. After sufficient growth, the membrane is carefully removed and transferred to the specimen stub for microscopic examination. In this way, colonial growth can be observed virtually undisturbed. Roth (1971), using a dissecting knife, cut agar blocks from agar plates containing colonies and placed them directly on to specimen stubs. Another technique for observing undisturbed growth is to grow cells on a microcoverslip adhered to a specimen stub. At the desired growth stage, the mounted specimen is immediately prepared for microscopic observation.

E. Specimen surface coating

Most biological specimens are poor electrical conductors, and when bombarded by an electron beam, build up a negative charge on their surface. To prevent this build-up and to increase conductivity, it is necessary to coat them with a thin film (10–15 nm) of conducting material. The conducting material is usually evaporated carbon; it can also be a heavy metal such as aluminium, silver, gold, or palladium; or it can be both. A popular and efficient biological coating material is gold-palladium. Organic antistatic agents also have been developed to reduce the charging phenomenon (Sikorski and Sprenkman, 1968; Owen and Merworth, 1970). When desired, samples can be observed uncoated. However, uncoated samples must be examined at a considerably reduced accelerating voltage in order to avoid the harmful charging effects on their surface. This procedure does not allow for maximum resolution because of limited primary electron penetration of the specimen.

Coating is carried out in a high-vacuum evaporator (Fig. 10a) by vapourizing the coating material on to the specimen. Ideally, the coating film should be uniformly continuous and at a thickness of about 10 nm.

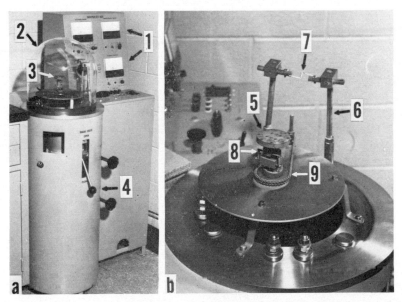

Fig. 10. Photograph of Denton DV-502 high-vacuum evaporator: (a) entire instrument showing (1) control panel; (2) glass dome lid; (3) rotary shadower specimen stage assembly; (4) vacuum pump assembly; (b) close-up view of rotary shadower assembly; (5) stub carriage; (6) electrode post; (7) platinum wire basket used to hold coating material; (8) rotary shadower tilting device; (9) chain drive.

Practically, this thickness is difficult to achieve on samples with highly ornate surfaces. To increase efficiency of coating, the vacuum evaporator should possess a rotary shadower with a tilting device (see Fig. 10b). Such a device enables all areas of the specimen surface to be exposed to the vapourized metal. Another method used to ensure uniform coating when no tilting device is available is to place the coating material in two separate positions, one at about 30° angle to the centre of the rotary plate and the other directly above the plate.

Image clarity of the scanned object depends upon specimen preparation. A critical aspect of successful scanning electron microscopy is monitoring (usually by light microscopy) of the specimen during preparative steps. To know such things as degree of cleanliness, approximate number of cells and their morphological state, and finally, spatial arrangement of mounted cells is mandatory for good end results.

IV. APPLICATIONS

When the first commercial scanning electron microscope became available, its use in biological research was limited to examination of plant and animal tissues and to micropaleontological investigations. Since then, use of this microscope has expanded to microbiology. It would be cumbersome to describe here all the applications of scanning microscopy to microbiology; therefore, only a few selected examples are given. Prominent areas of microbiology in which scanning microscopy is being used currently are systematics (Heywood, 1971), spore germination and outgrowth (St. Julian et al., 1971; Rousseau et al., 1972), bacterial spore morphology (Murphy and Campbell, 1969; Bulla et al., 1969), bacterial colonial morphology (Roth, 1971), effects of antimicrobial agents on cell surfaces (Klainer and Perkins, 1971), phytopathology (Locci, 1969b; Locci, 1970; Locci and Bisiach, 1970), microflora of plants (Barnes and Neve, 1968; Leben, 1969), and soil (Locci, 1969a), fungal spore wall development (Hawker and Gooday, 1968), estimation of bacterial cell volumes (Boyde and Williams, 1971), elemental analysis of algae (Thurston and Russ, 1971), air pollution (Bulba, 1968), and ecology of polluted streams (Small and Ranganathan, 1970).

A. Bacterial spore morphology

Some of the earliest work involved descriptive morphology of bacterial spores (Murphy and Campbell, 1969; Bulla et al., 1969). Several examples are portrayed in Fig. 11. The sporangium of a *Bacillus thuringiensis* sporulated cell in Fig. 11a contains a parasporal body as well as a spore.

Fig. 11. Scanning electron micrographs of bacterial spores: (a) *Bacillus thurin-giensis* showing parasporal body (p) spore (s) both enclosed in a sporangium (sp); (b) *Bacillus popilliae* extrasporangial spore showing ridges; (c) *Bacillus lentimorbus* extrasporangial spore with ridges; (d) *Bacillus polymyxa* extrasporangial spore with ridges. *B. polymyxa* photograph courtesy of J. A. Murphy and L. L. Campbell.

The spore and parasporal body are held together in a loose-fitting, smoothly textured sporangium. Fig. 11b is an extrasporangial spore of *Bacillus popilliae* which exhibits distinct continuous ridges that extend along the entire length of the spore. Extrasporangial spores of *Bacillus lentimorbus* also possess highly pronounced ridges (Fig. 11c). Longitudinal ridges are interconnected by short ridges perpendicular to them. *Bacillus polymyxa* has a peculiar ridge formation clearly seen in Fig 11d. Longitudinal ridges extend from end to end and fuse in polygonal fashion at the end of the spore.

B. Bacterial colony morphology

The structure of bacterial colonies has been studied by scanning microscopy (Roth, 1971) to gain a better understanding of structural interrelationships of individual cells within a colony. Afrikian, St. Julian, and Bulla (unpublished data) have examined colonies of bacteria freshly isolated from soil and found various cellular arrangements within different areas of the colonies. Figure 12a is a micrograph of the edge of a *Bacillus cereus* colony. As can be seen, the edge is one cell-layer thick. The individual cells are oriented in uniform chains that lie adjacent and concentric to one another. Cells in the centre of the colony (Fig. 12b) have no specific orientation; they are randomly stacked. Figure 12c reveals the edge of a *Bacillus subtilis* colony in which the longitudinal axis of the individual cells is perpendicular to a tangential plane drawn through the colony edge. The centre of the colony is characterized by layers of cells bound together by an extracellular material (Fig. 12d). Figure 12e depicts the edge of a *Bacillus mycoides* colony. Its cellular arrangement is similar to that of *B. cereus*. Note, however, that not only are the chains curled, but also the individual cells. The central area of the colony (Fig. 12f) is different from that of either of the other two colonies examined. It is one cell thick and is composed of uniform, parallel chains of cells.

C. Systematics

Systematic studies of micro-organisms have been greatly facilitated by the scanning electron microscope. Locci and Quaroni (1970) have examined some 28 species and varieties of ascosporic aspergilli and have gathered valuable morphological information for taxonomic purposes. Ellis *et al.* (1970) examined a number of *Rhizopus* sporangiospores and categorized them into four groups according to their morphology. Fennell, Bulla, St. Julian, and Baker (unpublished data) are using a scanning electron microscope in a systematic analysis of aspergilli. From part of the latter work are presented ascospores of four species of *Aspergillus* (Fig. 13a–d) which represent three of the *Aspergillus* groups according to Raper and Fennell (1965). Figure 13a is *Aspergillus variecolor* var. *astellatus*, a member of the *nidulans* group. As can be readily seen, the ascospore body of this organism is smooth, convex, and bicrested. The architecture of both crests reveals radially developed ridges that extend close to the border of the crests. Figure 13b is *Aspergillus stramenius*, which is within the *fischeri* series of the *fumigatus* group. This ascospore is bicrested, but the body is echinulate and convex. The crests are smooth and distinctly separated. Four parallel rows of small rounded echinulations lie between the crests in an equatorial fashion. Figure 13c portrays lenticular ascospores of *Aspergillus rugulosus*, another member of the *nidulans* group. These spore bodies

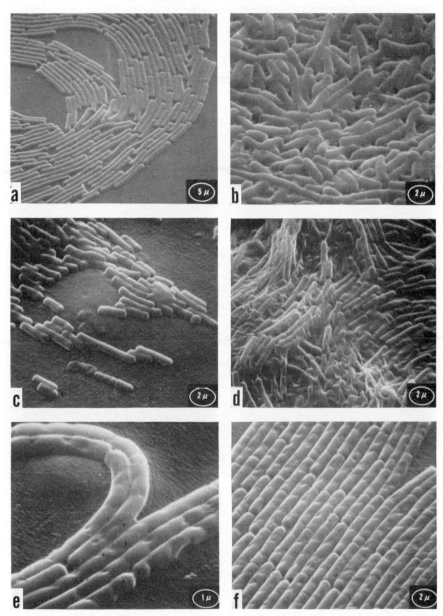

Fig. 12. Arrangement of *Bacillus cereus* vegetative cells at (a) periphery of colony and (b) centre of colony; *Bacillus subtilis* vegetative cells at (c) edge of colony and (d) centre of colony; *Bacillus mycoides* vegetative cells at (e) edge of colony and (f) centre of colony. Photographs courtesy of E. G. Afrikian *et al.*

Fig. 13. Scanning electron micrograph of (a) *Aspergillus variecolor* var. *astellatus* ascospore; (b) *Aspergillus stramenius*; (c) *Aspergillus rugulosus*; (d) *Aspergillus cremeus*. Photographs courtesy of D. I. Fennel *et al.*

are convex and discontinuously ridged. The equatorial crests are smaller than those of *A. variecolor* var. *astellatus* (compare with Fig. 13a) which also is within the *nidulans* group. The crests are uniformly ribbed and are separated by a smooth equatorial crevice. The ascospore of *Aspergillus cremeus* (Fig. 13d) of the *cremeus* group appears very delicate. In the centre of the top surface are indefinite ridges with no apparent symmetry. The same configuration is contained on the opposing surface (not shown.) The two equatorial crests are large, smooth, and flexuous; the furrow between the crests is subtly echinulated.

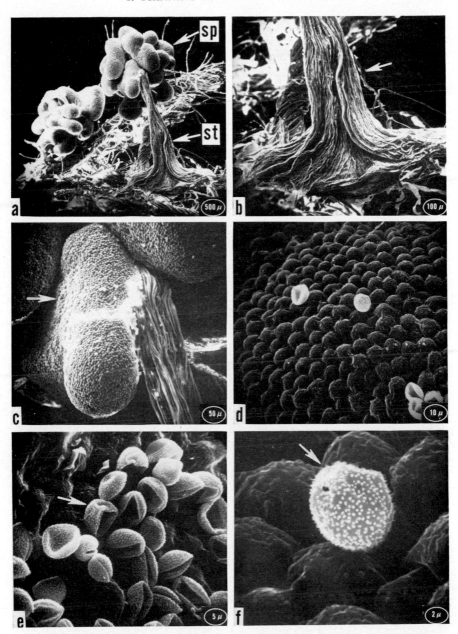

Fig. 14. Fruiting stage of *Physarum polycephalum*: (**a**) peridial sac or sporangium (sp) on a stalk or stipe (st); (**b**) bundled filaments of stipe (arrow); (**c**, arrow, and **d**) sporangium; (**e** and **f**) individual exposed spores (arrows). Photographs courtesy of J. A. Murphy and L. L. Campbell.

In other systematic studies, Murphy and Campbell (unpublished data) are investigating morphological properties of the acellular slime moulds (Myxomycetes) whose taxonomy thus far is based primarily on light microscopic observations. Figure 14 is a montage of micrographs demonstrating the fruiting stage of a slime mould *Physarum polycephalum*. The entire fructification (Fig. 14a) contains a cluster of peridial sacs or sporangia on a stalk or stipe. A closer look at the stipe (Fig. 14b) reveals a composition of many bundled filaments comprised of smaller strands. The sporangial surface (Fig. 14c and d) contains a layer of spores overlaid with a membrane-like material. In Fig. 14e and f are exposed spores whose entire surface is marked by rounded punctate projections.

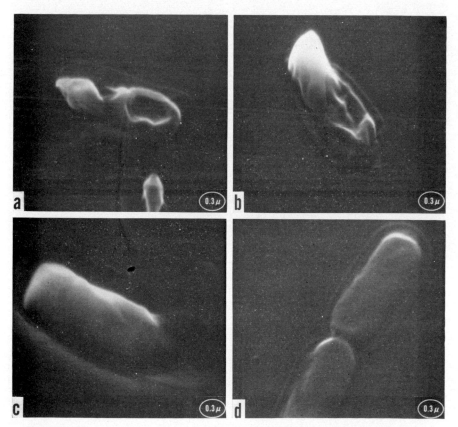

Fig. 15. Germination and outgrowth of *Bacillus thuringiensis* spore: (a) germinated spore with parasporal body; (b) early outgrowth; (c) late outgrowth; (d) a newly divided (first generation) vegetative cell.

D. Spore germination and outgrowth

Scanning electron microscopic examination of bacterial and yeast spore germination and outgrowth has revealed distinctive changes in spore surface and overall anatomy during the developmental process (St. Julian *et al.*, 1971; Rousseau *et al.*, 1972). Fig. 15 presents selected stages of

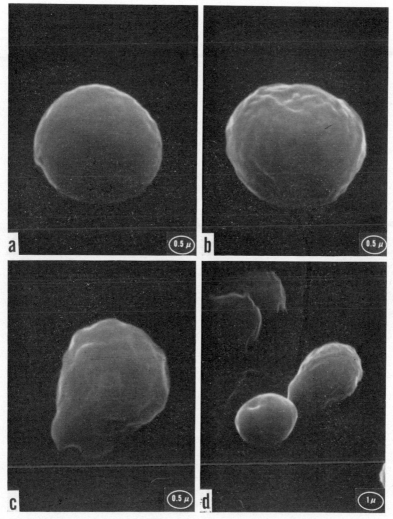

Fig. 16. *Saccharomyces cerevisiae* spore germination and outgrowth: (a) un-germinated spore; (b) early germinated spore; (c) beginning outgrowth; (d) bud formation. Photographs courtesy of P. Rousseau *et al.*

morphological development in the bacterium *B. thuringiensis*. Figure 15a is a germinated spore with accompanying parasporal body. The gnarled cell in Fig. 15b represents an early outgrowth stage and Fig. 15c is a late outgrowth stage. Note that there is a loss of the parasporal body during outgrowth. A newly divided cell in Fig. 15d represents the termination of spore outgrowth.

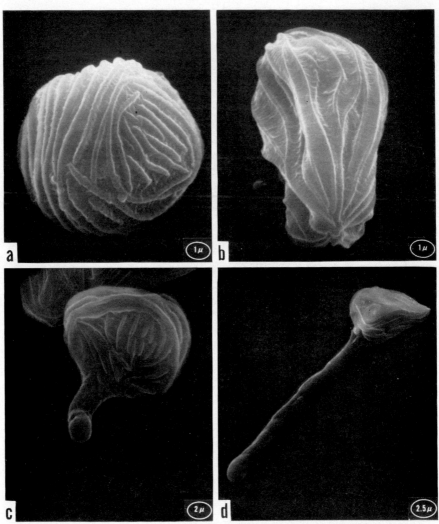

Fig. 17. *Rhizopus stolonifer* spore germination and outgrowth: (a) ridged germinated spore; (b) beginning outgrowth; (c) germ tube elongation; (d) extended elongation of germ tube. Photographs courtesy of J. L. Van Etten *et al.*

For the yeast *Saccharomyces cerevisiae*, several stages of spore development are disclosed in Fig. 16. A single ungerminated spore (Fig. 16a) has a slightly irregular surface whereas an early germinated stage (Fig. 16b) exhibits a rough surface with continuous ridges. During outgrowth, the spore changes shape, and surface irregularity becomes heightened

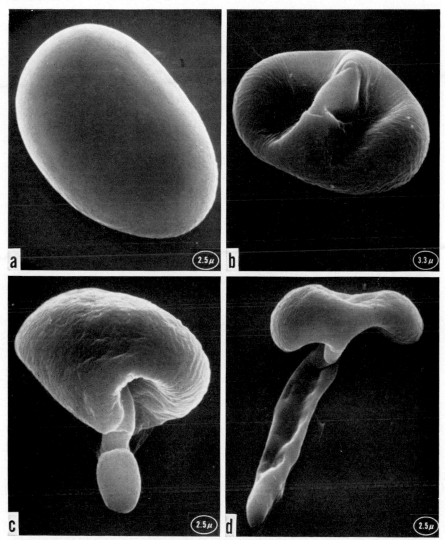

Fig. 18. *Botryodiploidia theobromae* spore germination and outgrowth: (a) germinated spore; (b) beginning outgrowth; (c) elongation of germ tube; (d) extension of germ tube. Photographs courtesy of W. P. Wergin *et al.*

(Fig. 16c). A final stage of development is bud formation (Fig. 16d); the smooth surface of the bud resembles that of the outgrown area of the parent cell.

Van Etten, St. Julian, and Bulla (unpublished data) have investigated morphological and surface structural modifications during germination and outgrowth of *Rhizopus stolonifer* spores. *R. stolonifer* represents a genus of Mucorales that is characterized by cylindrical ridges traversing the entire surface of the sporangiospore. An ungerminated sporangiospore of *R. stolonifer* in Fig. 17a exhibits this kind of ridge formation. Upon germination, the spore elongates (Fig. 17b) and forms a germ tube (Fig. 17c). In Fig. 17d germ tube formation is near completion.

Wergin, Dunkle, Van Etten, St. Julian, and Bulla (unpublished data) are carrying out similar studies with a higher fungus, *Botryodiploidia theobromae*. For this organism, cellular differentiation during germination and outgrowth is a very dramatic process (Fig. 18). An ungerminated spore (Fig. 18a) is ellipsoidal and relatively smooth-surfaced. However, upon germination, surface modification occurs in a localized area (Fig. 18b) through which a germ tube emerges (Fig. 18c) and eventually forms a hypha (Fig. 18d).

V. ANCILLARY TECHNIQUES

In addition to the contrast mechanisms listed in Section II.D, there are several complementary techniques with potential value for microbiological research that should be noted.

A. Scanning transmission electron microscopy

By using a transmission accessory with the scanning instrument, sectioned material that has been fixed and stained with heavy metal salts can be examined. Materials as thick as 0·5 μm which are unamenable for conventional transmission electron microscopy are readily observed in the transmission mode of a scanning microscope. Because lower operating voltages are possible with a scanning microscope than with a transmission instrument, there is less damage to sectioned material. Crewe (1971) has developed a scanning transmission electron microscope with a field emission source that will record single atoms within a molecular structure.

B. Three-dimensional analysis

A useful method to quantitate the topography of specimen surfaces is to construct stereopairs (Dorfler and Russ, 1970). A stereopair is made by photographing the same area of a specimen at two different beam angles. When the two photographs are properly aligned, parallax measurements are made of identical image points on the photographs. With this information, along with the magnification and tilt angle between the two photographs, height differences of the image points can be calculated.

C. Y-modulation

Another way in which quantitative information from the various contrast modes can be gathered is by adding the video signal to the y-sweep deflection signal (Kelly *et al.*, 1969). Figure 19 shows y-modulation of a sporulated cell of *B. thuringiensis*. Outline images are produced over the

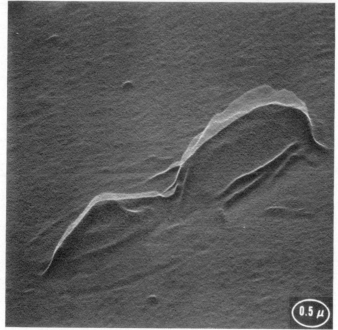

Fig. 19. Y-modulation of *Bacillus thuringiensis* spore and parasporal body.

entire surface of the specimen (compare Fig. 19 to Fig. 11a which is the same specimen without a y-sweep deflection signal). By modulating the video signal in this way, the surface topography, i.e. ridges, flat spots, depressions, etc., can be measured.

D. Ion etching

Ion etching allows examination of structures beneath a specimen surface. Echlin *et al.* (1969) have described a system by which various parts of a specimen can be selectively removed within a microscope column and then be examined immediately at low accelerating voltages. The ion source is a cathode argon discharge unit and can be manipulated so that an ion beam is directed at different angles on the specimen stub. A hazard of this technique lies in image interpretation of the etched material because various materials and structures etch at different rates. It is difficult to know whether selective etching results from either specimen resistance or a combination of other undetermined factors, or both.

E. Low voltage operation

There are several advantages to low voltage (1 to 5 kV) operation. In the emissive mode, an uncoated sample can be examined rapidly at medium resolution. Adverse charging effects and other artifacts are avoided and, therefore, interpretation of the final image is easier. Low accelerating voltage also is necessary for obtaining useful information in the luminescent mode of operation, i.e. cathodoluminescence and X-ray analysis. It should be understood that when using a standard tungsten filament electron gun (see Fig. 4) at a low voltage, spot size is increased with a resultant decrease in resolution. There are available lanthanum hexaboride electron guns which provide high resolution at low accelerating voltages. However, they are much more expensive than the ordinary tungsten electron guns.

VI. CONCLUSION

At its present stage of development, the scanning electron microscope is a valuable adjunct to other methods of microscopic observation. It cannot be used alone to study fine structure and extreme surface detail; but in association with optical and transmission electron microscopy, it can provide concise definitive information on cellular morphology.

Two striking features that make scanning electron microscopy particularly exciting are the illusion of three-dimensional images and the extremely large depth of field. The depth of field is about 300 times larger than that of transmission electron and optical microscopes. These factors alone have elicited increased interest and use of the instrument in microbiology.

The scanning electron microscope is a closed television circuit and, as such, has varied and powerful techniques of information gathering and transmission. It is quite believable that this microscope will eventually become an indispensable tool for analysis of micro-organisms. Within this decade there should be tremendous improvement in video quality, pattern recognition, coating materials, and reduction in instrument size and cost. Furthermore, it is probable that image formation will become computer controlled. If so, the scanning electron microscope will revolutionize microscopic examination of micro-organisms.

VII. SOME SCANNING ELECTRON MICROSCOPE MANUFACTURERS*

Advanced Metals Research Corp. (AMR), 149 Middlesex Turnpike, Burlington, Massachusetts 01803.

Coates and Wetter Instrument Corp. (Cwikscan), 777 North Pastoria Avenue, Sunnyvale, California 94086.

Etec Corporation (Autoscan), 3392 Investment Boulevard, Hayward, California 94545.

Hitachi Ltd. (Scanscope), Tokyo, Japan.

Japan Electron Optics Laboratory Co., Ltd. (Jeolco), Chicago Office— 2 Talcott Road, Parkridge, Illinois 60068.

Kent Cambridge Scientific, Inc. (Stereoscan), 8020 Austin Avenue, Morton Grove, Illinois 60053.

Ultrascan Company, 18530 Miles Parkway, Cleveland, Ohio 44128.

REFERENCES

Anderson, Thomas F. (1952). *In* "Extrait du Congres De Microscopie Electronique" Sec. 5, 567–576. Editions de la Revue d'Optique, Paris.

Barnes, G., and Neve, N. F. B. (1968). *Trans. Brit. Mycol. Soc.*, **51**, 811–813. Printed in Great Britain.

Boyde, A., and Williams, R. A. D. (1971). *Arch. Oral Biol.*, **16**, 259–267. Printed in Great Britain.

Boyde, A., and Wood, C. (1969). *J. Microsc.*, **90**, 221–249.

Bulba, E. (1968). *Review in Current Laboratory Practice*, **1** (1), 6–11.

Bulla, L. A., St. Julian, G., Rhodes, R. A., and Hesseltine, C. W. (1969). *Appl. Microbiol.*, **18**, 490–495.

Crewe, A. V. (1971). *Phil. Trans. Roy. Soc. London, Ser. B.*, **261**, 61–70.

Dorfler, G., and Russ, J. C. (1970). *In* "Proceedings of the Third Annual Scanning Electron Microscope Symposium", pp. 65–72. IIT Research Institute, Chicago, Illinois 60616, U.S.A.

Echlin, P., Kynaston, D., and Knights, D. (1969). *In* "Proceedings of the 27th Annual Meeting of the Electron Microscopic Society of America" (Ed. C. J. Arcenaux), pp. 10–11.

Echlin, P., Paden, D., Dronzek, B., and Wayte, R. (1970). *In* "Proceedings of the Third Annual Scanning Electron Microscope Symposium", pp. 49–56. IIT Research Institute, Chicago, Illinois 60616, U.S.A.

Ellis, J. J., Bulla, L. A., St. Julian, G., and Hesseltine, C. W. (1970). *In* "Proceedings of the Third Annual Scanning Electron Microscope Symposium", pp. 145–152. IIT Research Institute, Chicago, Illinois 60616, U.S.A.

Hawker, Lillian, and Gooday, M. A. (1968). *J. Gen. Microbiol.*, **54**, 13–20.

Hayes, T. L., and Pease, R. F. W. (1968). *In* "Advances in Biological and Medical Physics" (Ed. John H. Lawrence and John W. Gofman, Asst. Ed. Thomas L. Hayes), Vol. 12, pp. 85–137. Academic Press, New York and London.

* The mention of firm names or trade products does not imply that they are endorsed or recommended by the U.S. Department of Agriculture over other firms or similar products not mentioned.

Heywood, V. H. (1971). "Scanning Electron Microscopy", Proceedings of an International Symposium held at the Department of Botany, University of Reading (Ed. V. H. Heywood), Vol. 4, pp. 1–331. Academic Press, London and New York.

Klainer, A. S., and Perkins, R. L. (1971). *In* "Proceedings of the Fourth Annual Scanning Electron Microscope Symposium", pp. 329–336. IIT Research Institute, Chicago, Illinois 60616, U.S.A.

Kelly, T. K., Lindqvist, W. F., and Muir, M. D. (1969). *Science*, **165**, 283–285.

Leben, Curt. (1969). *Can. J. Microbiol.*, **15**(3), 319–321.

Locci, R., and Bisiach, M. (1970). *Rivista Di Patalogia Vegetale*, Serie IV, Vol. VI, pp. 21–28. Istituto Di Patologia Vegetale, Universita Di Milano.

Locci, R. (1970). *Rivista Il Riso*, Anno XIX, pp. 99–109. Instituto Di Patologia Vegetale, Universita Di Milano.

Locci, R., and Quaroni, S. (1970). *Rivista Di Patologia Vegetale*, Serie IV, Vol. VI, pp. 141–192. Istituto Di Patologia Vegetale, Universita Di Milano.

Locci, R. (1969a). *Rivista Di Patalogia Vegitale*, Serie IV, Vol. V, pp. 167–178. Istituto Di Patologia Vegetale, Universita Di Milano.

Locci, R. (1969b). *Rivista Di Patologia Vegetale*, Serie IV, Vol. V, pp. 199–206. Istituto Di Patologia Vegetale, Universita Di Milano.

MacDonald, N. C. (1971). *In* "Proceedings of the Fourth Annual Scanning Electron Microscope Symposium", pp. 89–96. IIT Research Institute, Chicago, Illinois 60616, U.S.A.

Murphy, Judith, A., and Campbell, L. L. (1969). *J. Bacteriol.*, **98**(2), 737–743.

Oatley, C. W., Nixon, W. C., and Pease, R. F. W. (1965). *In* "Advances in Electronics and Electron Physics" (Ed. L. Marton and C. Marton), Vol. 21, pp. 181–247. Academic Press, London.

Ogilvie, Robert, E. (1969). *In* "Proceedings of the Second Annual Scanning Electron Microscope Symposium", Vol. 2, pp. 21–26. IIT Research Institute, Chicago, Illinois 60616, U.S.A.

Owen, C. J., and Merworth, W. R. (1970). *Res. Develop.*, **21**, 66.

Pease, Daniel C. (1964). "Histological Techniques for Electron Microscopy" (Second Edition). Academic Press, New York and London.

Raper, K. B., and Fennell, D. I. (1965). "The Genus Aspergillus". Williams and Wilkins Company, Baltimore.

Roth, I. L. (1971). *In* "Proceedings of the Fourth Annual Scanning Electron Microscope Symposium", Part I, pp. 321–328. IIT Research Institute, Chicago, Illinois 60616, U.S.A.

Rousseau, Paul, Halvorson, Harlyn O., Bulla, Lee A., Jr., and St. Julian, Grant. (1972). *J. Bacteriol.*, **109**(3), 1232–1238.

Sacks, L. E. (1969). *Appl. Microbiol.*, **18** (3), 416–419.

St. Julian, G., Bulla, L. A., Jr., and Hesseltine, C. W. (1971). *Can. J. Microbiol.*, **17**, 373–375.

Small, E. B., and Ranganathan, V. S. (1970). *In* "Proceedings of the Third Annual Scanning Electron Microscope Symposium", pp. 177–184. IIT Research Institute, Chicago, Illinois 60616, U.S.A.

Small, E. B., and Marszalek, D. S. (1969). *Science*, **163**, 1064–1065.

Sikorski, J., and Sprenkman, W. (1968). *Melliand Textilber*, **49**(4), 471–473.

Stintzing, H. (1929). German Patent No. 485,155. Date of application 13 May 1927. Granted October 1929.

Thornton, P. R. (1968). "Scanning Electron Microscopy". Chapman and Hall, Ltd., London E.C.4.

Thurston, E. L., and Russ, J. C. (1971). *In* "Proceedings of the Fourth Annual Scanning Electron Microscope Symposium", pp. 511–516. IIT Research Institute, Chicago, Illinois 60616, U.S.A.

Von Ardenne, M. (1938). *Z. Tech. Phys.*, **19**, 407–416, and *Z. Phys.*, **109**, 553–572.

Zworykin, V. K., Hillier, J., and Snyder, R. L. (1942). *ASTM Bull.*, **117**, 15–23.

CHAPTER II

Mathematical Models in Microbiology

H. H. Topiwala

Shell Research Limited, Borden Microbiological Laboratory, Sittingbourne,
Kent, England

I.	Introduction	35
II.	Need for Formulation of Objectives	37
III.	Classification	37
IV.	Formulation of Models	39
	A. Mass balances and rate expressions	39
	B. Mass balances in a microbiological system	40
V.	Examples of Microbiological System Models	41
	A. Waste treatment plants	42
	B. Continuous culture	42
	C. Antibiotic production	43
	D. Thermal death of bacteria	43
VI.	Aids to Mathematical Work	46
	A. Introduction	46
	B. Graphical methods	46
	C. Comparison of theoretical and experimental work	47
	D. Empirical curve fitting	47
	E. Linear graph paper	49
	F. Semilogarithmic graph paper	49
	G. Logarithmic graph paper	52
	H. Least-square fitting	53
	I. Digital computer solutions	56
	J. Simulation languages	58
	K. Stability of microbiological systems	58
References		58

I. INTRODUCTION

Mathematical models are now used in such diverse fields as economics and biochemistry. The word "models" has thus varied connotations and it is unrealistic to attempt a comprehensive definition for it. For our purposes, the word may be defined as a mathematical specification of the inter-relationships between various parts of a system. The specification takes the form of mathematical statements or equations. A system may be broadly defined as any set of physical or abstract objects. With the development of accurate measurement techniques there is a growing need for interpretation of quantitative data in microbiology. However, biological systems are by nature extremely complex and the actual system has to be replaced by an imaginary model system which is mathematically tractable. The model system is arrived at by making simplifying assumptions and generalizations about the nature of the microbiological system. The results of the mathematical analysis are applicable only to the model system. The applicability of the results to the biological system will depend on the validity of the assumptions.

Fig. 1 shows some of the steps in model construction. Sections II, III and IV of this Chapter discuss the underlying principles in formulation of mathematical models while Section VI presents some simple aids to mathematical analysis of models. No attempt has been made to review the literature of models of microbiological systems though selected examples are cited in Section V.

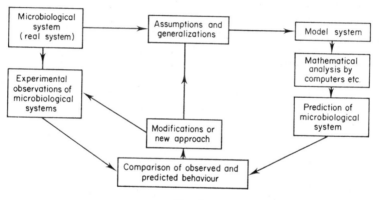

FIG. 1.

It must be remembered that apparently successful models do not constitute final proof of the assumptions since two or more alternative models may lead to similar conclusions. On the other hand, if a given theory cannot be successfully modelled it is unlikely to be correct. While models have serious drawbacks they can be useful tools when their limitations are fully understood.

The main purpose of mathematical models can be summarized:

1. Construction of such models provides a systematic way of studying behaviour of specific systems for which experimental data are available. This approach encourages the microbiologist to be rigorous in his statements and definitions. Terms like growth yield, oxygen uptake, etc., have to be expressed in the form of mathematical statements which allow no ambiguity in meaning.

2. Realistic and tested models provide useful guides for design and operation of industrial microbiological processes. An engineer seeks, in his dynamic model, relations that exist between performance and control system parameters in order to optimize the process.

3. In research, models are used as conceptual tools to gain insight into biological mechanisms. They can be used to predict behaviour in some as yet untested situation or to test the plausibility of various suggested mechanisms. This approach often points to a critical region where further experiments should be carried out.

II. NEED FOR FORMULATION OF OBJECTIVES

The systems microbiologists have to study are too complicated to permit models which will mimic the real system in all respects. A comprehensive model of microbial growth which incorporates, among other aspects, DNA synthesis, the complex activities of all the enzymes and the physiological effects of environmental factors would be mathematically cumbersome. Moreover, the complexity of such a model would itself be a hindrance. The criterion by which we should judge the success or failure of any model-building exercise is the extent to which we have constructed a tool which enables us to achieve a specified objective. Only those features of the system which are pertinent to the objective should be considered. Thus a model builder exercises a considerable amount of judgement in formulating and working his model. In the microbiological field he has to draw on knowledge of the organisms and their interaction with the environment to suggest a likely set of hypotheses which may be used to interpret data. Of course, the hypotheses will be based, as far as possible, on known principles of physical, chemical and biological sciences. Some of the difficulties in modelling microbiological systems will arise as a result of the diversity and complexity of biological principles. If the model is to be useful in practice it is imperative to answer questions such as—what intermediate factors exert so small an influence that they can be neglected? Can certain factors be lumped together?

III. CLASSIFICATION

The literature of mathematical models abounds with confusing terminology. This situation arises partly as a result of the different approaches to classification of the various types of models. One type of classification depends on the description used to represent the internal physical detail of the system. The three main levels of description are the molecular, the microscopic and the macroscopic. The level of description used will depend on the system under consideration and will reflect the interests of the model builder. Another classification may be based on the nature of the mathematical equations of the model. In this context terms such as deterministic *vs* probabilistic, linear *vs* nonlinear and steady state *vs* dynamic are used. Himmelblau and Bischoff (1968) give an excellent review of models based on the above mentioned dichotomies.

Microbiological system models deal mostly with populations of organisms. Variables chosen for the models highlight aspects such as microbial growth, population death rates and production of metabolites. A very useful classification of models of populations of micro-organisms was suggested by Tsuchiya *et al.* (1966) and is shown in Fig. 2.

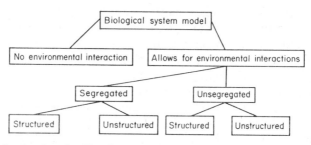

Fig. 2. A simple classification of mathematical models of populations of micro-organisms.

The first distinction is made between models that account for interactions between the organisms and the environment and those that do not. A culture of organisms has, at any instant, individual cells of various masses and sizes. The individual cell's internal composition, metabolic activity and other factors, which may be described in terms of a "physiological state", also change during the cell's life cycle. A model that takes into account the differences between individual cells is called "segregated". If the physiological state could be defined in terms of certain cell parameters and a relationship be found that relates the physiological state to reproduction, a rigorous mathematical treatment of microbial populations would be possible. Attempts have been made by various workers to introduce the concept of segregation by assigning a parameter to describe the physiological state of the cells. For instance, Fredrickson and Tsuchiya (1963) used age while Eakman *et al.* (1966) have used cell mass as an index of the physiological state in their models. However, these models are not very satisfactory for two primary reasons. First, they often have to rely on statistical correlations and second, the analysis of the equation arising out of the segregated models becomes quite complicated.

The most common mathematical approach to modelling of microbial growth has been one where the entire population is taken as protoplasmic mass distributed throughout the culture. These "unsegregated models" treat the cellular mass of the culture as the fundamental variable and ignore the presence of individual cells. This approach reduces the complex growth process to one of simple biological reaction kinetics. Monod (1949) was one of the first workers to propose a simple unsegregated model for bacterial growth. The model accounted for the interaction of the micro-organisms with the environment by the concept of growth dependence on a limiting substrate. Monod's model is an unstructured model because it does not account for any physiological variations in the culture mass. As a consequence, the history of the culture is of no relevance to the future growth of the culture. However, the mass can be thought of as consisting of different components which vary in their kinetic behaviour. The behaviour of the culture at any particular instant will depend on the relative amounts of these components and hence the history of the culture. Ramkrishna (1965) in his unsegregated but structured model divides the biomass into two component parts of G-mass and D-mass. The G-mass is taken to be the nucleic acids in the cells and the D-mass includes the rest of the biomass.

A biochemically sound structured model may contain a number of constants whose numerical values cannot be determined by simple manipulation of experimental data. Thus resort has to be made to parameter estimation by curve fitting techniques, and that, coupled with the fact that routine measurement of the components of cell mass can be difficult, limits the use of these models.

IV. FORMULATION OF MODELS

A. Mass balances and rate expressions

Mathematical models are constructed by the application of laws of conservation of mass, energy and momentum with due regard for biological, physical and thermodynamic principles. A balance of conservation over an elemental volume in a small interval of time can be expressed as:

$$\begin{bmatrix} \text{Net} \\ \text{accumulation} \end{bmatrix} = \begin{bmatrix} \text{Transport in} \\ \text{through surface} \end{bmatrix} - \begin{bmatrix} \text{Transport out} \\ \text{through surface} \end{bmatrix} + \begin{bmatrix} \text{Net} \\ \text{generation} \end{bmatrix} \quad (1)$$

Most mathematical models of microbiological systems are essentially mass balances. A material balance of any component can be drawn up in the form:

$$\begin{bmatrix} \text{Change of moles} \\ \text{within element} \end{bmatrix} = \begin{bmatrix} \text{Moles} \\ \text{entering} \\ \text{element} \end{bmatrix} - \begin{bmatrix} \text{Moles} \\ \text{leaving} \\ \text{element} \end{bmatrix} + \begin{bmatrix} \text{Moles} \\ \text{generated} \\ \text{(growth)} \end{bmatrix} \quad (2)$$

The above microscopic balance is valid at any given point within the whole system. To make further progress we need to make assumptions about (a) spatial distribution of the component in the system and (b) the form of growth rate equation.

In the kinetic approach to microbiological systems, the growth process is assumed to be the result of interaction between the component and factors such as concentrations of other components, mass transfer processes, temperature (T), pressure (P), etc. For instance, the growth rate expression (R_c) for a component c, may be expressed in the form

$$R_c = f(c(1), c(2), \ldots c(n), T, \text{pH}, P, \ldots) \qquad (3)$$

where $c(1)$, $c(2)$, etc., represent biomass component, nutrient and product concentrations. Normally such kinetic expressions are considered to be deterministic, i.e. they will have a fixed value for a given set of conditions. To make equations (2) and (3) compatable, R_c can be defined as moles produced per unit volume per unit time in a given volume element. Mathematical methods used to incorporate the distribution of components in a system can be found in chemical engineering literature (Himmelblau and Bischoff, 1968). Advanced concepts of micro and macro mixing (Danckwerts, 1958; Zwietering, 1959; Kattan and Adler, 1972) are being used in formulating microbiological models (Tsai, Erickson and Fan, 1969). They are considered outside the scope of this particular article. It must be emphasized that all real systems are distributed but approximations regarding the distribution can be made provided they do not conceal important features of the system. In the next Section we shall restrict ourselves to the simple but most commonly used idealized approximation of distribution, i.e. a perfectly mixed system.

B. Mass balances in a microbiological system

To illustrate the formulation of a mathematical model, a specific microbiological system is now defined. The system consists of a submerged culture of micro-organisms in a vessel (Fig. 3). In order to describe the microbiological process in the environment of the physical system some assumptions are made: (1) The organisms are considered suspended in a single liquid phase of fixed volume (V); (2) the microbiological rate processes do not affect the density of the liquid phase, and hence the total inlet flow rate equals the outlet flow rate (F); (3) the contents of the vessel are stirred vigorously to ensure that the concentration of any component in the outgoing stream, at any instant, is the same as that throughout the vessel.

The premise of complete mixing also implies that the contents of the vessel are homogeneous with regard to environmental factors such as

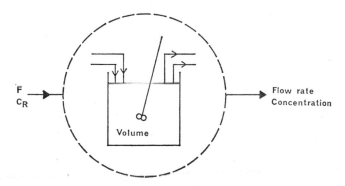

FIG. 3. A stirred tank fermenter.

temperature and pressure. Consequently, the reaction rate for any component (eqn. (3)), is uniform throughout the system and a mass balance can be made for the vessel as a whole:

$$\frac{dc}{dt} = \frac{F}{V}(c_R - c) + R_c \qquad c = c(1),\ c(2),\ \ldots c(n) \qquad (4)$$

where F/V is defined as the dilution rate (D). The set of first order differential equations given by eqn. (4) forms the mathematical model of the microbiological flow system described above. To solve the mathematical model the rate expressions R_c have to be specified in terms of the state variables, and the boundary conditions given. Some techniques used in analysing models of this type are discussed in Section VI.

The stirred tank fermenter described above is widely used in industry and is variously designated as C.F.S.T.R. (continuous flow stirred tank reactor), C.S.T.R. and C*. In practice, most flow systems lie between the two extremes of the perfectly well mixed and the idealized tubular type with no mixing (Denbigh and Turner, 1971). Many real situations can be modelled by various combinations of ideal C.S.T.R. and tubular fermenters (see Ricica, this Series, Vol. 2). The choice of the most efficient fermenter scheme to meet any specified design criterion has been discussed by Bischoff (1966).

V. EXAMPLES OF MICROBIOLOGICAL SYSTEM MODELS

The examples given below have been selected to illustrate the different types of microbiological systems where the modelling approach has proved useful. The models themselves are all unsegregated and structured.

A. Waste treatment plants

A serious disadvantage of microbiological waste treatment plants has been the difficulty in controlling the process when subjected to dynamic loadings. Reliable mathematical models are being developed to obtain better design and control criteria. The mathematical approach to such complex biological systems has been indicated by the success of the models in predicting results which are commonly observed in the field (Andrews, 1971).

Curds (1971) studied the population dynamics of mixed cultures of micro-organisms in an activated sludge plant. The model considered the microbial population to consist of three primary groups of organisms, namely, dispersed sewage bacteria, the flocculating sludge bacteria and protozoa. The two types of bacteria were in competition with one another for the single limiting nutrient while the protozoa fed on the sewage bacteria. The rate reactions were assumed to obey simple Monod kinetics. The establishment of activated sludge populations was observed by computer solution of the differential equations. The equations were also analysed to yield steady-state populations at various dilution and sludge waste rates. Theoretical results, relating the quality of effluent to the microbial ecology, supplied quantitative explanations for observed phenomena.

B. Continuous culture

Sinclair and Topiwala (1970) observed that the steady-state viability of continuous cultures was a function of dilution rate. A model was proposed for bacterial growth which considered the bacterial mass to be made up of viable and non-viable fractions. Viable cells were assumed to lose mass owing to endogenous metabolism and also to be converted into dead cells. The rate of endogenous metabolism and the production of dead cells were both considered proportional to the viable cell mass. It was also assumed that dead cells do not lyse to any appreciable extent. The rates were expressed as:

Rate of generation of non-viable mass $= \gamma x_v$

Rate of consumption of substrate $\quad = \mu x_v/Y_p = \dfrac{\mu_m s x_v}{(K_s+s)Y_p}$

Rate of generation of viable mass $\quad = \mu x_v - K x_v - \gamma x_v$

where $\gamma =$ the cell death constant, $K =$ the endogenous metabolism constant, $Y_p =$ the yield factor, $\mu_m =$ the rate constant and $K_s =$ the rate saturation constant. A mass balance (eqn. (4)) in terms of the viable cell mass (x_v), non-viable cell mass (x_d) and substrate concentration (s) gives the following three differential equations for the case of a single-stage continuous culture:

$$\frac{dx_v}{dt} = \frac{\mu_m s\, x_v}{K_s + s} - Kx_v - \gamma x_v - Dx_v$$

$$\frac{dx_d}{dt} = \gamma x_v - Dx_d \tag{5}$$

$$\frac{ds}{dt} = D(s_R - s) - \frac{\mu_m s}{K_s + s}\,\frac{x_v}{Y_p}$$

The equations that result from a steady state analysis of the model (obtained by setting the derivatives to zero) were successful in fitting data from the literature. Figure 4 shows the simulation of steady-state data from experiments of Postgate and Hunter (1963). Transient predictions of the model were obtained by digital solutions of the equations. The theoretical responses of the total cell mass (x_t) and substrate concentration (s) to a step change in dilution rate are shown in Fig. 5. The large fraction of non-viable mass results in an initial washout of the culture, although x_t attained a higher value at the final steady state. This sort of dynamic behaviour is difficult to predict without the use of a model. The model itself could profitably be explored for cultures operating at low dilution rates, e.g. biotreaters.

C. Antibiotic production

Recently, a model which describes the production of the antibiotic griseofulvin has been proposed (Calam et al., 1971). The mechanistic model was developed by simulation of the main biochemical pathways. Seventeen differential equations were used to incorporate the postulated reaction mechanisms. The reactions represented the conversion of corn-steep liquor to pyruvate and ammonia, cell production, griseofulvin biosynthesis, production of ATP, formation of glucose from pyruvate, and fat metabolism. The model simulated semi-batch fermentations reasonably well and was used to predict the effects of changing operating conditions such as feed rates. The model drew attention to features of the fermentation which could not be foreseen in practical work.

D. Thermal death of bacteria

Mathematical models of kinetics of thermal death of organisms are of great practical interest since many industrial processes involve destruction of bacteria. Moats (1971) postulated a model of thermal death which explained many experimental observations. He hypothesized that death

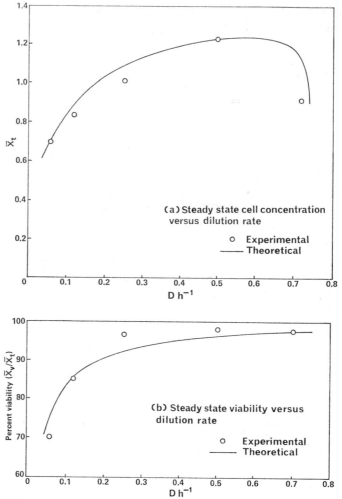

Fig. 4. Comparison of Postgate and Hunter's (1963) experimental data with steady-state model given by eqn. (6). Parameters for theoretical curves: $s_R = 2$, $\mu_m = 0.85$, $Y_p = 0.71$, $K_s = 0.01$, $K = 0.081$, $\gamma = 0.02$.

results from inactivation of a fixed number of "critical" sites whose nature is unknown. The model makes three fundamental assumptions: (1) that inactivation of individual sites occurs at random and follows first order kinetics; (2) that critical sites are of equal heat resistance; and (3) that the population is homogeneous with respect to its heat resistance. The model accounted for features such as initial lag in death rate, sublethal injury and dependence of death rate on the nature of heating and recovery media.

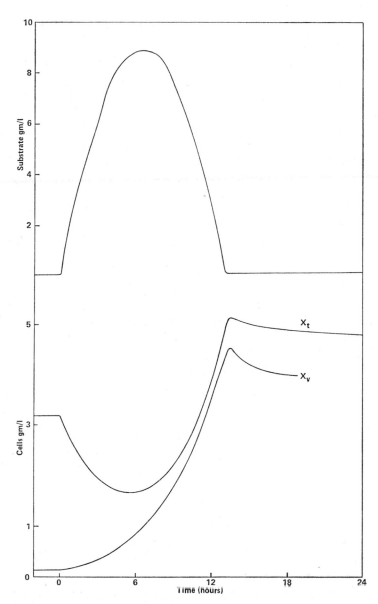

FIG. 5. Theoretical transient responses to step change in dilution rate according to eqn. (5). Parameters: $\mu_m = 0\cdot6$, $Y_p = 0\cdot4$, $K_s = 0\cdot01$, $K = 0\cdot07$, $\gamma = 0\cdot05$, $s_R = 15$, $D_1 = 0\cdot004$, $D_2 = 0\cdot24$.

VI. AIDS TO MATHEMATICAL WORK

A. Introduction

This Section is not intended as a general course in mathematics for the microbiologist but rather as a brief introduction to some mathematical tools which are commonly used in modelling microbiological systems. Excellent introductory texts for biologists with no formal training in mathematics are available (Saunders and Fleming, 1957; Smith, 1966).

The mathematical equations representing a model may be algebraic, differential, finite difference, etc., depending upon the system under investigation and the detail of its description. For instance the steady state of the system described in Section V.B is represented by a set of algebraic equations whereas the unsteady state is represented by a set of first order differential equations. The equations consist of symbols which may be classified in certain broad terms. A *variable* is a symbol representing a quantity whose magnitude is allowed to change in the particular situation the model is seeking to describe. Furthermore, *independent* variables can be varied by choice while there is no direct control over a dependent variable. There is a cause and effect relationship between independent and dependent variables. The term *parameters* describes the symbols whose magnitude is not allowed to change. The steady state description of the model in Section V.B is given by the equations:

$$\bar{x}_t = \frac{(D+\gamma)\ Y_p}{(D+\gamma+K)}\ (s_R - \bar{s})$$

$$\bar{s} = \frac{K_s(D+K+\gamma)}{\mu_m - (D+K+\gamma)} \tag{6}$$

If the dilution rate (D) is the only quantity changed by the experimenter the symbols can be classified as

$$\text{Independent variables} = D$$

$$\text{Dependent variables}\ \ = \bar{x}_t,\ \bar{s}$$

$$\text{Parameters}\ \ \ \ \ \ \ \ \ \ \ \ = Y_p,\ \mu_m,\ K_s,\ K,\ \gamma,\ s_R$$

B. Graphical methods

Visual display of results in the form of graphs aids comprehension and facilitates analysis of both experimental and theoretical work. Though the use of graphs is normally restricted to two variables, contour representation of three variables is not uncommon. Pictorial representation of more than three variables is impractical. For multivariable systems graphs can still be used by choosing two variables at a time and treating the other variables as parameters. In the treatment that follows the discussion will be confined to systems of two variables.

C. Comparison of theoretical and experimental work

A theoretical relationship between two variables y and x might be arranged in the form

$$f_1(y) = bf_2(x) + a \qquad (7)$$

From experimental measurements of y and x, values of the functions $f_1(y)$ and $f_2(x)$ are calculated and plotted in a graphical form. If the plotted points do not indicate a straight line relationship the proposed theory which yielded the theoretical relationship can be assumed to be invalid. Some scatter of experimental points about the straight line is not unusual even if the theory is correct. The scatter is due to random error in experimental results.

The type of linear transformation involved in the derivation of eqn. (7) can be illustrated by rearranging the Michaelis–Menten relationship.

$$\mu = \frac{\mu_m s}{K_s + s} \qquad (8)$$

to

$$\frac{1}{\mu} = \frac{K_s}{\mu_m} \left[\frac{1}{s} \right] + \frac{1}{\mu_m} \qquad (9)$$

A plot of the reciprocal of the variable μ vs the reciprocal of variable s will yield a straight line of slope K_s/μ_m and intercept $1/\mu_m$. If the random error is present only in one variable a "best" fitting line can be obtained by the method of least-squares (see Section VI.H). The value of the parameters K_s, μ_m can then be obtained from the slope and intercept of the "best" fitting line.

Special optimization techniques are employed (Rosenbrock and Storey, 1966; Megee, 1971) in dealing with complex models where the "best" values of a large number of parameters are required. These techniques are used to find the values of parameters in both algebraic and differential equations. As the number of model parameters increases, a large amount of experimental data has to be subjected to analysis for confidence in the numerical values of the parameters. There are instances when a best model has to be selected from a group of proposed models. This problem of model discrimination is discussed by Kittrell (1970).

D. Empirical curve fitting

In the absence of theoretical relationships, empirical equations which relate two or more variables are often sought to present results in a summarized form. However, with no guidance available from theory, the simplest equation which satisfactorily fits the data should be chosen. Though a polynomial with the same number of terms as experimental points can always be used to fit any set of data such an approach can only lead to cumbersome equations of little practical use. It is also dangerous to predict the value of a variable beyond the fitted points by extrapolating an empirical equation since equations which yield similar results over one range may diverge over other ranges (see Fig. 6).

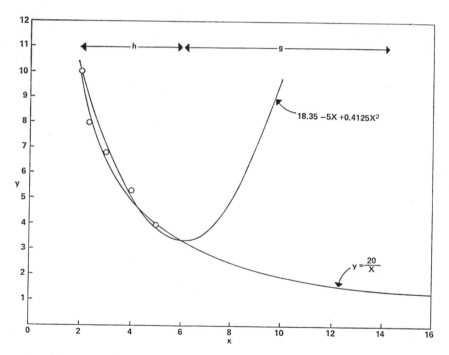

FIG. 6. Dangers of extrapolating empirical equations beyond experimental points. Both the equations give reasonable fits in range "h" but deviate in range "g".

Graphs with suitably chosen co-ordinates can be used to great advantage to deduce empirical relationships between the two variables x and y. A preliminary examination of the fundamental properties of the empirical equation is extremely useful in choosing the correct representative curve. Does the curve pass through the origin? How does its gradient change? Answers to questions of this type are rewarding since considerable time could otherwise be spent on the pursuit of wrong equations. On a linear graph paper a straight line gives a relationship of the type

$$y = bx + a \qquad (10)$$

while a slightly curved graph will indicate a relationship of the form

$$y = a + bx + cx^2 \qquad (11)$$

Caution should be exercised in the choice of scales on the graph since undue compression of one axis may lead to difficulty in detection of slight curvatures. Higher order polynomials may be used to represent curves of greater complexity, and the values of parameters a, b, c, etc., can be obtained by either direct substitution of numerical values of x and y or by repeated graphical differentiation. For instance eqn. (11) can be differentiated to yield

$$\frac{dy}{dx} = b + 2cx \qquad (12)$$

Thus, a plot of the slopes of tangents to the curve (dy/dx) *vs* x will be a straight line with slope equal to $2c$ and intercept equal to b.

In cases where the graphs display a rapidly changing slope, logarithmic or exponential relationships may be more suitable. An exponential relationship is given by the expression

$$y = ae^{bx} \qquad (13)$$

and a logarithmic relationship by

$$y = bx^n \qquad (14)$$

The use of special graph papers greatly facilitates the calculation of the parameters a, b, n in such relationships.

E. Linear graph paper

This type of graph paper has its axes divided into equal intervals which are usually subdivided into ten divisions. Thus it is good practice to choose a decimal scale which avoids factors of 3 and 7. Graph paper is often used for integration of the general equation $y = f(x)$ with respect to x. The area between the curve and the limits of integration is calculated by counting the enclosed squares.

F. Semilogarithmic graph paper (exponential growth and disappearance)

In the analysis of microbial systems one often encounters some variable which is increasing or decreasing at a rate which is directly proportional to the magnitude of the variable itself. The increase of biomass in the exponential region of a batch culture and the logarithmic death rate of micro-organisms during heat sterilization can be cited as examples. The equation of exponential change can be written as

$$\pm \frac{dy}{dx} = ky \tag{15}$$

where

  $x =$ independent variable
  $y =$ dependent variable
and $k =$ a constant of proportionality

Taking x to be time, t, eqn. (15) can be rearranged to obtain

$$\left(\pm \frac{dy}{dt}\right)\Big/ y = k \tag{16}$$

According to the above equation, the proportional rate of change of y is equal to the constant k which has the dimensions of reciprocal time. Eqn. (16) can be integrated to yield.

$$\log_e y = \log_e A \pm kt \tag{17}$$

or

$$y = Ae^{\pm kt} \tag{18}$$

where A is the constant of integration which is equal to the value of y when $t = 0$. There are two general ways of specifying the rate of exponential change. One is to give the value of the constant k in the appropriate unit, e.g. h^{-1}. The second is the time required for y to change to some factor of the original value. Hence the term "doubling time" specifies the time taken for y to double with exponential growth, while "half time" in the case of exponential decrease specifies the time for y to decrease to half its original value. In either case this time can be obtained from eqn. (17) as:

$$\text{doubling time or half time} = \frac{\log_e 2}{k} \tag{19}$$

Introducing a new dependent variable, Y, eqn. (17) can also be expressed as:

$$Y = \pm kx + \log_e A \tag{20}$$

where $Y = \log_e y$. A plot of Y against x will give a straight line of intercept $\log_e A$ and slope $\pm k$.

 Since exponential expressions are frequently used semilogarithmic graph paper (Fig. 7) is available which has one normal arithmetic scale and one scale divided logarithmically. This type of graph paper permits

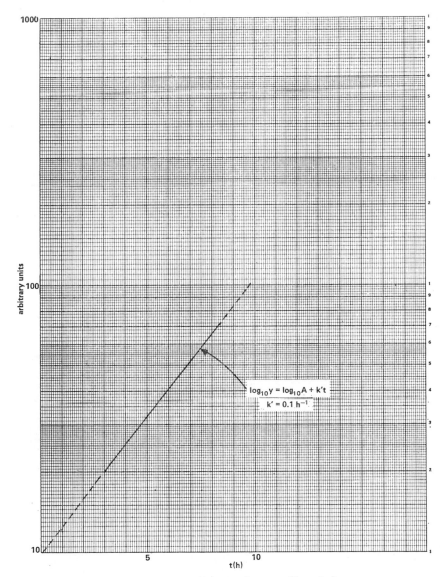

FIG. 7. A semilog graph paper (2 cycles).

the values of y to be plotted directly and saves evaluating Y first and then plotting on linear scales. The logarithmic scale is available in a variety of cycles. Each cycle represents a single $\log_{10}$ unit and hence a 10-fold range of numbers. Caution should be exercised in determining the parameter $\pm k$ of eqn. (20) by the use of semilogarithmic graph paper. In eqns. (17) and (20) the logarithms are taken to the base e whereas a straight line drawn on a semilogarithmic scale has the equation:

$$\log_{10} y = \log_{10} A \pm k't \tag{21}$$

where $k' = 0.4343$ k. Moreover, the gradient k' must not be determined by reading the scales which give values of y. If the gradient is determined by linear measurement of sides it must be corrected for the scales of the axes.

G. Logarithmic graph paper

In many situations (e.g. dimensional analysis) an empirical equation of the form

$$y = bx^n \tag{14}$$

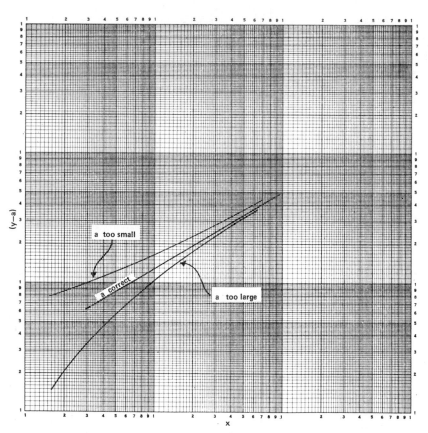

FIG. 8. A log-log graph paper (3×3 cycles). The straight line has the equation $y = a + bx^n$.

proves very useful. The logarithmic form of such an equation can be written as

$$Y = nX + B \tag{22}$$

where $Y = \log_e y$, $X = \log_e x$ and $B = \log_e b$. A graph paper with both scales divided logarithmically can thus be used to plot values of y and x directly. Logarithmic graph paper is also used for curve fitting empirical equations of the type:

$$y = a + bx^n \tag{23}$$

by estimating values of "a" and plotting $(y - a)$ *vs* x. The correct value of "a" results (see Fig. 8) in a straight-line relationship.

H. Least-square fitting

As stated previously, this method is used to fit the "best" straight line to a set of data consisting of N pairs of results for x and y. The method assumes that the quantity y is liable to random error while x is a quantity with negligible error. The equation of the best straight line is:

$$y = mx + c \tag{24}$$

and the method seeks the values of the slope m and intercept c which minimize the sum of the squares of the vertical deviations (Fig. 9) from the straight line. To obtain positive representation for the errors (error may be positive or negative) the deviations are squared. If the individual deviation of each point from the line is represented by the symbol "l", the sum of the squares of deviations is given by:

$$L = \sum_{n=1}^{N} l_n^2$$

where $l_n = y_n - mx_n - c$. For L to be minimum

$$\left(\frac{dL}{dm} \right)_c = 0 \text{ and } \left(\frac{dL}{dc} \right)_m = 0$$

The resultant equations can be solved to yield the values of m and c:

$$m = \frac{N \sum x_n y_n - \sum x_n \sum y_n}{N \sum x_n^2 - (\sum x_n)^2} \tag{25}$$

$$c = \frac{\sum x_n^2 \sum y_n - \sum x_n y_n \sum x_n}{N \sum x_n^2 - (\sum x_n)^2} \tag{26}$$

Manual calculation of m and c can be tedious if the number of experimental points (N) is large but the problem can be easily tackled on most minicomputers.

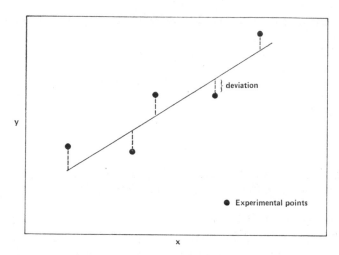

y

x

FIG. 9. The least-square fit line.

Section VI.C showed how a non-linear equation such as the Michaelis–Menten relationship can be transformed so that a straight line graph could be utilized to obtain "best" values of parameters such as K_s and μ_m. However, prior to fitting a transformed equation to unweighted data it must be ascertained that the method has not resulted in distortion of error. Fig. 10a shows the plotted relationship between μ and s according to the theoretical equation:

$$\mu = \frac{\mu_m s}{K_s + s} \tag{8}$$

The dotted line shows the influence of a constant experimental error of $0\cdot05\ \mathrm{h}^{-1}$ above and below the true value of the rate μ. Fig. 10b shows the straight line plot of the transformed relations:

$$\frac{1}{\mu} = \frac{K_s}{\mu_m}\left[\frac{1}{s}\right] + \frac{1}{\mu_m} \tag{9}$$

The broken line shows the effect of the random error in μ on the plot of $1/\mu$ vs $1/s$. It can be seen that the constant error in μ has an enormous influence on the points which represent the slower rates. Because of the fixed error the experimental points representing the high rates are more reliable but are bunched near the intercept. Thus when determining the best straight line for Fig. 10b the more reliable points must be given far more weight.

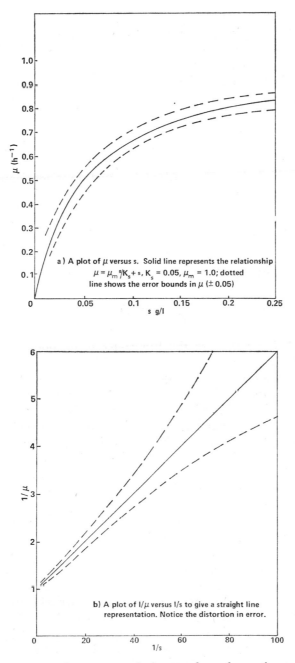

a) A plot of μ versus s. Solid line represents the relationship $\mu = \mu_m \frac{s}{K_s + s}$, $K_s = 0.05$, $\mu_m = 1.0$; dotted line shows the error bounds in μ ($\pm\,0.05$)

b) A plot of $1/\mu$ versus $1/s$ to give a straight line representation. Notice the distortion in error.

FIG. 10. Least-square fit for transformed equation.

I. Digital computer solutions

Many models of microbiological systems give rise to series of ordinary differential equations such as equation (5). Generally they are of first order but non-linear. Analytical solutions of such equations are rare and resort has to be made to the use of computers. Analogue computers are quite adequate for the study of simple problems but for more complex problems digital computers have several advantages. They can deal with a large number of equations with great accuracy. Statistical and optimization techniques can be readily incorporated in the overall solution.

Various numerical techniques (Rosenbrock and Storey, 1966) are available for the solution of first order differential equations. Simple methods such as the Trapezium rule and Simpson's rule can be utilized for solution of equations of the type:

$$\frac{dy}{dx} = f(x) \tag{27}$$

For more complicated problems such as:

$$\frac{dy}{dx} = f(x, y) \tag{28}$$

advanced techniques such as the Runge–Kutta methods are employed. These iterative methods start from the initial conditions ($y=y_0$, $x=x_0$) and estimate values of y at $x=x_0+h$ where h is an adjustable integration interval. The solution is by means of a series of small step lengths from the initial to the final value of the independent variables. Some differential equations have widely separated *eigen-values* and present severe numerical integration problems of stability. Such equations are called "stiff" equations and special techniques (Seinfeld *et al.*, 1970) have to be employed to solve them. Higher order differential equations are also solved by numerical methods since an nth order equation can be converted to "n" simultaneous first order equations.

The digital computer has to be provided with an orderly sequence of instructions (programme) to enable it to solve the problem under consideration (see Ware, this Series, Vol. 7A, for a general account). Though the computer actually obeys instructions in a "machine code" most users supply the "programme" in a "higher level" language such as FORTRAN. The manufacturer supplies the computer with a compiler which translates the instruction from the user language to the machine code. The first step in writing a programme for a digital computer is to draw a flow chart which organizes the solution of the problem in logical steps. Figure 11 shows a flow chart which was used for the solution of the differential equations

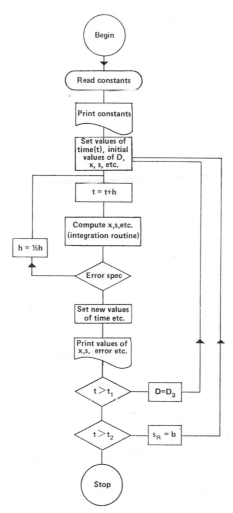

FIG. 11. Generalized flow diagram for the programme to solve eqn. (5). h = integration interval; D_2, t_1, t_2 and b = preset constants.

presented in Section V.B. It is evident that the programme can be divided into three distinct sections of (a) reading of data, (b) principal calculations, and (c) presentation of results. It is often found that many sequences of instructions are basically common to different programmes and are called "routines". Most high level languages provide previously prepared routines which can be readily utilized in programmes. Thus a programmer can call for library routines to perform operations such as reading arrays of numbers from a data tape or numerically integrate differential equations without having to write all the programme instructions every time the same operation has to be performed.

J. Simulation languages

For workers who have no desire to learn digital computer programming but have the need to use large-scale digital machines, problem-orientated programmes have been devised (I.B.M. Ltd., 1969). The programmes provide basic sets of functional blocks with which the components of the mathematical model are represented. The use of a simulation language through an online teletype permits rapid setting up of complex models. Moreover, it provides for an interactive approach so that values of parameters in a model can be adjusted during a simulation exercise.

K. Stability of microbiological systems

Recently there has been considerable (Boddy *et al.*, 1967; Strickland and Ackerman, 1966; Koga and Humphrey, 1967; Degn and Harrison, 1969) interest in the dynamic analysis of microbiological models. Information about stability of the system is of interest not only to control engineers but also to microbiologists, since phenomena such as cyclic oscillations reveal interesting patterns in metabolic activity. Many mathematical techniques have been proposed for stability analysis of systems represented by non-linear differential equations. Some of these techniques have been used (e.g. Megee, 1971) to study the stability of continuous culture models.

REFERENCES

Andrews, J. F. (1971). "Biological Waste Treatment" (Ed. Canale, R.P.). Interscience Publishers, New York.
Bischoff, K. B. (1966). *Can. J. Ch. E.*, **44**, 281.
Boddy, A., Clarke, P. H., Houldsworth, M. A., and Lilly, M. D. (1967). *J. gen. Microbiol.*, **48**, 137.
Calam, C. T., Ellis, S. H., and McCann, M. J. (1971). *J. appl. Chem. Biotechnol.*, **21**, 181–189.
Curds, C. R. (1971). *Water Res.*, **5**, 793.
Danckwerts, P. V. (1958). *Chem. Eng. Sci.*, **8**, 93.
Degn, H., and Harrison, D. E. F. (1969). *J. Theoret. Biol.*, **22**, 238–248.
Denbigh, K. G., and Turner, J. C. R. (1971). "Chemical Reactor Theory". C.U.P., London.
Eakman, J. M., Fredrickson, A. G., and Tsuchiya, H. M. (1966). *Chem. Eng. Proc. Sympos. Ser. No.* 69, **62**, 37–49.
Fredrickson, A. G., and Tsuchiya, H. M. (1963). *AIChE J.*, **9**, 459–468.
Himmelblau, D. M., and Bischoff, K. B. (1968). "Process Analysis and Simulation". John Wiley and Sons, New York.
I.B.M. Limited, Manual No. H 20-0367-2 (1969) and revisions. System/360 Continuous Modelling System Program (360A-CX-16X). I.B.M. Corporation, New York.

Kattan, A., and Adler, R. J. (1972). *Chem. Eng. Sci.*, **27**, 1013–1028.
Kittrell, J. R. (1970). *Advan. Chem. Eng.*, **8**, 97–183.
Koga, S., and Humphrey, A. E. (1967). *Biotech. Bioeng.*, **9**, 375.
Megee, R. D. (1971). Ph.D. Thesis, University of Minnesota, Minneapolis, Minnesota.
Moats, W. A. (1971). *J. Bact.*, **105**, 165 171.
Monod, J. (1949). *Ann. Inst. Pasteur*, **79**, 390.
Postgate, J. R., and Hunter, J. R. (1963). *J. appl. Bact.*, **26**, 295.
Ramkrishna, D. (1965). Ph.D. Thesis, University of Minnesota, Minneapolis, Minnesota.
Rosenbrock, H. H., and Storey, C. (1966). "Computational Techniques for Chemical Engineers". Pergamon Press, New York.
Saunders, L., and Fleming, R. (1957). "Mathematics and Statistics for Use in Pharmacy, Biology and Chemistry". Pharmaceutical Press, London.
Seinfeld, J. H., Lapidus, L., and Hwang, M. (1970). *Ind. Eng. Chem. Fundamen.*, **9**, 266–275.
Sinclair, C. G., and Topiwala, H. H. (1970). *Biotech. Bioeng.*, **12**, 1069.
Smith, C. A. B. (1966). "Biomathematics". Charles Griffin and Company Limited, London.
Strickland, E. H., and Ackermann, E. (1966). *Nature, Lond.*, **209**, 405.
Tsai, B. I., Erickson, L. E., and Fan, L. T. (1969). *Biotech. Bioeng.*, **11**, 181.
Tsuchiya, H. M., Fredrickson, A. G., and Aris, R. (1966). *Advan. Chem. Eng.*, **6**, 125–206.
Zwietering, Th. N. (1959). *Chem. Eng. Sci.*, **11**, 1.

CHAPTER III

Isolation, Growth and Maintenance of Anaerobic Free-living Spirochetes

E. CANALE-PAROLA

Department of Microbiology, University of Massachusetts, Amherst, Massachusetts 01002, U.S.A.

I.	Introduction	61
II.	Isolation	63
	A. Selection by filtration	63
	B. Selection by migration through agar media . . .	65
	C. Filtration and migration method	66
III.	Growth	68
	A. *Spirochaeta stenostrepta*	68
	B. *Spirochaeta litoralis*	69
	C. *Spirochaeta zuelzerae*	70
	D. *Spirochaeta aurantia*	71
IV.	Maintenance of spirochetes	71
References	. . . .	73

I. INTRODUCTION

Strictly anaerobic and facultatively anaerobic, free-living spirochetes occur commonly in aquatic environments, such as the water and mud of ponds, lakes, rivers and oceans. Presently these bacteria are classified in the genus *Spirochaeta*. This genus includes five species, listed in Table I. Species one to four (Table I) have been isolated and studied (Canale-Parola *et al.*, 1967 and 1968; Breznak and Canale-Parola, 1969; Hespell and Canale-Parola, 1970a and 1970b; Holt and Canale-Parola, 1968; Joseph and Canale-Parola, 1972; Veldkamp, 1960). They were found to be saccharolytic and to ferment carbohydrates mainly to acetate, ethanol, CO_2 and H_2, except for *S. zuelzerae* which does not form ethanol but produces lactate and succinate. Lactate is formed only as a minor product by the other three species.

S. aurantia is capable of growing aerobically as well as anaerobically and, in the presence of O_2, its colonies are yellow-orange, due to the synthesis of carotenoid pigments (Breznak and Canale-Parola, 1969).

The main chemical role that known species of *Spirochaeta* play in nature is the degradation of carbohydrates. However, the natural occurrence of anaerobic and facultatively anaerobic, free-living spirochetes capable of dissimilating other compounds is likely. The use of appropriate selective enrichment techniques will probably yield such strains.

The currently accepted classification of anaerobic and facultatively anaerobic, free-living spirochetes is a provisional one (Canale-Parola *et al.*, 1968). A revision will undoubtedly become necessary as additional information on poorly characterized species (e.g. *S. plicatilis*, the type species) and on new isolates is obtained. Most likely such a revision will result in the assignment of the strictly anaerobic free-living spirochetes to one genus, and of the facultatively anaerobic forms to another (Canale-Parola *et al.*, 1968).

Selective isolation methods have been developed for the small free-living spirochetes (Table I) and these organisms can be cultured in readily

TABLE I

Characteristics of recognized species of *Spirochaeta*[a]

Organisms	Size (μm)	No. of axial fibrils	Relation to O_2	GC content of DNA[b] (moles %)
I. Small spirochetes				
1. *S. stenostrepta*	0·2 to 0·3 by 15 to 45, up to 300	2	Obligate anaerobe	60·2
2. *S. zuelzerae*	0·2 to 0·35 by 8 to 16	2	Obligate anaerobe	56·1
3. *S. litoralis*	0·4 to 0·5 by 5 to 7	2	Obligate anaerobe	50·5
4. *S. aurantia*	0·3 by 10 to 20	2	Facultative anaerobe	56·7–60
II. Large spirochetes				
5. *S. plicatilis*	0·5 to 0·75 by 100 to 200, up to 500	Many	Unknown	Not determined

[a] Data are from Canale-Parola *et al.* (1968); Breznak and Canale-Parola (1969); Hespell and Canale-Parola (1970b); Blakemore and Canale-Parola, in press; Breznak and Canale-Parola, in press.

[b] Guanine + cytosine (GC) content of DNA determined by buoyant density in CsCl for species 1–3, and by thermal denaturation for species 4.

prepared media. Because of their ease of cultivation these bacteria constitute useful tools for the study of the fundamental biological properties of spirochetes in general.

II. ISOLATION

Two selective factors have been frequently used for the enrichment and isolation of thin, free-living spirochetes. The first is the ability of the spirochetes to pass through filters with pore diameters small enough (0·2 to 0·45 μm) to retain most other bacteria. The second selective factor is the ability of spirochetes to migrate readily through agar media containing as much as 1 g of agar per 100 ml. Migration of other bacteria is largely prevented at this agar concentration. The two selective factors have been combined in some isolation procedures.

A. Selection by filtration

Thin, anaerobic spirochetes present in mud are separated from the majority of the accompanying microbial flora by filtration of mud suspensions through cellulose ester filter discs (Millipore). The slender and flexible spirochetes pass through the small pores of the filter discs, whereas most other bacteria do not. The resulting filtrate is inoculated into appropriate culture broths to allow growth of the spirochetes.

This type of procedure has been used successfully for the isolation of strict anaerobes, such as *S. stenostrepta* (Canale-Parola *et al.*, 1967 and 1968) and *S. litoralis* (Hespell and Canale-Parola, 1970b), which are typically present in H_2S-containing aquatic environments.

Strains of *S. stenostrepta* have been isolated as follows. Black mud was collected at the edge of fresh-water ponds and streams. To promote H_2S production by micro-organisms present in the mud, some mud samples were mixed with $CaSO_4$ and cellulose powder (approx. one part by volume of each per ten parts of mud), and were kept in a container at room temperature for one or more months. Mud, from which an odour of H_2S emanated, was suspended in a sulphide solution (1 vol. mud per 2 vol. 0·02% $Na_2S.9H_2O$, w/v). The mixture was filtered through filter paper (Whatman No. 40) to remove large particles, and the filtrate passed through a sterile cellulose ester filter disc (Millipore, 0·45 μm pore dia.). One ml samples of the resulting filtrate were added aseptically to 60 ml glass bottles containing approximately 30 ml of sterile isolation medium (Table II). Each bottle was then completely filled with the medium, sealed with a ground-glass stopper, covered with a sterile 50 ml beaker, and incubated at 30°C. After approximately one week of incubation, the microbial population in many of the bottles consisted predominantly of thin spirochetes. Thin rods and spirilla were frequently present. Pure cultures of the spirochetes were obtained by using dilution shake cultures, with sterile paraffin layered over the medium, or by pour-plating serial dilutions and incubating the plates anaerobically (e.g. Bray dishes, A. H. Thomas, P.O. Box 779, Philadelphia,

TABLE II

Isolation medium for *Spirochaeta stenostrepta*[a]

Distilled water	875 ml
Glucose	5 g
Peptone	2 g
Yeast extract	0·3 g
Vitamin B_{12}	10^{-5} g
Phosphate solution[b]	15 ml
Salts solution[c]	100 ml
Sulphide solution[d]	10 ml

[a] The medium is sterilized by heat. A precipitate present in the freshly autoclaved medium disappears upon cooling to room temperature. The pH of the complete, sterilized medium is 6·9.

[b] KH_2PO_4, 3 g; K_2HPO_4, 7 g; dist. water, 100 ml.

[c] The salts solution is prepared as follows. Ethylenediamine tetra-acetic acid (EDTA), 0·2 g, is added to 800 ml of dist. water. The EDTA is dissolved by heating and the pH of the solution is adjusted to 7 with KOH. Then, the following salts are added: $MgSO_4.7H_2O$, 2 g; $CaCl_2.2H_2O$, 0·75 g; $FeSO_4.7H_2O$, 0·1 g; trace element solution, 5 ml. The volume of the salts solution is adjusted to 1000 ml with dist. water. The trace element solution is prepared as follows. Each of the salts listed below is dissolved separately in dist. water. The pH of the Na_2MoO_4 and $NaVO_3$ solutions is adjusted to a value below 7. The salt solutions are mixed in the order in which they are listed below, beginning with the $AlCl_3$ solution. The following salts are added (g per 1800 ml final volume): $AlCl_3.6H_2O$, 0·5; KI, KBr, LiCl, 0·25 each; $MnCl_2.4H_2O$, 3·5; H_3BO_3, 5·5; $ZnCl_2$, $CuCl_2·2H_2O$, $NiCl_2.6H_2O$, $CoCl_2.6H_2O$, 0·5 each; $SnCl_2.2H_2O$, $BaCl_2.2H_2O$, 0·15 each; $Na_2MoO_4.2H_2O$, 0·25; $NaVO_3$, 0·05. The pH of the mixture is adjusted to a value between 3 and 4 with HCl. At first a yellow precipitate is present which changes to a fine white precipitate after a few days. The solution may be kept at room temperature and should be thoroughly mixed before use. This trace element solution is a modification of that described by Pfennig (1965).

[d] $Na_2S.9H_2O$, 2 g; dist. water, 100 ml. Sterilized separately, added immediately before inoculation.

Pa., U.S.A.). The isolation medium, solidified with 1·5 g of agar (Difco) per 100 ml, was used. After 5 to 6 days of incubation at 30°C colonies of spirochetes were present.

S. litoralis was isolated from marine H_2S-containing mud by a method similar to that described for *S. stenostrepta* (Hespell and Canale-Parola, 1970b). However, a different isolation medium was used (Table III), and the cultures were incubated at 22 to 23°C. The mud serving as source of the organism was suspended in isolation medium (1 : 5, v/v), rather than in sulphide solution, prior to filtration.

TABLE III

Isolation medium for *Spirochaeta litoralis*

Distilled water	100 ml
Tryptone	0·3 g
Yeast extract	0·05 g
NaCl	2 g
M K phosphate buffer (pH 7·4)	2 ml
Salt solution[a]	0·2 ml

The pH of the medium is adjusted to 7·3 before sterilization by heating. Immediately before inoculation the sterilized medium is supplemented with the following sterile solutions:

Glucose soln. (25 g/100 ml dist. water)	2 ml
$Na_2S.9H_2O$ soln. (10 g/100 ml dist. water)	0·5 ml

[a] Dist. water, 75 ml; tetrasodium ethylenediamine tetra-acetate, 1 g; $CaCl_2.2H_2O$ 3·75 g; $MgCl_2.6H_2O$, 12·5 g; $FeSO_4.7H_2O$, 0·5 g. To 75 ml of this mixture 25 ml of trace element solution (see Table II) are added.

B. Selection by migration through agar media

Anaerobic free-living spirochetes are isolated readily from their natural environment by methods which allow them to migrate through agar media. The migration is probably due to chemotaxis toward the substrate. In these procedures spirochete-containing mud may be placed in a "well" dug in the centre of a plate of agar medium. During anaerobic incubation the spirochetes grow and diffuse into the agar medium, away from the "well", forming a subsurface growth veil which extends toward the periphery of the plate. The growth of most contaminants is restricted to the "well". The rate of migration of saccharolytic spirochetes is greater in media containing low sugar concentrations (e.g. 0·02% glucose, w/v). Spirochetes from the growth veil are used to obtain pure cultures by standard techniques.

The following is a procedure successfully used for the isolation of spirochetes from marine mud. The isolation medium contains: beef extract (Lab-Lemco), yeast extract, and peptone, 0·1 g each; Ionagar No. 2 (Oxoid, Colab Lab. Inc.), 0·7 or 0·8 g; distilled water, 50 ml; sea water, 50 ml. Thick plates of this medium are prepared in 60×20 mm sterile plastic Petri dishes (Lab–Tek Products, Division of Miles Lab., Westmont, Ill., U.S.A., cat. No. 4036) and are allowed to stand at room temperature for several hours. A small cylindrical "well" (2 or 3 mm wide) is dug in the centre of each plate by aspirating some of the agar medium with a thin-walled, sterile pipette (e.g. a Pasteur pipette) connected to a suction apparatus. The depth of the "well" should be approximately one half that of the agar plate. Liquid which oozes out from the agar gel into the "well" is removed by suction. Then a small volume of spirochete-containing mud or water is placed in the "well" and the plates are incubated in argon atmosphere at 30°C. A small amount of moisture-absorbing material (e.g. anhydrous $CaSO_4$) should be added to the container in which the plates are incubated, to minimize condensation.

The medium contains trace amounts of carbohydrates which are utilized by the spirochetes for growth. Occasionally growth of contaminants occurs on the plate surface near the "well" and masks the spirochetal growth veil. When liquid is allowed to overflow from the "well", or liquid resulting from excessive condensation is present on the agar medium, contaminants may grow and spread extensively on the plate surface. This surface growth generally prevents the formation of the spirochetal growth veil.

After the appearance of a growth veil consisting of spirochetes, cells from the outermost edge of the veil are used to obtain pure cultures by procedures involving either dilution through shake cultures (layered with paraffin) or plating and anaerobic incubation (e.g. Bray dishes).

C. Filtration and migration method

A combination of the filtration and migration methods has been used for the isolation of facultatively anaerobic spirochetes e.g. *S. aurantia* (Breznak and Canale-Parola, 1969). Other bacteria, such as thin spirilla and small vibrios, may also be isolated by this procedure (Canale-Parola *et al.*, 1966).

Sterile cellulose ester filter discs (Millipore, 47 mm disc dia., 0·3 or 0·45 μm pore dia.) are placed on the surface of isolation medium plates (Table IV). One filter disc is placed on the surface of each plate, in the centre. From 0·05 to 0·1 ml of pond water or pond water-mud slurry, prefiltered through filter paper (Whatman No. 40) to remove large particles, is added to the centre of each filter disc. The plates are incubated at 30°C for 12 to 24 h to allow spirochetes in the inoculum to move through the filter discs on to the medium surface. Then the filter discs are removed aseptically from the plates and incubation is continued. The plates are examined periodically for the appearance of subsurface, semi-transparent, veil-like growth of spirochetes. The growth veil migrates toward the periphery of the plate, away from colonies of other small micro-organisms which have passed through the filter pores. Growth of spirochetes becomes apparent after five to 10 days of incubation. Generally, if spirochetes are microscopically visible in the inoculum, 10% to 20% of the plates yield spirochetal growth veils. Pure cultures are obtained by streaking cells from the outer edge of the growth veil on plates of isolation medium (Table IV) or other suitable media (maltose broth, GTY broth, plus 1% agar; see Table V).

TABLE IV

Isolation media for *S. aurantia*

Medium components[a]	Amounts[b]		
	Medium HE	Medium PEP	Medium GYP
Distilled water (ml)	50	100	100
Peptone	0·1	0·5	0·2
Yeast extract	0·1	0·05	0·2
Glucose	—	—	0·2
K_2HPO_4 (anhyd.)	—	0·01	—
Hay extract[c] (ml)	50	—	—
Agar (Difco)	1	1	1

[a] Prior to sterilization the pH of HE medium is adjusted to 6·5, and that of GYP medium to 7·5.

[b] Expressed in grams, unless otherwise indicated.

[c] Prepared by boiling 0·5 g of dried barn hay in 100 ml of distilled water for 10 min. The boiled mixture is filtered through Whatman No. 40 filter paper. The filtrate (hay extract) is used for medium preparation.

TABLE V

Growth media

Medium component[a]	Amount[b]			
	GYPT medium	Maltose broth	GTY broth	SZ medium
Distilled water (ml)	100	99	99	100
Glucose	0·5	—	0·2	0·2
Maltose	—	0·2	—	—
Yeast extract	0·2	0·4	0·2	0·4
Peptone	0·2	0·2	—	—
Trypticase (BBL)	—	—	0·5	—
Na thioglycolate (or L-cysteine)	0·05	—	—	0·05
$CaCl_2.2H_2O$	—	—	—	0·004
$MgSO_4.7H_2O$	—	—	—	0·05
$NaHCO_3$	—	—	—	0·1
KH_2PO_4	—	—	—	0·1
M K phosphate buffer, pH7 (ml)	—	1	1	—

[a] pH adjustments prior to sterilization: medium GYPT, pH 7·3–7·6; maltose and GTY broths, pH 7·5; SZ medium, pH 7·2. The M K phosphate buffer, $NaHCO_3$ and KH_2PO_4 are added to the sterile media as separately sterilized solutions.

[b] Expressed in grams unless otherwise indicated.

Spreading growth veils are occasionally formed by other bacteria which swim through the pores of the filter discs. Most frequent among these organisms are thin spirilla resembling *Spirillum gracile* (Canale-Parola *et al.*, 1966) and relatively long (10 μm) motile rods of small diameter (0·3 μm), which are extremely flexible.

III. GROWTH

Most of the free-living anaerobic and facultatively anaerobic spirochetes which have been cultured grow abundantly in media containing a fermentable carbohydrate and complex nutritive materials such as yeast extract and peptone. Addition of small amounts (0·05 g/100 ml) of reducing agents, such as sodium thioglycolate, L-cysteine or sodium sulphide. to culture media for the strictly anaerobic forms is either required for growth or helps initiate growth.

The obligately anaerobic spirochetes may be grown in Florence flasks filled to the neck with culture broth, or in test-tubes (e.g. 16×150 mm tubes each containing 12 ml of medium). The media are cooled to approximately 30°C after sterilization by heat and are inoculated immediately. Media which have been stored after sterilization are heated for 5–10 min in a boiling water bath or a steamer to drive off dissolved oxygen, and then are rapidly cooled to 30°C prior to inoculation. Cultures incubated in air are layered with sterile paraffin. However, a paraffin seal is not necessary for broth cultures if a relatively large volume of a log phase culture is used as inoculum (e.g. 5×10^8 to 10^9 cells in 5 ml of culture used to inoculate 100 ml of medium).

The strictly anaerobic species grow readily in media gelled by the addition of 1 or 1·5 g of agar per 100 ml. In these agar media *S. stenostrepta* (GYPT medium, Table V), *S. litoralis* (isolation medium, Table III), and *S. zuelzerae* (SZ medium, Table V) usually form white or cream-coloured, spherical, fluffy subsurface colonies, which range from 1 to 5 mm in dia. depending on the length of incubation and on other growth conditions.

S. aurantia is cultured by techniques commonly used for the cultivation of facultatively anaerobic bacteria. The colony morphology of this spirochete is described in a following Section.

A. *Spirochaeta stenostrepta*

Information available on the growth and nutritional characteristics of *S. stenostrepta* has been derived mainly from studies on strain Zl (Canale-Parola *et al.*, 1967 and 1968; Hespell and Canale-Parola, 1970a).

S. stenostrepta grows in medium GYPT (Table V) to final yields of 2×10^8 to 3×10^8 cells/ml. The generation time in this medium is approximately 6 h and growth ceases when the pH of the cultures reaches values between 5·5 and 5·3, even though glucose is still available in the medium. From 10^8 to 10^9 cells are used as inoculum per 100 ml of medium GYPT. Incubation temperature is 30°C.

Greater yields, up to 10^9 cells/ml, are obtained by buffering medium GYPT with N-2-hydroxyethylpiperazine-N'-2-ethanesulphonic acid (HEPES) or piperazine-N,N'-bis(2-ethanesulphonic acid) (PIPES) at final concentrations of 0·033M (initial pH of complete medium, 7·5). On the other hand, the addition of phosphate or Tris buffers (pH 7, sterilized separately) to medium GYPT at levels as low as 0·02M inhibits growth, the final yield being less than 10^7 cells/ml (Hespell and Canale-Parola, 1970a).

When large numbers of cells are desirable it is possible to obtain higher cell yields of *S. stenostrepta* by increasing the buffer content of the medium. This may be accomplished by adding greater amounts of yeast extract to medium GYPT and by repeated additions of $NaHCO_3$ or Na_2CO_3 to the growing culture. For example, the organism may be mass-cultured in 20-litre flasks filled with GYPT medium including 0·6 g of yeast extract per 100 ml. After the cultures enter the second half of the exponential growth phase, the pH is maintained above six by periodic additions of $NaHCO_3$ solution. Under these conditions, final yields approximating 10^{10} cells/ml have been obtained (Hespell and Canale-Parola, 1970a).

In addition to D-glucose, *S. stenostrepta* ferments a variety of hexoses, pentoses, and disaccharides. Exogenous supplies of biotin, riboflavin, and vitamin B_{12} are either required or stimulatory for growth. Furthermore, the organism apparently requires a growth factor present in yeast extract (Hespell and Canale-Parola, 1970a).

B. *Spirochaeta litoralis*

The growth and nutrition of *S. litoralis* strain R1 were studied by Hespell and Canale-Parola (1970b). This organism has been cultured routinely in isolation medium (Table III), in which it grows to densities of 6×10^8 to 9×10^8 cells/ml. Substitution of L-cystcine, sodium thioglycolate, or L-ascorbic acid for sulphide, in the isolation medium, results in lower growth yields. Media to which a reducing agent is not added do not support growth. The initial pH and the buffer content of the medium affect the final growth yield of *S. litoralis*. Highest cell yields were obtained at initial pH values between 7 and 7·5. Increasing the amount of phosphate buffer, in the isolation medium, to a concentration of 0·06M results in final growth yields slightly greater than 10^9 cells/ml. This may be contrasted with the response of *S. stenostrepta* and *S. aurantia*, neither of which grows when the phosphate buffer concentration in the medium is 0·06 M.

A modified isolation medium, useful for mass-culturing *S. litoralis*, contains 0·25% (w/v) yeast extract and 0·06M (final concentration) potassium phosphate buffer. In this medium the final growth yield approaches 10^{10} cells/ml at 30°C and the generation time is 2·2 h. At 25°C or 35°C the generation time is 3·5 h, and at 15°C the rate of growth is very low. No detectable growth occurs at 5°C or above 40°C.

D-Glucose serves as a fermentable substrate for *S. litoralis*, and the omission of this sugar from the isolation medium prevents growth. Other fermentable substrates are various pentoses, hexoses, and disaccharides. Amino-acids, sugar alcohols, tricarboxylic acid cycle intermediates, and other organic acids are not fermented (Hespell and Canale-Parola, 1970b).

S. litoralis may be grown in a chemically defined medium containing glucose, amino-acids, growth factors, NaCl, Na_2S, and other inorganic salts. This medium, which supports growth yields of $5·5 \times 10^8$ cells/ml, has been used to investigate the growth factor requirements of the organisms (Hespell and Canale-Parola, 1970b). It was found that exogenous supplements of biotin, niacin and coenzyme A are required for growth. Pantothenate, a component of the coenzyme A molecule, replaces coenzyme A as an exogenous growth factor, but the resulting growth yields are low. The addition of thiamine to the medium stimulates growth.

S. litoralis is a marine spirochete, grows readily in media prepared with sea water, and has specific requirements for Na^+ and Cl^- ions. The organism does not grow in fresh water media containing less than 0·05M NaCl (final concentration). The highest cell yields have been obtained when the NaCl concentration in the medium was 0·35M (Hespell and Canale-Parola, 1970b).

C. *Spirochaeta zuelzerae*

Veldkamp (1960) investigated the growth characteristics of *S. zuelzerae* ATCC 19044 (originally named *Treponema zuelzerae*), the only strain of this species which has been isolated. Like *S. stenostrepta* and *S. litoralis* this spirochete ferments pentoses, hexoses, and disaccharides. Veldkamp (1960) reported that the addition of $NaHCO_3$ to the medium is necessary for growth. He found that the organism does not grow when $NaHCO_3$, which maintains the pH of the medium within a favourable range and serves as a source of CO_2, is replaced by phosphate buffers. Replacement of $NaHCO_3$ by buffers other than phosphate has not been attempted.

S. zuelzerae may be cultured in medium SZ (Table V; Joseph and Canale-Parola, 1972) and in other media described by Veldkamp (1960). Incubation temperature is 30 to 40°C. The highest growth yields are obtained when the initial pH of the medium is between seven and eight.

The generation time is 3 to 4 h at 37°C (Veldkamp, 1960).

D. *Spirochaeta aurantia*

The growth and nutritional properties of seven strains of *S. aurantia* were investigated by Breznak and Canale-Parola (1969, and manuscript in press). The strains studied by these authors included representatives of the two morphological types characteristic of *S. aurantia*: (1) strains exhibiting a loose, sometimes angular coiling of the cell, and (2) more tightly coiled strains, with approximately one-half the coil amplitude of the loosely coiled forms. The studies did not reveal significant differences in growth and nutritional characteristics between the loosely and tightly coiled strains.

S. aurantia may be grown in maltose broth, GTY broth (Table V) or similar media, either aerobically or anaerobically. Aerobic cell yields of strain J1 in maltose broth are in the vicinity of 9.8×10^8 cells/ml, with generation times of 3·8 h at 30°C. Under anaerobic conditions (e.g. under N_2) at the same temperature the growth yield of strain J1 in maltose broth is 3×10^8 cells/ml, with a generation time of 5 h. The highest growth yields of all strains studied are obtained when the initial pH of the medium is between 7 and 7·3. Optimum growth is at 30°C, whereas at 25°C the rate of growth is lower, and at 37°C the cells grow poorly or not at all.

S. aurantia readily forms colonies in media including 1% (w/v) agar, but growth of some strains is inhibited at higher agar concentrations. Colonies growing aerobically on agar plates (maltose or GTY broths, plus 1% agar) are generally 1–4 mm in diameter, yellow-orange to orange in colour, round or nearly so. The colonies develop within the agar gel, just under the medium surface, and sometimes have a slightly raised central portion. On plates of media low in carbohydrates (e.g. 0·01% maltose or glucose) the colonies diffuse through the agar gel in the shape of discs or circles, have a low cell density, and their pigmentation is not apparent. Subsurface, anaerobic colonies developing within the agar medium are white, spherical, somewhat fluffy, and approximately 1–2 mm in diameter.

Carbohydrates such as pentoses, hexoses and disaccharides serve as energy sources for *S. aurantia*, whereas amino-acids and various organic acids tested do not. Amino-acids, but not inorganic ammonium salts or nitrate, are utilized as sole nitrogen sources. Exogenously supplied thiamine is required for growth by all known strains, riboflavin by most, and biotin is required by one strain (J1) and is stimulatory to the growth of others,

IV. MAINTENANCE OF SPIROCHETES

Free-living spirochetes can be preserved in a viable condition for several years by maintaining them in the frozen state at the temperature of liquid nitrogen ($-196°C$). Since frequent subculturing of cells preserved by this method is not necessary, the occurrence of mutants is minimized and, presumably, genetic change of the strains is largely prevented. Free-living spirochetes stored in liquid nitrogen for as long as three years in my laboratory were actively motile upon thawing, and grew readily when transferred to culture media.

Spirochetes may be prepared for liquid nitrogen storage as follows. Cell pellets, obtained by aseptic centrifugation of young cultures, are suspended in five times their volume of growth medium, which has been sterilized and then supplemented with dimethyl sulphoxide (4 or 5 ml/ 100 ml of medium). Then, 1-ml samples of the suspension are syringed aseptically into sterile glass ampoules (A. H. Thomas Co., Philadelphia, Pa., U.S.A.). The ampoules are sealed using the flame of a gas torch and are placed into metal holders or "canes" (Shur-Bend Mfg. Co. Inc., 5709 29th Ave. North, Minneapolis, Minn., U.S.A.). The ampoules, in the holders, are immersed in 95% ethyl alcohol contained in a 500-ml glass graduated cylinder. The cylinder, containing the ampoules, is placed in an ultralow temperature freezer (Revco Inc., Deerfield, Mich., U.S.A.) set at $-85°C$. After the alcohol bath has been cooled to approximately $-85°C$ the ampoules are placed, still in their holders, in a liquid nitrogen refrigerator (Linde, type LR-35-9; Union Carbide Corp., Speedway, Ind., U.S.A.). When cells are to be transferred into a growth medium, the ampoules are immersed in a beaker containing lukewarm water (35 to 40°C) to thaw the contents. Then the necks of the ampoules are broken aseptically, the thawed cell suspension is withdrawn using a sterile syringe, and is inoculated into the growth medium.

Sterile polypropylene tubes (38 × 12·5 mm) with screw caps and silicone washers (Vanguard International, Red Bank, New Jersey, U.S.A., cat. No. 1076) may be used instead of glass ampoules for liquid nitrogen storage of cells. The screw-capped polypropylene tubes can be sealed more conveniently than the glass ampoules. Furthermore, storage in poly-propylene tubes eliminates the uncertainties of using glass ampoules, which occasionally explode upon removal from liquid nitrogen, or are otherwise subject to breakage. Safety eye goggles should always be worn when handling liquid nitrogen or frozen glass ampoules.

Strictly anaerobic and facultatively anaerobic free-living spirochetes may be maintained in agar medium stabs. After inoculation the stabs are incubated at 30°C until growth becomes visible and, then, are stored at 5°C. Stab cultures of obligately anaerobic spirochetes are layered with sterile paraffin immediately after inoculation.

To maintain viability, cells from the stab cultures stored at 5°C generally are transferred to culture broths not later than 3 or 4 weeks after inoculation and, after growth, new stab cultures are prepared. Some spirochetes, such as *S. litoralis*, survive only for a short period of time in stab cultures. The latter organism, when maintained in isolation medium (Table III) stab cultures, remains viable for approximately one week of storage at 5°C. However, *S. litoralis* retains viability for at least three months in "depression" cultures (Canale-Parola and Wolfe, 1960; Canale-Parola, 1970; Hespell and Canale-Parola, 1970b). To prepare a "depression" culture of *S. litoralis* approximately 800 ml of sterile isolation medium (Table III), to which 2% (w/v) agar has been added, are allowed to gel in a 1-litre Erlenmeyer flask. After a few days, when the agar medium is free of surface water, a small well or depression is melted in the centre of the medium in the flask, using a sterile pipette, the tip of which has been heated in a flame. Finally, two drops (0·1 ml) of a young culture of *S. litoralis* are placed in the depression. The cultures are incubated for 2 days at room temperature and then at 15°C to allow slow growth of the spirochete. Excreted metabolic products, which may be toxic to *S. litoralis*, become diluted throughout the large amount of agar medium.

REFERENCES

Breznak, J. A., and Canale-Parola, E. (1969). *J. Bacteriol.*, **97**, 386–395.
Canale-Parola, E. (1970). *Bacteriol. Rev.*, **34**, 82–97.
Canale-Parola, E., Holt, S. C., and Udris, Z. (1967). *Arch. Mikrobiol.*, **59**, 41–48.
Canale-Parola, E., Rosenthal, S. L., and Kupfer, D. G. (1966). *Antonie van Leeuwenhoek*, **32**, 113–124.
Canale-Parola, E., Udris, Z., and Mandel, M. (1968). *Arch. Mikrobiol.*, **63**, 385–397.
Canale-Parola, E., and Wolfe, R. S. (1960). *J. Bacteriol.*, **79**, 857–859.
Hespell, R. B., and Canale-Parola, E. (1970a). *J. Bacteriol.*, **103**, 216–226.
Hespell, R. B., and Canale-Parola, E. (1970b). *Arch. Mikrobiol.*, **74**, 1–18.
Holt, S. C., and Canale-Parola, E. (1968). *J. Bacteriol.*, **96**, 822–835.
Joseph, R., and Canale-Parola, E. (1972). *Arch. Mikrobiol.*, **81**, 146–168.
Pfennig, N. (1965). *Zbl. Bakt., I. Abt. Orig., Suppl. 1*, 179–189.
Veldkamp, H. (1960). *Antonie van Leeuwenhoek*, **26**, 103–125.

CHAPTER IV

Borrelia

OSCAR FELSENFELD

*Department of Tropical Medicine and Parasitology, Tulane University School of
Public Health and Tropical Medicine, New Orleans, and Tulane University Delta
Regional Primate Research Centre, Covington, Louisiana, U.S.A.*

I.	Introduction	75
II.	Staining Methods	78
	A. Aniline dyes	78
	B. Silver impregnation methods	81
	C. Fluorescent antibody technique	82
	D. Other methods	83
III.	Culture Methods	84
	A. *In vitro* methods	84
	B. Developing chick embryos	85
	C. Tissue cultures	85
IV.	Methods of Preservation	86
	A. In culture media	86
	B. In developing chick embryos	86
	C. In vectors	86
	D. In hosts	87
	E. By freezing	87
V.	Serological Methods	88
	A. Neutralization and protective antibody formation	88
	B. Agglutination and precipitation	89
	C. Complement fixation	89
	D. Immobilizine and lysin	90
	E. Adhesin	91
VI.	Animal Inoculation	92
	A. Rodents and monkeys	92
	B. Xenodiagnosis	93
VII.	Summary	93
	References	94

I. INTRODUCTION

The genus *Borrelia* consists of various species which cannot be differentiated from one another on the grounds of morphological characteristics.
Most of them are difficult to grow in culture media. *Borellia* species and

types do not show enzymatic characteristics in artificial media that would permit their classification. The serological reactions of the individual strains are variable, particularly when the organisms are exposed to antibodies in the infected person or animal. Qualitatively different antibodies may develop during subsequent attacks of relapsing fever. Borreliae isolated from the second and later febrile episodes usually acquire antigenic properties that are different from those found in the organisms that were separated from the blood during previous attacks. Antibodies circulating in the blood of man or animal after an initial attack react with borreliae from the first episode but only incompletely or not at all with organisms isolated during subsequent febrile periods. However, serum drawn after the last attack usually reacts with borreliae collected from all previous febrile episodes.

A further obstacle to the classification of borreliae is the presence of antigenic components present in most borreliae and at least one factor common to the majority of all treponemes.

The nomenclature of members of the genus *Borrelia* is rather arbitrary. As a matter of fact there is some doubt as to whether the *Borrelia* species listed in various text books actually represent different species and subspecies. It is possible that these "species" represent only variants and mutants of one single species that has adapted itself to various vectors and hosts. However, practical considerations dictate that species designations are used in diagnostic microbiology until the taxonomy of borreliae is further clarified.

The extensive literature on species and sub-species of *Borrelia* requires the consideration of some facts related to the ecology and pathogenicity of this genus. Among these are the reasons for the division of *Borrelia* strains into four groups. One is related to human relapsing fever. Human relapsing fever may be louse-borne (epidemic) or tick-borne (endemic). The vector of the causative agent of epidemic relapsing fever, *Borrelia recurrentis*, is the human body louse *Pediculus humanus*. Endemic relapsing fever is caused by a number of *Borrelia* strains which are harboured by ticks of the genus *Ornithodoros*. Lice are cosmopolitan, whereas the various *Ornithodoros* species live within certain geographical boundaries. With a few possible exceptions, one species of *Ornithodoros* carries only one species of *Borrelia*. The names of the species of borreliae are often derived from the tick vectors.

The second group of borreliae causes disease in animals. The only *Borrelia* generally recognized as a pathogenic agent in large domestic animals is *B. theileri* that has been found in Africa and Australia. The vector of this *Borrelia* is at present the subject of debate.

The third group of borreliae again consists of one single organism which,

TABLE I
Principal *Borellia* strains

Borrelia	Vector	Geographical area	Medical importance
recurrentis	Pediculus hominis	May become cosmopolitan	Human relapsing fever, epidemic
duttonii	Ornithodorus moubata	Africa	Human relapsing fever, endemic
hispanica	O. erraticus	Middle East, Mediterranean	
persica	O. tholozani	Middle East, Central Asia	
latyshevyi	O. tartakovskyi	Central Asia	
turicatae	O. turicata	North and South America	
hermsii	O. hermsi	North America	
parkerii	O. parkeri	North America	
venezolensis	O. rudis	South America	
crocidurae subgroup	O. erraticus	Middle East, Africa	Seldom pathogenic
theileri	?	Africa, Australia	Cattle and horse fever
anserina	numerous	Potentially world-wide	Avian disease
vincentii	none	World-wide	Vincent's angina in man

however, has numerous serologically different strains. This *Borrelia*, which infects birds in nature, is *B. anserina*. There may be several vectors of this organism. It may be transmitted without the mediation of an arthropod.

The fourth group encompasses borreliae found in the oral cavity. Most of them were classified as borreliae because of their morphological appearance. Only one acquired a taxonomic status: *B. vincentii*. This organism usually appears together with fusiform bacilli. It can be cultured in artificial media with relative ease. Only this member of the fourth group of borreliae will be discussed in this Chapter.

Borreliae cannot be differentiated on a morphological basis. They are usually 10 μm to 20 μm long and 0.2 μm to 0.5 μm wide. Smaller and larger forms have been observed frequently, varying in length from 3 μm to 25 μm. The size, particularly the thickness of these organisms, varies according to the method used to stain them for microscopy.

Borreliae have 4 to 30 wide coils of uniform amplitude when at rest.

They move rapidly by contraction and relaxation of the coils, bending, looping, and a corkscrew-like motion. The spirals of the borreliae change their amplitude during motion. They appear uneven in samples prepared for microscopy according to the phase of movement during which the fixative or the drying proces skilled the organism.

Electron microscopy is seldom used in the routine study of borreliae. They differ from other Treponemataceae principally by having 15 to 25 fibrils.

Borreliae are present in the peripheral blood during the febrile paroxysm but not before, nor during and after the crisis. Therefore blood examinations are most successful if carried out in the beginning and during the first days of the febrile attack.

Not all *Borrelia* strains penetrate into the cerebrospinal fluid, particularly not during the first attack. The examination of organs in relapsing fever is rewarding only between attacks and at autopsy. In aves, blood and liver are usually examined for *B. anserina*. The search for *B. vincentii* may be undertaken at any time.

II. STAINING METHODS

Borreliae differ from other Treponemataceae by having a strong affinity for aniline dyes. However, in tissues they are visualized with greater ease by silver impregnation methods.

The selection of the staining method is a matter of personal choice and experience.

The most frequently used method in searching for borreliae is the examination of blood smears. Concentration methods may precede the examination of blood for borreliae.

Usually thin and thick smears are prepared on the same slide.

The thick smear is carefully dehaemoglobinized with distilled water. The thin smear may be fixed with absolute methanol or acetone for 3 to 5 min if the stain itself does not contain a fixing agent.

A useful method to dehaemoglobinize both thick and thin smears is that of Du (1931). A 6% acetic acid solution in 95% ethanol is permitted to act on the slides for 5 sec, followed by staining with an aniline dye that contains phenol.

A. Aniline dyes

(i) A handy aniline dye is the carbol fuchsin of Ziehl–Neelsen. This is prepared by dissolving 1 g basic fuchsin in 10 ml absolute ethanol. In another bottle 5 ml liquid carbolic acid are dissolved in 100 ml distilled water. The two solutions are mixed. Filtration is mandatory before use.

The slides are stained for 1 min with this solution, then carefully washed with distilled water and air-dried.

(ii) Methylene blue is a satisfactory stain for borreliae, particularly in combination with concentration using a bile acid salt. Simons (1939) introduced the following method:

One ml of a saturated solution of methylene blue solution in physiological saline is mixed with 2 ml of 10% sodium taurocholate in physiological saline. This mixture keeps for about one month.

Equal volumes (3 to 5 loopfuls) of the blood to be examined and of the stain are mixed, a smear prepared from the mixture, and covered with a cover slip. The staining is completed within 1–2 min.

(iii) Of the combined stains, those of the Jenner–Romanowski group, namely Leishman, Wright, Giemsa and their combinations are most frequently used. They are difficult to prepare in the laboratory and, therefore, purchased from reliable manufacturers (Gurr, London; Harleco, Philadelphia; Grübler, Berlin; and others). Should the need arise to prepare them in the laboratory, perhaps Leishman's is easier prepared than the others if the proper ingredients are available but the results of the staining vary from one batch to another.

It is essential to guard all stains against contamination with water.

(a) **Leishman's stain.** A 1% solution of Methylene blue is heated in a 0·5% aqueous solution of sodium carbonate at 65°C for 12 h, then left to stand for 10 days. An 0·1% aqueous solution of Eosin B "extra" is prepared. Equal amounts of both solutions are mixed. After 12 h the precipitate is collected on a filter. The precipitate is washed with distilled water until the washings are colourless. It is then dried and triturated. Approximately 15 mg aliquots of the resulting fine powder are ground in 10 to 20 ml aliquots of absolute methanol, allowed to stand for 1 min, then the supernate filtered into a bottle. This is repeated until 150 mg of the precipitate have been dissolved in 100 ml absolute methanol. The stain is permitted to stand for 4 weeks before use.

The smears are air-dried and placed on a staining rack.

They are covered with a measured amount of the stain for 1 min.

Then 0·01M phosphate buffer pH 6·6 to 6·8 is added until a metallic scum appears. Approximately two volumes of the buffer are required.

The diluted stain is permitted to act for 3–5 min.

The slides are washed with the phosphate buffer until the thin parts of the smear appear pink, or until examination under the microscope shows that differentiation is satisfactory.

If the slide is over-differentiated, it is decolourized with 95 to 96% ethanol rinsed with distilled water, and re-stained.

The slides are dried by standing on one end.

(b) **The Wright stain** is available in solution or in powder-form. Of the latter, 1 g is dissolved in 600 ml absolute methanol.

The staining method is the same as with the Leishman stain but a 0·01M phosphate buffer of pH 6·4 to 6·6 is preferred. An approximately equal volume of the buffer is necessary to produce the formation of a metallic scum.

If acid-free methanol is used and the washings are carefully carried out, either of these staining methods gives satisfactory results.

(c) **Panoptic** staining is best achieved by combining the methods of May–Grünwald and Giemsa. Both stains are available commercially.

The smears are air-dried and fixed for 5 min in absolute methanol or ethanol.

May–Grünwald stock stain (commercial) is freshly diluted with 2 volumes of 0·01M phosphate buffer pH 6·8.

The slides are stained for 3 to 5 min.

In a Coplin jar, 1·5 ml stock (commercial) Giemsa solution are diluted with 1 ml absolute methanol and 50 ml phosphate buffer pH 6·8.

The slides are placed in the jar, standing on their edge, and allowed to stain for 12 to 18 h, then differentiated in a solution of 1 ml acetic acid in 1 litre distilled water. When the thin part of the smears appear reddish-pink, they are rapidly rinsed in three changes of the phosphate buffer pH 6·8.

The smears are dried standing on the edge.

(d) An alternate **panoptic** staining method consists of fixation and application of the May–Grünwald stain as under (c). Then without washing, the slides are transferred to freshly diluted stock (commercial) Giemsa stain. Nine volumes of 0·01M phosphate buffer pH 6·8 are used to dilute the stock.

The smears are stained for 10 min in this diluted Giemsa stain.

Differentiation is carried out in three quick changes of the phosphate buffer, then the slides are left in the fourth change of the same buffer until the thin part of the smears appears a reddish-pink.

The slides are dried standing on end.

The phosphate buffers can be purchased in powder form which is diluted in an indicated amount of distilled water. Many laboratory workers use distilled instead of buffered water.

(iv) Additional staining methods are:

(a) Combined stain. Felsenfeld (1965) used Wright's stain, followed by 1% Crystal violet for 10 to 30 sec, and differentiation in distilled water.

(b) Concentration before staining. Saurino and DeLamater (1952) found filtration, differential centrifugation, centrifugation and flotation, addition of fibrinogen to heparinized infected blood, and combinations of these procedures of little use in attempts to separate borreliae from blood and tissue. They recommended the following method, principally for the concentration of *B. anserina*:

Heparinized blood is gently centrifuged at low speed, then filtered through an "F" grade fritted glass disc. The filter is washed with an equal amount of physiological saline, which is added to the filtrate. The filtrate is centrifuged at 3000 rpm (800 *g*) for 1 h. The packed borreliae are washed three times with physiological saline, then resuspended in 1 ml saline.

These authors also recommended Nelson's medium. An equal part of this medium and of heparinized blood are mixed and permitted to sediment at 37°C overnight. The supernate containing the borreliae is carefully removed, and the organisms concentrated by centrifugation at 5000 *g*.

B. Silver impregnation methods

These serve principally for the demonstration of borreliae and other treponemes but mycotic elements and many bacteria, often also reticulin, are stained by them.

Scrupulous cleanliness of all glassware and instruments, high purity chemicals and adaptation of the methods to local conditions are prerequisites.

(i) A routinely used and rather slow method is that of Levaditi which is feasible for staining tissue blocks. These are first fixed in formalin, then stained, and finally embedded in paraffin. Another routine procedure, that of Krajan (1939) and its modifications, are useful for the rapid staining of frozen sections as well as paraffin blocks.

(ii) A short and reliable method that can be applied to smears, formol-saline fixed tissues as well as paraffin embedded sections (after hydration) is that of Faulkner and Lillie (1945).

The method employs acetic acid–acetate buffer pH 3·6 which is made up by mixing 46·3 ml of 1·155% solution of glacial acetic acid in distilled water, 3·7 ml of 1·641% solution of anhydrous sodium acetate, and distilled water to 1 litre.

A stock solution of gelatin, made up by heating 10 g gelatin in 200 ml acetate buffer for 1 h at 58°C and to which 2 ml of 1 : 10,000 merthiolate (sodium ethylmercurithiosalicylate, Thimerosal, Mertamin) are added after cooling, is prepared.

From each block or blood sample three sections or slides are made, washed with the acetate buffer that has been diluted 1 : 25 with distilled water, for 5 min. Then the slides are exposed to a 1% solution of silver nitrate in 1 : 25 diluted acetate buffer for 45 min at 60°C.

In the meantime, 15 ml of the gelatin stock solution are heated to 60°C in an oven and 3 ml of 2% silver nitrate in acetate buffer heated to the same temperature, are added. Just before the heating of the slides is completed, 3% hydroquinone in acetate buffer are added to this mixture.

The slides are flooded with the mixture which should be warm. When the sections become golden brown and/or the developing mixture turns brownish black, the slides are rinsed with water heated to 55 to 60°C. Each of the three slides should be developed for a slightly different time.

After a rinse with distilled water, the slides are dehydrated, cleared and mounted as for other histological sections.

C. Fluorescent antibody technique

The antigen is prepared by bleeding a susceptible rodent at the peak of the borrelaemia. Blood containing at least 100 borreliae per oil immersion field should be used.

(i) Allinne and Marx (1966) collect the blood into citrated saline, centrifuge it at a few hundred rpm (200–300 g) to separate the plasma, add to the plasma formalin to a final concentration of 0·2%, then centrifuge the supernate at 5000 rpm (1000 g) for 8 min.

The sediment, which consists of borreliae, is washed with physiological saline, then suspended in an equal volume of 0·4% formol-saline. It should contain approximately 50 borreliae per microscopic field at × 400 magnification.

Drops of this antigen are deposited on carefully cleaned slides, dried in the air, and fixed with absolute acetone for 10 min.

Several smears are prepared of each antigen.

The indirect fluorescent antibody method is recommended.

All sera used in this test should be absorbed with sonified Reiter's spirochaete (available from Difco and Baltimore Biological Laboratory) to avoid cross-reactions with *Treponema*. The sera are diluted 1 : 5 with phosphate buffered saline pH 7·2 (PBS), then mixed with an equal amount of sonified Reiter's organisms for 10 min, and centrifuged at 1000 g for 30 min. The supernate is the absorbed serum.

Sera conjugated with fluorescent dyes may be absorbed after conjugation without significant loss of activity.

Species-specific anti-*Borrelia* sera prepared in rabbits with known and frequently checked titres should be kept on hand, as well as positive and negative control sera.

If an unknown serum is tested, two-fold dilutions with PBS are prepared, usually 1 : 5 to 1 : 400.

One drop of each serum dilution is added to a separate slide with the

Borrelia antigen. After 30 min standing in a moist chamber the slides are washed with PBS for 10 min, then one drop of anti-human rabbit, goat, sheep or donkey serum labelled with fluorescein isothiocyanate is added to each slide. After 10 min the slides are washed with PBS, mounted in a mixture of one part glycerol in nine parts of PBS, and observed under the fluorescent microscope. (See Walker *et al.*, this Series, Vol. 5A for technical details.)

Appropriate controls with negative and positive sera are set up. If the positive control serum was prepared in rabbits, fluorescent dye labelled anti-rabbit goat, sheep or donkey serum is used to visualize the reaction and to establish the end-titre of the serum.

If the species of the *Borrelia* is unknown, a set of slides is prepared as for the testing of unknown sera. *Borrelia* species-specific rabbit antisera, diluted with PBS to 1 : 2, 1 : 5 and 1 : 10 of their titres, are used. These sera do not have to be absorbed with *Treponema*. One drop of each dilution of each antiserum is added to a slide with the unknown antigen (*Borrelia*). Then the reaction is carried out according to the procedure recommended for the indirect fluorescent antibody technique with unknown sera as described above.

Cross-reactions may appear also with some anti-*Borrelia* sera which are properly absorbed with other borreliae. Therefore animal tests are recommended for further studies of the unknown organism.

Nichol's strain can be used instead of Reiter's treponeme for the absorption. Sera prepared in rabbits permit the differentiation of *B. vincentii* from other cultivable treponemes in this test (Meyer and Hunter, 1967). The fluorescent antibody test was found superior to immobilization and lysin determination in rodents by Coffey and Eveland (1967) who used *B. hermsii*.

(ii) The method of Maestrone (1964) can be applied to demonstrate borreliae in tissues. It is feasible for frozen sections as well as for formol-fixed tissues.

The tissue sections are exposed to acetone for 5 min, dried at 37°C, then flooded with 1% ammonia for 3 to 5 min. The slides are washed with 3% Tween 80 (polyoxyethylene/20/sorbitan mono-oleate, polyethylene oxide sorbitan mono-oleate, Polysorbate 80, Sorlate, Monitan) in phosphate-buffered saline pH 7·2, blotted dry, then treated with rabbit anti-*Borrelia* serum or globulin, then with fluorescent dye—labelled anti-rabbit serum or globulin as in method (a).

D. Other methods

Mercurochrome (dibromohydroxymercurifluorescein, Merbromin, Gallochrome) has been used to stain borreliae. When it is used alone, the organisms seldom stain uniformly. The staining may be weak. An advantage of mercurochrome is that the borreliae are less often distorted than after fixation with alcohols.

The method of Young (1951) is recommended. A saturated aqueous solution of Mercurochrome and a concentrated aqueous solution of Methyl violet are filtered just before use. The smears are air-dried, then stained with Mercurochrome for 3 min. After rinsing with distilled water, the Methyl violet solution is applied for a period established in preliminary tests because various makes of the stain give different results. The smears are washed with distilled water and air-dried.

III. CULTURE METHODS

Not all strains of *Borrelia* causing human relapsing fever can be cultured. These organisms do not multiply in most of the hitherto proposed media but may remain alive in them for some time. Successful passages have been observed in the developing chick embryo. Growth in tissue cultures does not yet give consistent results.

Blood defibrinated by shaking with glass beads and sometimes blood laked with distilled water yield more frequently viable cultures than citrated blood. For the preparation of antisera to borreliae, from chick embryo cultures, the use of blood collected at the height of the borrelaemia from the vessels of the inoculated embryos is recommended.

Culture experiments may be negative when an antibiotic has been administered.

A. *In vitro* methods

After Noguchi reported in 1912 that borreliae can be cultured in ascitic fluid containing fragments of rabbit kidney and covered with a liquid paraffin seal, numerous modifications of this medium were described. It became apparent that the paraffin seal serves to prevent the penetration of atmospheric O_2 into the medium; that tissue fragments contribute to an increased CO_2 tension in their vicinity; that the medium should be slightly alkaline; and that serum or other protein-rich materials such as ascitic fluid and egg-white enhance the survival of the borreliae.

The medium used to date with the greatest success is that of Wolman and Wolman (1945).

One ml aliquots of egg albumin are put into culture tubes and coagulated at 80°C. A mixture containing one part human ascitic fluid, three parts of phosphate-buffered saline pH 7·8 and one part 1% dextrose is prepared and sterilized by Seitz or micropore filtration. Ten ml of this mixture are added to each of the tubes containing the coagulated egg albumin. The media are sealed with liquid paraffin and heated on three consecutive days at 56°C for 1 h. The most useful inoculum is the sediment of centrifuged laked blood.

Duplicate cultures are incubated at 32°C and at 28°C.

B. Developing chick embryos

Saurino and DeLamater (1952) summarized the history of attempts to culture *B. anserina* and concluded that the most successful method is to inoculate fertile hen's eggs. Various media containing fresh tissue, ascitic fluid, serum and/or broth, as well as inactivated or coagulated serum or egg white covered with inactivated serum and/or blood sustained but did not support the multiplication of borreliae.

The oldest method is the inoculation of the chorioallantoic membrane with defibrinated and centrifuged blood.

(i) Chabaud (1939) recommended 4 and 5 day old fertilized eggs, whereas others prefer 7 to 12 day old embryos. According to strain, the borreliae begin to multiply 2 to 4 days after inoculation and may or may not cause death of the embryos. Sometimes, when the chorioallantoic membrane is inoculated only 2 or 3 days before hatching, the borreliae may appear in the blood circulation of the newly hatched chicks.

(ii) Yolk-sack inoculation with borreliae was initiated by Chen (1941). The number of borreliae reaches its maximum 3 to 5 days after inoculation. Nine to 10 day old embryos are recommended. The borreliae disintegrate after the embryos die. Therefore blood has to be drawn for examination and passage 3 to 4 days after inoculation. The chorioallantoic vessels are bled and the blood is permitted to mix with the allantoic fluid. A sufficient amount of sodium citrate is added to prevent coagulation.

Opinions differ concerning the age of the fertilized hen's egg, the optimal temperature of incubation, and the route of infection. Many strains lose their virulence during passage through chick embryos; others show morphological changes. However, egg passage is feasible for the propagation of many *Borrelia* strains.

This method is not yet recommended for diagnostic purposes.

C. Tissue cultures

(i) Allantoic membrane cultures served as a growth substrate of borreliae for Manteufel and Dressler (1933).

(ii) Our group tested several tissue cultures, including HeLa, human embryonic kidney, vervet kidney, rabbit embryonic lung and kidney cell lines as growth supporting media for *B. turicatae* without satisfactory results. The greatest obstacles encountered in attempts to grow borreliae in tissue cell cultures are the "natural" resistance of some cell lines to borreliae, pH, osmotic pressure and respiratory requirements.

IV. METHODS OF PRESERVATION

It is difficult to propagate and to maintain borreliae in artificial media. A convenient method is to keep alive tick-borne strains in their vectors. The borreliae do not undergo mutations and variations in the infected tick, and do not appear to cause pathological changes in the *Ornithodoros*. *Ornithodoros* ticks have a long life time during which the borreliae survive in their coelomic cavity. Another method is to maintain borreliae by animal passages but antigenic variations may be induced in the organisms. A convenient method is to store borreliae at low temperatures. The latter is particularly helpful in the preservation of *B. recurrentis*. The various procedures recommended for the maintenance of borreliae are:

A. In culture media

(i) *B. vincentii* is conveniently kept in serial passages in Nichol's medium (*vide Treponema*).

(ii) The medium of Wolman and Wolman (*vide* III.A) is feasible for the maintenance of *B. recurrentis* and several other borreliae if the full-grown culture is stored at 3 to 5°C.

B. In developing chick embryos

Inoculation of 9 to 10 day old fertilized hen's eggs yields the best results (see Section III.B (ii)). However, the borreliae have to be transferred to other developing chick embryos every third day.

C. In vectors

This method is very helpful for the maintenance of *B. duttonii, B. hispanica, B. persica* and the North American borreliae. The respective *Ornithodoros* species serving as vectors remain alive for several years. Nymphs from early generations may lose the organisms after repeated moulting which takes place after each feeding. Fortunately most *Ornithodoros* species remain alive without a blood meal for a long time, even for years.

The ticks may be kept either in a glass or plastic box into which a dead newborn mouse is dropped at feeding time. An alternate method is to put the ticks into small test-tubes containing a strip of filter paper, insert a lose cotton plug, and place the tubes into a desiccator. A saturated aqueous solution of ammonium chloride is poured into the bottom of the desiccator. The ticks are fed on the shaved skin of young mice.

Uninfected ticks may be fed on these mice during the borrelaemia. This is helpful in increasing the number of infected *Ornithodoros*. This method is of value when infection of mammals is contemplated by the natural route, i.e. by feeding infected ticks on them. *Ornithodoros* often take their blood meals at long intervals, usually once in several months. Therefore a supply of infected ticks which are ready to feed (and transmit the infection) may be desirable.

D. In hosts

(i) Borreliae can be propagated by drawing blood from infected animals, particularly mice, into citrate-containing tubes, then inoculate other rodents with the blood intraperitoneally.

The infection in mice is of short duration. Rats, if susceptible to the respective strain, have a longer lasting borrelaemia. Guinea-pigs are particularly suitable for the serial propagation of *B. persica*. The number of circulating borreliae may be low in experimentally infected rodents, particularly in *B. latishevyi*, *B. hermsii* and *B. parkerii* infections. The organisms may undergo phase variations in animals. Therefore the results of serological reactions must be evaluated carefully, particularly if relapses occured.

(ii) The brains of rats and guinea-pigs have been recommended for the preservation (*sit venia verbo*) of borreliae. Pampana (1931) suggested this method principally for the maintenance of borreliae which have an affinity to the central nervous system of these species of rodents. For instance, *B. hispanica* can be recovered from the brain of guinea-pigs at least 2 months, frequently 6 months to 3 years, after infection by injecting the emulsified brain into fresh guinea-pigs. Mice are not feasible for such experiments.

The limitations of this method are obvious.

E. By freezing

(i) Weyer and Mooser (1957) established that borreliae can be preserved in the deep freeze at -70 to $-72°C$. The freezing is best carried out at a uniform rate by lowering the temperature by $1°C$ each minute. Ampoules are sealed after freezing and kept at $-70°C$.

(ii) Lyophillzation was shown to be helpful in the preservation of borreliae by Hanson and Cannefax (1964). If the procedure is carried out *in vacuo*, 2% lactose in skim milk is a good vehicle. The ampoules are kept at $-70°C$.

(iii) Organs and ticks containing borreliae have been conserved at low temperatures by Bourgain (1946). Liquid N_2 may be used for this purpose.

The surfaces of tissue blocks are dusted with talcum powder to absorb water before immersion into N_2.

The viability of various *Borrelia* strains differs in the deep freeze, from one to approximately 12 years. Repeated freezing and thawing destroys the organisms. Therefore it is advisable to prepare several ampoules of each batch, each containing enough borreliae for one experiment.

V. SEROLOGICAL METHODS

Serological tests with borreliae are not always specific because of the presence of antigens cross-reacting with antibodies not only against borreliae but also against other treponemes. Moreover, phase variation, which is common in borreliae causing relapsing fever and develops during subsequent attacks, may lead to false conclusions.

Serological tests may give false results when the patient is receiving antibiotics or arsenicals.

Frequently employed tests are:

A. Neutralization and protective antibody formation

(i) Prevention of the development of borrelaemia in mice with serum from the patient has been recommended in the past but this test has only historical significance today.

(ii) Resistance to superinfection with the same strain is often helpful in the classification of borreliae.

Groups of at least three young mice and guinea-pigs are inoculated with strains of *Borrelia*. Guinea-pigs are not used for testing organisms suspected of belonging to the *crocidurae* subgroup and *B. recurrentis*. The known strains used in the experiments should not be virulent enough to kill the animals. One group of mice and one group of guinea-pigs serve as controls regardless of the expected strain. They are not infected. The animals are observed for borrelaemia at least for one week after inoculation.

Two weeks after the end of the borrelaemia, the unknown organism is injected into all animals, including the controls.

The age of the animals has to be considered in the evaluation of the results since, in addition to susceptibility of the selected rodents to various *Borrelia* strains it may influence the outcome of the experiments.

The sera of the infected and recovered animals are tested against known *Borrelia* strains in the complement fixation and lysin immobilizing tests. The unknown borreliae are examined against specific rabbit anti-*Borrelia* sera by the same methods.

B. Agglutination and precipitation

(i) The agglutination reaction with borreliae has been introduced by Novy and Knapp in 1906. It may be carried out as a slide test. The results are evaluated by darkfield illumination.

The tube test, recommended by Stein (1944) gives a slowly developing, loose and fluffy sediment.

The most frequently used procedure is to mix saponin-treated borreliae (*vide* III. C) with equal volumes of two-fold serum dilutions. The mixtures are incubated for 2 h at 37°C, then overnight in the refrigerator. The final titre is the highest dilution giving a 2+ reaction.

(ii) Saurino and DeLamater (1952) observed mild cross-reactions between *Treponema pallidum* and *B. anserina* using an antigen extract prepared with 0·5N hydrochloric acid. This was mixed with the organisms for 10 min at 56°C. The supernatant, representing the antigen, was neutralized with 1N sodium hydroxide.

(iii) Agar-gel diffusion tests proved feasible to demonstrate *B. anserina* antigen in the liver of infected chickens (Al-Hilly, 1969). This organ gave the best results, and the precipitin lines were more distinct when the plates were kept in a refrigerator. Sera of chickens after recovery from the disease as well as sera of immunized animals gave positive results.

This method has not yet been applied successfully to borreliae causing human relapsing fever. Immunoprecipitation takes place with sonicates of some of these borreliae against sera having a high (1 : 1000 or higher) titre in the direct precipitation test.

Cross-reactions are not uncommon. If they occur, cross-absorption is recommended before re-testing the sera. Absorption with Reiter's treponema enhances the specificity of the test.

C. Complement fixation

(i) The complement fixation reaction may be carried out according to the method of Stein (1944).

Stein recommended mixing four volumes of blood with one volume of 2% solution of sodium citrate in physiological saline, then the addition of $1\frac{1}{3}$ volume of 10% saponin, with subsequent centrifugation and recentrifugation of the mixture to separate borreliae for the preparation of the antigen.

The procedure consists of mixing 0 1 ml of a suspension of borreliae containing approximately 80 organisms per oil-immersion field, 0·1 ml each of ten-fold increasing dilutions of the test serum, and 0·1 ml of guinea-pig complement containing two standard units. The mixture is incubated in a water bath for 30 min at 37°C. Then 0·2 ml of sensitized sheep red blood cells containing amboceptor, two haemolytic units, and an equal amount of 5% erythrocytes are added. After ten additional minutes at 37°C the results are read and expressed on a scale from 0 to 4+. This test frequently gives cross-reactions with various *Borrelia* strains.

(ii) Another method, recommended by Wolstenhome and Gear (1948) consists of the inoculation of 7 day old chick embryos through the air-sac with 0·3 to 0·4 ml of heart blood from experimentally infected mice. After one week's incubation, the chorioallantoic vessels are opened and permitted to bleed into the allantoic fluid. One-tenth of an ml of the resulting mixture is inoculated into a new series of 7 day old embryos. After ten passages, 0·5% phenol in physiological saline is added to the last blood-allantoic fluid mixture which is then cleared by centrifugation. This antigen should contain approximately 100 borreliae per oil immersion field. It is tested in various dilutions (1 : 10 to 1 : 200) in the complement fixation test against known antisera.

The final titres are usually 1 : 10 to 1 : 400 with sera from infected animals and man one month after infection. Cross-reactions are frequent but absorption of the sera with Reiter's or Nicol's organism may increase specificity.

D. Immobilizine and lysin

Levaditi *et al.* (1952a) studied immobilizines in rodents and man. They found that high-speed centrifugation which may influence the reactive titres of syphilitic sera, only slightly influences the outcome of the immobilization test in borreliosis. If complement is present, immobilization and later lysis may take place (Levaditi *et al.*, 1952b). Cross-reactions between *B. duttonii* and *B. hispanica* were observed but not with *T. pallidum* (Levaditi *et al.*, 1952c).

Further studies of immobilizines (Vaisman and Haemlin, 1954) demonstrated that these antibodies are homologous in reinfected animals and in rodents infected first with one, than with the other of these borreliae. Similar results were obtained by Ranque *et al.* (1957).

Schuhardt (1942) and Felsenfeld (1965, 1971) demonstrated that immobilizine and lysin may or may not be related to each other but lysins may represent a complement-dependent form of immobilizines. Neither reaction has been standardized as yet. The methods presented here appear to yield the most specific results.

(i) The immobilizine test is usually performed by mixing equal amounts of inactivated serum and a suspension of live borreliae containing 20 to 30 organisms per microscopic field at ×400 magnification.

0·005M phosphate-buffered saline pH 7·2 with 5mM calcium chloride is a suitable diluent for both immobilizine and lysin determinations.

After 10 and 30 min incubation at 37°C on a slide covered with a cover slip and sealed with liquid paraffin, the proportion of immobilized borreliae is determined in the serum-*Borrelia* mixture, as well as in a control in which buffered saline has been substituted for the serum.

The results are expressed in % of the borreliae immobilized.

This test may be performed with increasing serum dilution and the titre of the highest serum dilution immobilizing 50% of the borreliae reported.

(ii) The lysin (borreliolysin) test is usually carried out according to the technique of Schuhardt (1942).

Antigen and antibody are mixed in equal proportions. They are drawn into a capillary tube with a rubber bulb. The contents of the capillary are expelled from the tube into a welled slide, mixed, and redrawn into the capillary which is sealed with wax or clay and incubated for 2 h at 37°C. The sealed end is broken and the contents emptied on to a slide.

The number of borreliae are counted under darkfield illumination and compared with the number of organisms in the control which contains buffered saline instead of serum.

(iii) Inactivated serum is used in another method (Felsenfeld, 1971).

Guinea-pig complement, suspended in phosphate-magnesium chloride buffer is preferred, usually in 1 : 100 dilution. The diluting fluid supplied with commercially available desiccated complement should not be used because it often contains a preservative that may destroy borreliae. The antigen is the same as in the immobilizine test. Equal parts of antigen and inactivated serum are mixed and incubated at 37°C for 30 min, then one part of diluted complement is added and incubated at 37°C for 90 min. The surviving borreliae are counted and compared with the controls that contain buffer instead of serum. The results are reported as in the immobilizine test.

The outcome of the lysin test may be expressed as the highest dilution of serum causing the lysis of 50% of the borreliae. The borreliae should be counted in at least 10 to 15 microscopic fields in both tests. The titres of both tests increase after the first attack. Titres to 1 : 400 and 1 : 800 are not unusual. However, lysin-fast borreliae may develop.

E. Adhesion

This test is difficult to carry out and to interpret. Spontaneous agglutination and adhesion are not uncommon in *Borrelia* suspensions.

The usual method is to mix equal parts of a suspension of borreliae containing 80 to 100 organisms per ×400 microscopic field, two-fold serum dilutions and a 10^4 suspension of *Escherichia coli* per ml.

After incubation at 30°C for 30 min, samples are examined by darkfield illumination. Adhesion of the borreliae to the colon bacilli is considered a sign of a positive test, provided that this does not occur in the control which contains physiological saline instead of the serum.

VI. ANIMAL INOCULATION

A. Rodents and monkeys

(i) The examination for *B. vincentii* does not require tests in animals.

(ii) *B. anserina* can be transferred to chickens but not as a rule to rodents, monkeys and cold-blooded animals. Blood or organ suspensions of sick or recently dead birds are injected into chickens. Young chickens are preferred. Borreliae appear in the blood of the infected birds in approximately 4 days.

(iii) Borreliae causing relapsing fever in mammals including man can be isolated by injecting intraperitoneally six to eight young mice each with 0·4 to 0·5 ml blood of the patient.

Beginning with the third day, blood samples of the mice, usually collected from the tail vein, are examined daily for at least 7 days. If borreliae are found, a cardiac puncture is performed, citrated blood collected and injected into other animals.

Table II offers a selection of laboratory rodents and monkeys indicating the degree of their susceptibility to various *Borrelia* strains. It may be helpful in the differential diagnosis of these organisms.

TABLE II
Susceptibility of some laboratory animals to *Borrelia*

Strain or group of *Borrelia*	Primary inoculation			Secondary inoculation				
	Young mice	Young guinea-pigs	Adult guinea-pigs	Adult mice	Young rats	Old rats	European hedge-hogs	Monkeys
recurrentis	3+, 4+	mostly neg.	1+, 2+	irregular, often 0				1+, 2+
duttonii	4+	3+	2+	2+, 3+	3+	1+	0	3+, 4+
hispanica	3+	4+	4+	1+, 2+	3+	1+	2+	0 to 2+
persica	4+	4+	4+	0, 1+	2+	0	4+	only young
North American borreliae	4+	2+	1+	2+	4+	1+	?	2+
crocidurae subgroup	2+	0 or 1+	0 or 1+	0, 1+	0 or 1+	0	1+	seldom

(iv) Spinal fluid is suitable for animal inoculation but the amount available is usually small, necessitating the use of fewer mice in the primary inoculation.

Mice seldom have relapses after infection with borreliae. Several periods of borrelaemia may be seen in rats as well as in monkeys inoculated with those borreliae to which they are highly susceptible.

Animal inoculation is the most reliable method of diagnosing borreliae causing relapsing fever, provided that the patient is not receiving antibiotics and the blood specimens are collected during the early part of the febrile paroxysm.

B. Xenodiagnosis

This procedure consists of feeding several ticks from a *Borrelia*-free *Ornithodoros* colony on a patient who has a febrile attack.

The haemolymph of the ticks is taken up into a capillary and examined for borreliae 2 or 3 weeks later.

Many *Borrelia* strains are taken up only by *Ornithodoros* species in which they are found in nature. Therefore xenodiagnosis is most feasible in areas where only one *Borrelia*-carrying *Ornithodoros* strain is present. Geigy (1968) used this method successfully in a part of Africa where *B. duttonii* prevails.

VII. SUMMARY

The diagnosis of borreliosis depends on the causative strain. The examination of mucous membranes and excreta for *B. vincentii* is seldom difficult.

B. anserina may be diagnosed in smears and organs of fowl by microscopic methods, serological tests and inoculation of the blood into other susceptible avian species, most frequently into chicken.

The most reliable diagnostic method for borreliae causing human relapsing fever is the inoculation of young mice with blood collected during the early phase of the febrile paroxysm. Microscopic preparations stained with aniline dyes give less reliable results but are useful. The serological tests may show cross-reactions and the phase variation of borreliae during subsequent fever episodes may cause differential diagnostic difficulties. The identification of the *Borrelia* strain is best carried out by inoculating several animal species, using both young and adult rodents. The immunological responses to borreliae require further investigation before antigen–antibody reactions suitable for diagnostic use in routine laboratories can be developed.

REFERENCES

Al-Hilly, J. N. A. (1969). *Amer. J. Veterin. Res.*, **30**, 1877–1880.

Allinne, M., and Marx, R. (1966). *Ann. Inst. Pasteur*, **111** (Suppl. 5), 28–35.

Bourgain, M. (1946). *Bull. Soc. pathol. exot.*, **39**, 185–187.

Chabaud, A. (1939). *Bull. Soc. pathol. exot.*, **32**, 483–485.

Chen, K. C. (1941). *Proc. Soc. Exptl. Biol. Med.*, **46**, 638–639.

Coffey, E. M., and Eveland, W. C. (1967). *J. infect. Dis.*, **117**, 23–28.

Coles, A. C. (1936). *J. Trop. Med. Hyg.*, **39**, 77–81.

Du, S. D. (1931). *Chinese med. J.*, **45**, 657–660.

Faulkner, R. R., and Lillie, R. D. (1945). *Stain Techn.*, **20**, 81–83.

Felsenfeld, O. (1965). *Bacteriol. Rev.*, **29**, 46–74.

Felsenfeld, O. (1971). *"Borrelia"*, pp. 121–127. W. H. Green Publ. Co., St. Louis, Missouri.

Geigy, R. (1968). *Infect. Dis.*, **2**, 175–216.

Hanson, A. W., and Cannefax, G. R. (1964). *J. Bacteriol.*, **88**, 811.

Krajan, A. A. (1939). *Amer. J. Syph.*, **23**, 617–620.

Levaditi, C., Vaisman, A., and Hamelin, H. (1952a). *Ann. Inst. Pasteur*, **83**, 256–260.

Levaditi, C., Vaisman, A., and Hamelin, A. (1952b). *Ann. Inst. Pasteur*, **83**, 260–262.

Levaditi, C., Vaisman, A., and Hamelin, A. (1952c). *Ann. Inst. Pasteur*, **83**, 437–442.

Maestrone, G. (1965). *Nature, London*, **197**, 409–410.

Manteufel, P., and Dressler, I. (1933). *Zentralbl. Bakt. Abtg. I. Orig.*, **130**, 188–193.

Meyer, P. E., and Hunter, E. H. (1967). *J. Bacteriol.*, **93**, 784–789.

Pampana, E. J. (1931). *Arch. ital. sci. med. colon.*, **12**, 257–263.

Ranque, J., Depieds, R., and Faure, A. (1957). *Bull. Soc. pathol. exot.*, **50**, 360–363.

Saurino, V. D., and DeLamater, E. D. (1952). *Amer. J. Syph.*, **36**, 353–367.

Schuhardt, V. T. (1942). *In* "Symposium on Relapsing Fever in the Americas". pp. 58–66. Amer. Soc. Adv. Sci. Monogr. No. 18. Washington, D.C.

Stein, G. J. (1944). *J. exptl. Med.*, **79**, 115–128.

Vaisman, A., and Hamelin, A. (1954). *Ann. Inst. Pasteur*, **86**, 107–109.

Weyer, F., and Mooser, H. (1957). *Zeitschr. Tropenmed. Parasitol.*, **8**, 294–304.

Wolman, B., and Wolman, M. (1945). *Ann. Trop. Med. Parasit.*, **39**, 82–93.

Wolstenhome, B., and Gear, J. H. S. (1948). *Trans. Soc. Trop. Med. Hyg.*, **41**, 513–517.

Young, H. (1951). *Ann. Biol. Chim.*, **9**, 318–322.

CHAPTER V

Methods for Assessing Damage to Bacteria Induced by Chemical and Physical Agents

A. D. RUSSELL AND A. MORRIS*

Welsh School of Pharmacy, University of Wales Institute of Science and Technology, Cathays Park, Cardiff, Wales

AND M. C. ALLWOOD

Department of Pharmacy, The University, Manchester, England

I.	Introduction	96
II.	Methods of Treatment	96
	A. Effect of drugs	97
	B. Physical process	99
III.	Bacterial Viability	102
	A. Exposure to chemicals	102
	B. Exposure to physical processes	103
IV.	Resistance to Antibacterial Agents	106
	A. Choice of test strains	106
	B. Impermeability to drugs	106
	C. Methicillin-resistant staphylococci	112
	D. Drug inactivation	113
	E. Resistance (R) Factors	117
V.	Repair of Injury	118
VI.	Determination of Binding of Drugs	119
	A. Theoretical considerations of adsorption	120
	B. Outline of procedure for quantitative studies . . .	120
	C. Other methods	122
VII.	Physical and Morphological Changes	124
	A. Changes in morphology and size—indirect methods . .	124
	B. Measurements of changes in cell size	125
VIII.	Cell Wall Damage	126
	A. Cell wall synthesis	126

* Present address: Bacterial Chemotherapy Unit, Glaxo Research Laboratories, Greenford, Middlesex, England.

IX.   Membrane Damage 131
      A.   Introduction 131
      B.   Methods 132
      C.   Protoplasts, spheroplasts and L-forms 135

 X.   DNA Damage 140
      A.   DNA synthesis 140
      B.   Interaction of drugs with DNA 141
      C.   Mutagenic effects 150
      D.   Photoproducts in ultraviolet-irradiated bacteria . . 150
      E.   Strand breakage 159

XI.   RNA damage 163
      A.   Ribosome breakdown and loss of activity 164
      B.   Changes induced in RNA 165
      C.   RNA synthesis 166

XII. Protein Damage 166
      A.   Protein synthesis 166
      B.   Substances inducing protein misreading 168

XIII. Conclusions 173

References 173

I. INTRODUCTION

Studies on the mode of action of chemotherapeutic agents and the mechanism of death in bacteria exposed to physical agents form an important aspect of microbiology. While such investigations have traditionally been considered as being mainly of academic interest, they are now of more widespread importance because they have greatly increased our knowledge of the structure and especially the biosynthetic processes of the bacterial cell. They have also helped provide information on the mechanisms of resistance of bacteria to various drugs and to physical processes. There is also the hope that such knowledge may lead to the design of new and improved chemotherapeutic drugs.

This Chapter will deal with methods of studying the effects of antibiotics and other chemotherapeutic agents and of heat, ionizing and ultraviolet radiations on bacteria at the cellular, biochemical and molecular levels. It is obviously impossible in such a broad type of essay to describe the many and varied techniques employed by investigators over the past 15 years or so, and we have, therefore, concentrated mainly on damage to the bacterial cell wall, cytoplasmic membrane, protein and nucleic acids. No attempt has been made to provide a comprehensive list of all authors who have used a particular technique. The book edited by Hugo (1971) should be consulted for reviews dealing with the inhibition and destruction of microbial cells by physical and chemical processes.

II. METHODS OF TREATMENT

A. Effect of drugs

Initial experiments should be carried out to determine the minimum concentration of the substance which inhibits the growth in broth of various bacterial strains. This concentration is the minimum inhibitory concentration (MIC) and details of the procedure are given in Chapter IV, Volume 7B of this Series, by Sykes and Spooner. The minimum sporostatic concentration can be determined in a similar manner. The MIC gives a useful starting point for other experiments. However, an exception to this rule occurs with glutaraldehyde, which interacts to a considerable extent with broth constituents, so that the MIC with non-sporing bacteria may be some 50 times higher than would be expected from other experiments (Rubbo, Gardner and Webb, 1967; Munton and Russell, 1970a).

Subsequent experiments should be carried out with both growing and non-growing bacteria or, if necessary, with bacterial spores.

1. *Non-growing bacteria*

Bacteria which have grown overnight in a nutrient medium are washed free of the medium in several changes of sterile glass-distilled water, and aliquots of the washed suspension added to solutions of the chemical agent under test. Samples are removed at intervals, and viable counts made as described below. Antibiotics or other antibacterial agents which inhibit some cellular synthetic process will have no effect on the viability of such suspensions, whereas substances with a so-called "direct" action will be lethal to sensitive bacteria. It must be added that an organism which is resistant could be so by virtue of impermeability to the drug (p. 106) drug inactivation (p. 113) or drug excretion, e.g. proflavine (Kushner and Khan, 1968) and actinomycin D and certain mutants (Voll and Leive, 1970).

2. *Growing bacteria*

Bacteria inoculated into growth media and incubated at the optimum growth temperature are treated with the drug (added at zero time or to exponentially growing cultures). Samples are removed at intervals for determining surviving numbers, as described below. Again, however, in certain cases, e.g. penicillins, cephalosporins, destruction of the test drug by enzymes possessed by the bacteria (p. 113) must be borne in mind.

3. *Bacterial spores*

Comparatively little information is as yet available as to the manner in which the few sporicidal agents available act on bacterial spores. There are various methods available for preparing aerobic bacterial spores. The method

5

used by the authors is similar to that described in the British Pharmacopoeia (1968). This involves growing the organisms for 7 days at 37–39°C
on the surface of an agar plate containing 0·0001% w/v manganese sulphate
(note that the heat resistance of spores can be altered considerably by the
incorporation of certain cations), and then washing off the growth with
sterile water. Spore suspensions can be stored for long periods at ca. 4°C
without any loss of viability. Because vegetative cells are more sensitive
to disinfectants, they must be removed before tests are made. One way of
carrying this out is to heat the spore-containing suspension to 80°C for
about 5 min; however, such a technique, although satisfactory for killing
vegetative bacteria, may render the spores more sensitive to various chemicals and is thus not to be recommended. A far better procedure is to
remove non-sporing cells by repeated centrifugation, and to examine the
suspensions under the phase-contrast microscope to ensure their absence;
spores then appear as phase-bright cells.

(a) *Sensitivity of spores to drugs.* This is best determined by a viable counting procedure, as described later. Extended periods of treatment (up to
100 h or longer) may be necessary in some cases, e.g. phenols, even to
show a slight effect, whereas 2% glutaraldehyde has a pronounced lethal
effect within 2 h.

(b) *Effect of drugs on germination.* Germination may be defined (Lund, 1962)
as changes between the mature, resting spore and the vegetative cell at the
stage of first division. During this process, the following changes occur in
bacterial spores (E. O. Powell, 1957; J. F. Powell, 1957; Powell and Hunter,
1955; Rode and Foster, 1962a, b; Powell and Strange, 1953): loss of heat
resistance accompanied by changes in staining properties, decrease of
refractive index, decrease in dry weight and optical density (O.D.) and
release of dipicolinic acid (DPA). There is also slight swelling of the spores
during germination, and oxygen uptake becomes detectable (Levinson
and Hyatt, 1956). Methods for studying the effects of a drug on germination
of spores will thus include (i) microscopical examination of spore-drug
systems (Gould, 1964), (ii) direct measurement of spore swelling, e.g. by
means of a Coulter counter model B (Parker, 1969), (iii) measurement of
O.D. changes (Parker, 1969), (iv) measurement of oxygen uptake in a
Warburg apparatus (Loosemore and Russell, 1964), or redox potential
measurement.

(c) *Effect of drugs on post-germinative development* (*outgrowth*). Hitchins,
Gould and Hurst (1963) recognized four stages in the post-germinative
process: (i) swelling, (ii) emergence from the spore coat, (iii) elongation of
the emergent organism, (iv) division of the elongated organism. They further

found three stages in the swelling of aerobic spores during the germination and post-germinative processes: swelling during germination, involving a rapid increase of ca. 20% in packed cell volume (pcv); pre-emergence swelling of up to 100% increase in pcv prior to emergence from the spore coat; and elongation. Thus, the effect of drugs on this stage can be studied microscopically (Gould, 1964), by measurement of spore swelling or by measurement of O.D. changes (Parker, 1969).

(d) *Effect of drugs on sporulation.* Comparatively little attention has been given to this. However, Vinter (1964) has shown that penicillin can inhibit sporogenesis throughout almost the whole of the phase of accumulation of calcium in the spores and of dipicolinic acid (DPA) synthesis. Calcium accumulation can be measured by means of $^{45}Ca^{2+}$, the concentration being determined in cells washed with 1 mN HCl; DPA can be determined colorimetrically. Spores formed in the presence of methicillin show a decreased content of hexosamine (see p. 127 for details of assay) and of DPA (Murrell and Warth, 1965).

B. Physical processes

1. *Heating processes*

To study the effect of moist heat on bacteria, a temperature controlled water-bath (a temperature variation of $\pm 0.01°C$ is adequate) is employed. Washed suspensions of the organism may be added at the required temperature, allowing for a heating-up period, or preferably one part is added to nine or 99 parts of diluent previously equilibrated at the required temperature. Regular or continuous mixing is essential during storage at the high temperature. The temperature itself should be carefully chosen and for mesophilic strains 50–60°C is recommended, although responses may vary even within this range (Allwood and Russell, 1968). Samples for analysis may be cooled by dilution or by placing in a container in a waterbath at the required temperature. Cooling rate and final temperature should be carefully selected; in particular, it should be borne in mind that cooling to 0°C may cause cold shock (see below).

2. *Low temperatures*

(a) *Cold shock.* The rapid cooling of bacteria to ca. 0°C may be lethal. However, cold shock is observed only with Gram-negative organisms, e.g. *Aerobacter aerogenes* (Strange and Dark, 1962), *Pseudomonas* species, *Escherichia coli* and *Salmonella typhi*. Chilling must be rapid, and the cells should be in the log phase of growth. It is most readily accomplished by dilution of the cell suspension into suspending menstruum held at the chilling temperature, e.g. Strange and Postgate (1964) diluted one part of a suspension to 0°C in nine parts or 49 parts of diluent; Sato and Takahashi (1968) added one part to 49 parts of buffer at 3°C. The suspending media can enhance or abolish shock, and injury appears in increasing amount with increasing exposure at 0°C.

(b) *Freezing and thawing.* Bacterial spores, and many Gram-negative non-sporulating species, especially cocci, are very resistant to this process. However, most types of bacteria are sensitive, dependent on a number of variables, viz. cooling velocity, temperature, suspending medium, storage time and temperature, and warming rate. For a comprehensive review see Mazur (1966). Mazur and Schmidt (1968) have summarized a series of methods for varying cooling rate, final temperatures and warming rate. A common method is to cool 5 ml aliquots of suspension in screw-capped bottles by immersion in dry ice-acetone mixture or liquid air which will freeze rapidly to -75 to $-78°C$. Warming can be carried out by transfer to a water-bath at 37°C. An initial slow cooling to -1 to $-3°C$ in an ethanol bath (Mazur and Schmidt, 1968) may be necessary to minimize supercooling. Moss and Speck (1966) employed a freezer to cool suspensions to $-20°C$, which provides for a slow cooling rate (0·5–1·5°C/min). The provision of even freezing may be difficult to accomplish. Postgate and Hunter (1963) suggested a rapid chilling method in which suspensions were frozen in drops (0·05 ml) in liquid nitrogen. Thawing was also rapid in buffer at room temperature.

3. *Ultraviolet radiation*

The source of u.v. light is an important consideration. It is preferable to use monochromatic light if possible. The maximum lethal effect of u.v. against bacterial cells is between ca. 250 and 275 nm, and the rate of death depends on the light intensity. The germicidal lamp (low pressure mercury vapour lamp) emits 95% of its light at 254 nm. Other broad spectrum lamps may also be employed together with filters to isolate or narrow the wavelength band (high pressure mercury vapour or tungsten lamp). Filters, however, usually reduce the intensity, which also depends on the distance between the u.v. source and the irradiated material: intensity varies inversely with the square of the distance between lamp and material. Transmission of u.v. light is considerably reduced by any liquid and by cells. Absorption may also occur by the constituents of the media (Meynell and Meynell, 1965). For example, there is only 30% transmission through 1 cm of a suspension containing $2·5 \times 10^8$ cells/ml (Smith and Hanawalt, 1969).

Ultraviolet dose rate may be measured in different ways, e.g. recent publications by Radman *et al.* (1970), Radman and Errera (1970) and

Monk, Peacey and Gross (1971) have used the Latarjet dosimeter (Latarjet, Morenne and Berger, 1953). Jagger (1961) described a small, inexpensive u.v. dose-rate meter. Howard-Flanders and Theriot (1966) used a General Electric Germicidal light meter, whilst Smith and Meun (1970) measured the photodecomposition of uranyl oxalate. See Smith and Hanawalt (1969) for a detailed discussion of the above parameters and of dosimetry determination.

The usual method of u.v. exposure is to place the bacterial sample (10 ml) in a 9 cm Petri dish with magnetic stirrer. The mean dose depends on the distance between the source and the surface of the suspension and concentration of cells. Care should be taken to prevent exposure to direct light after exposure, particularly if repair processes are under study (page 118). Temperature control may be important and cells should be cooled to 0°C after exposure to prevent enzyme repair processes if necessary (allowance should also be made for cold shock effect if relevant).

4. *Ionizing radiation*

The two most common sources of ionizing radiation used to study the effects on micro-organisms are as follows:

(a) *X-ray tubes.* The conditions of exposure to X-rays depend on the output of the tube. Low voltage tubes (ca. 50 Kvp) emit radiation of low energy, some of which will be readily absorbed by filter, container, atmosphere and suspending solution. A correction should be made for this absorption (e.g. Town *et al.*, 1970). Higher energy tubes (200 Kvp) with suitable filtration of any low energy radiation emit radiation which will not be significantly influenced by medium, container, etc. Temperature of irradiation is of little significance between 0 and 20°C.

(b) *γ-Radiation from a ^{60}Co source.* A source of activity of 1 Mrad is convenient, although this may present a rather too high dose rate for short exposure experiments. Glass containers or vials are suitable. The amount of oxygen present should be controlled, e.g. by bubbling oxygen or nitrogen through the system immediately before exposure. A more controllable system is one in which gas can be bubbled through the preparation during exposure. Temperature control may also be required. The composition of the suspending medium will influence the sensitivity of bacteria to γ-rays, because of the presence of sensitizing or protecting compounds. An inorganic buffer medium is often recommended, although defined minimal media may be more suitable (Pollard and Weller, 1967). To minimize the indirect effects of ionizing radiation, the a_w (water activity) of the system can be reduced by the addition of solutes, or by freezing or drying the suspension prior to exposure.

III. BACTERIAL VIABILITY

Any study dealing with the effects of chemical and physical processes on intact bacteria must be related to the effects of these processes on viability. The term "viability" is itself difficult to measure, however, because an organism could be considered to be dead or alive depending upon the practical conditions used. Viable counts are normally made by serial dilution of cultures in sterile water, phosphate buffer, normal saline or Ringer's solution, followed by plating into (pour-plate, roll-tube) or on to (surface-viable) nutrient agar. Alternatively, the most probable number (MPN) method with liquid media or the microscopical slide technique of Postgate, Crumpton and Hunter (1961), of particular use in studying the effect of drugs on the germination or outgrowth of bacterial spores, may be adopted. The Chapter by Postgate (1969) in Volume 1 of this Series should be consulted for valuable practical information. Nevertheless, difficulties may arise when determining the viability of bacteria which have been exposed to chemicals or physical agents, as discussed below. For reviews on damaged bacteria see Harris (1963), Russell (1964) and Roberts (1970).

A. Exposure to chemicals

After treatment of bacteria with a chemical, sufficient of the substance may adhere to the cells to be present when they are placed in a recovery medium and to hinder development. To counteract this, the recovery medium should contain a suitable "inactivating" or "neutralizing" agent, which must itself be non-toxic to bacteria and which, if it combines with the drug, must not result in the formation of a toxic product. Examples of appropriate inactivating agents for various inhibitory compounds are listed in Table I.

Many substances, e.g. phenols, cresols, glycerol, esters of p-hydroxy-benzoic acid, readily lose their activity on dilution, and this is a recommended method for eliminating the carry-over of inhibitory drug concentrations into the recovery medium.

Certain antibiotics cannot be inactivated solely by dilution, and no chemical or biological inactivator is as yet known for them. Examples of such substances are vancomycin, tetracyclines, chloramphenicol and methicillin and other penicillinase-resistant penicillins. Although dilution to a sub-inhibitory level is frequently practised, ideally an appropriate dilution of a (drug +bacteria mxiture) should be filtered through a membrane filter apparatus, the membrane washed *in situ* with sterile water or saline and the membrane placed on the surface of an agar medium for colony counts to be made after incubation.

TABLE I

Antibacterial agents and inactivating agents

Antibacterial agent	Inactivating agent	Comments
Penicillins	β-lactamase ("Neutrapen")*	Except Methicillin, Cloxacillin, Nafcillin, Flucloxacillin
Cephalosporins	β-lactamase from *Enterobacter cloacae* P99	Enzyme preparation: O'Callaghan *et al.* (1968)
Sulphonamides, sulphones	p-Aminobenzoic acid	
Mercury compounds organic arsenicals	Sodium thioglycollate	Possible inhibitory effect of thioglycollate on bacterial spores (Mossel and Beerens, 1968)
Quaternary ammonium compounds, biquanides	Lecithin ± Lubrol W	
Aldehydes	Sodium (bi) sulphite	Dilution a better method (Munton and Russell, 1970a)
Halogens	Sodium thiosulphate	

* Riker Ltd., Loughborough.

B. Exposure to physical processes

1. *Heat*

(a) *Vegetative cells*. Vegetative bacteria which survive exposure to temperatures above about 45°C may be sensitive to post-treatment recovery conditions, e.g. the composition and pH of the recovery medium and the temperature of incubation. Although the actual conditions may vary from organism to organism, it is recommended that a complex rather than a synthetic medium be used, and that with organisms such as staphylococci or *E. coli* the medium contain 1% w/v Difco brand yeast extract, which gives better recovery than other yeast extracts (Allwood and Russell, 1966). The pH of maximum recovery is c. 6 (Nelson, 1956), the actual optimum depending on the organism. The temperature of incubation for optimum recovery is ca. 32°C. The method of enumerating survivors is also of importance and higher counts are obtained by the pour-plate than by the surface-viable method (Baird-Parker and Davenport, 1965), although it might be expected that in the former technique, bacteria already damaged by a heating process were subjected to further harmful treatment when mixed with molten agar at c. 45°C, followed by exposure to room temperature whilst the agar set and then another temperature during incubation.

(b) *Bacterial spores.* The resistance of bacterial spores to heat has been considered in detail by Roberts and Hitchins (1969), Roberts (1970) and Russell (1971a). Their thermal resistance will depend on the composition of the sporulation medium (particularly the content of divalent metallic cations) and temperature of spore cultivation, the stage of development of the spores, the suspending menstruum during treatment and on water activity (a_w). The recovery and revival of heated spores depends upon the following factors:

(i) Composition of the recovery medium. The nutritional requirements of heat-damaged spores are greatly altered (Ernst, 1968). Thioglycollate broth is inhibitory to the outgrowth of *Bacillus* species used for monitoring steam and dry heat sterilization processes (Ernst, 1968). Bromocresol purple present in Oxoid brand Dextrose Tryptone Broth is harmful to heated spores of *Bacillus stearothermophilus* and should be used without the dye as a subculture medium for such spores (Cook and Brown, 1960). The value of enrichment substances in the recovery medium in eliminating the dormancy of heated, but not killed, spores is to be noted (Morrison and Rettger, 1930; Curran and Evans, 1937).

One other point is of interest, and this concerns the finding (Murrell *et al.*, 1950) that, as the period of heating increases, surviving spores become increasingly sensitive to inhibitors present in the recovery medium. Starch, charcoal and serum albumin which act presumably by adsorbing inhibitory substances present in the media improve the effectiveness of many but not all, recovery media (Olsen and Scott, 1950).

(ii) pH of the recovery medium. There is very little information available here, but *B. stearothermophilus*, after heat treatment, is very sensitive to pH, unlike *Clostridium perfringens* (Roberts, 1970).

(iii) Temperature and period of incubation. There is a marked variation in the claims of various authors (see Roberts, 1970), and consequently each investigator is recommended to determine optimal conditions, e.g. *Clostridium botulinum* type A recovered best at 20°C, *B. stearothermophilus* at 45–50°C. Long periods of incubation may be necessary, e.g. up to several months with some species of clostridia (Roberts, 1970).

2. *Cold shock*

When Gram-negative bacteria, e.g. *E. coli*, *Pseudomonas* sp. and *Aerobacter aerogenes*, are stored frozen or recovered immediately from the frozen state they are unable to grow on minimal agar medium which can support the growth of the organisms before freezing (Straka and Stokes, 1959; Postgate and Hunter, 1963; Moss and Speck, 1966; MacLeod, Smith and Gelinas, 1966). Higher counts of cold-damaged cells of these organisms are obtained on enriched agar media, and this must be borne in mind when assessing the effect of cold shock on such bacteria. Trypticase is the component of Trypticase Soy agar responsible for the recovery of injured cells of *E. coli* (Moss and Speck, 1966). As stated earlier, Gram-positive bacteria are relatively insensitive to freezing, and thus composition of the recovery medium, e.g. with *Staphylococcus aureus* (Baird-Parker and Davenport, 1965), is of little importance.

3. Ultraviolet radiation

The composition of the post-treatment recovery medium will influence the recovery of u.v.-irradiated bacteria. Greater recoveries of *E. coli* (Roberts and Aldous, 1949) or *Shigella sonnei* (Nakamura and Ramage, 1963) have been obtained on chemically defined media than on nutrient agar. The pH of the recovery medium should also be considered, since Weatherwax (1956) has reported that the number of colonies of u.v.-irradiated *E. coli* in agar at pH 7 was in some cases 1000 times the number at pH 8. The optimum recovery temperature is a third factor to be considered; whereas the recovery of *E. coli* exposed to X-rays is maximal at 12–21°C (Hollaender, Stapleton and Billen, 1953), the optimum temperature for the recovery of *S. sonnei* is 37°C (Nakamura and Ramage, 1963).

4. Ionizing radiation

The survival of *E. coli* after exposure to ionizing radiations is markedly influenced by the nature of the recovery medium (Stapleton, Sbarra and Hollaender, 1955; Freeman and Bridges, 1960), with surviving fractions smallest on media which were optimal for growth of untreated bacteria (Alper and Gillies, 1958, 1960); this need not necessarily be true for all other strains of vegetative bacteria (Bridges, 1963). Woese (1958) found that there was little or no difference in the survival on minimal or com-

TABLE II

Recovery conditions for damaged bacteria

Treatment	Post-treatment factors to be considered
Drug	Inactivation. Composition of medium, pH and temperature of incubation
Heat or cold shock	Composition of medium, pH, temperature of incubation and method of counting
Ultraviolet radiation	Composition of medium, pH, temperature of incubation, dark and light repair
Ionizing radiation	Composition of medium, pH, temperature of incubation.

plete media of X-ray treated bacterial spores. However, some recent data reviewed by Roberts (1970) suggest that the composition and pH of the recovery medium and the temperature of incubation are of considerable importance when dealing with irradiated spores.

A summary of recovery conditions which may be investigated is given in Table II.

IV. RESISTANCE TO ANTIBACTERIAL AGENTS

The terms "sensitive" and "resistant" are relative terms. The term "resistance" is frequently used when the majority of cells in a culture are not inhibited or killed by a concentration of a drug normally found *in vivo*, or when a strain is not inhibited or killed by a concentration of drug which is inhibitory or lethal to the majority of strains of that species. Note that it is possible to refer to a heterogeneously resistant culture, as with methicillin-resistant staphylococci (see later).

A. Choice of test strains

Initial testing experiments will indicate the extent and range of activity of a particular drug or a thermal or radiation process. The effects of a chemical or physical process can then be studied on a highly sensitive organism. However, information on how a process acts can also be obtained by studying a resistant strain, which may occur naturally or result from mutant development. Methods of producing mutant strains have been well documented by Hopwood (1970, this Series, Volume 3A).

B. Impermeability to drugs

1. *Gram-negative bacteria*

A drug may be unable to reach its site of action in the bacterial cell. This may be particularly so with Gram-negative bacteria, the cell wall of which is exceedingly complex and many-layered (Murray, 1968; de Petris, 1967). However, many Gram-negative bacteria after treatment with ethylenediamine tetra-acetic acid (EDTA) become sensitive to antibiotics and other agents to which they may normally be resistant (Leive, 1968; Russell, 1971b). EDTA releases a large proportion of the lipopolysaccharide (LPS) of the cell wall of these bacteria as well as surface enzymes (Heppel, 1965), and it is clear that such organisms contain an outer permeability barrier preventing access of a drug. EDTA is normally used in conjunction with Tris buffer, but the latter may itself remove components from the cell walls of Gram-negative bacteria (Voss, 1967).

The following techniques may be used to show this.

(a) *Pretreatment of cells with EDTA.* Tris buffer washed cells (there must be no chilling during this washing) (Leive and Kollin, 1967) are pretreated with EDTA (10^{-4}M) +tris (0.12M) at pH 8. However, it is important that this treatment should not be longer than 15 sec to 2 min, because EDTA + tris can cause degradation of 23s RNA and of nucleotides and nucleosides to bases (Neu *et al.*, 1967), if longer periods are used. Pretreatment for the short period described has no effect on bacterial viability, and represents an early change in permeability with RNA degradation occurring thereafter.

The system is then diluted 1 to 10 with growth medium, which effectively dilutes out the EDTA +tris, and the substance under test added. The sensitivity of the test organism to the test drug can then be determined in various ways, e.g.

    (i) determination of the dose (LD_{50}) of test drug necessary to kill 50% of the bacteria in a given time (Muschel and Gustafson, 1968);

   (ii) measurement, by non-radioactive methods, of protein, RNA and DNA synthesis;

  (iii) measurement of the effect of the drug on the incorporation of radio-active substances into trichloroacetic acid (TCA)—or perchloric acid (PCA)—insoluble material.

EDTA-pretreated cells can repair their permeability barrier and regain insensitivity to a drug, so that experiments (i)–(iii) must be carried out over a relatively short period, e.g. 60–120 min. Hence experiments involving determinations of MICs are of no value here.

(b) *Lysozyme EDTA spheroplasts.* The preparation of spheroplasts of Gram-negative bacteria by lysozyme, EDTA and tris is described later (p. 137). An example of their use is provided in are view on fusidic acid by Godtfredsen (1957) who states that whereas high concentrations of this antibiotic do not affect the incorporation of ^{14}C-phenylalanine into the protein fraction of *E. coli*, incorporation of spheroplasts is decreased by fucidin, so that the resistance of this organism may be the result of impermeability to the drug.

(c) *EDTA +drug combinations in broth.* In this method, EDTA and the test drug are incorporated into the culture medium into which bacteria are inoculated. The MIC of the drug $\pm$ EDTA is recorded after incubation. Suitable controls should be carried out to ensure that under such conditions EDTA is itself non-toxic to the bacterial cells. Concentrations of EDTA which may be used can vary from ca. 1×10^{-2}M to ca. 5×10^{-4}M. An isobologram is then constructed, in which the MIC of the test compound is

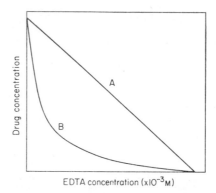

FIG. 1. Isobologram indicating (B) synergism, (A) additive effect.

plotted for various EDTA concentrations, as shown diagrammatically in Fig. 1. A synergistic response is shown by B in this figure, and an additive effect by A (Lacey, 1958).

This method does, however, suffer from the following possible disadvantages:

(i) EDTA may remove metals from the growth medium, so that the activity of drugs (e.g. vancomycin, tetracyclines) which are less potent in the presence of cations such as Mg^{++} (Best and Durham, 1964, 1965), is enhanced. However, concentrations of Mg^{++} necessary to overcome this inhibition may be considerably higher than those normally present in culture media (Garrod and Waterworth, 1969).

(ii) Any removal of metals from the growth medium may adversely affect the cells themselves, especially as Webb (1949) has shown that growth of Gram-negative bacteria such as *E. coli* in media containing limiting amounts of Mg ions occurs in the form of filaments. Filament formation in EDTA-containing media has yet to be examined in our experience.

(iii) Neu and Winshell (1970) have proposed that EDTA may render Gram-negative β-lactamase producers even more *resistant* to penicillins by increasing the access of enzyme to substrate. Strains of *E. coli* in which the β-lactamase is a surface enzyme are resistant to carbenicillin and ampicillin, whereas strains in which there are no such surface enzymes are sensitive to these drugs.

(d) *Agar diffusion method.* Weiser, Wimpenny and Asscher (1969) investigated the action of EDTA/antibiotic combinations on *Pseudomonas aeruginosa* by an agar diffusion method. In this, an agar plate seeded with the organism is poured, and two cups cut with their centres close to each other, e.g. 1·5 cm apart. One well is filled with EDTA, the other with the test drug. A synergistic effect is shown by the inhibition of growth in the area between the two cells (see Sykes and Spooner, this Series, Vol. 7B).

(e) *Other chelating agents.* Not only EDTA has an effect on bacterial permeability. Roberts, Gray and Wilkinson (1970) have studied the effects of EDTA and of other chelating agents (e.g. nitrilotriacetic acid, diethyl-enetriaminepenta-acetic acid) on *Ps. aeruginosa* and have shown that the bactericidal activities of these compounds are closely related to their affinities for Mg^{++} ions. It thus seems likely that at least some of these chelating agents could substitute for EDTA in the procedures described above, although it is doubtful whether any benefit would result.

(f) *Cell-free systems.* Details of the effects of drugs on cell-free bacterial systems are described later, when relevant. It is, however, interesting to note here that the results of experiments of EDTA treatment as described above may lead to the same conclusion as experiments involving cell-free systems, e.g. the peptidoglycan (mucopeptide) synthetase of *E. coli* is sensitive to vancomycin (Strominger *et al.*, 1968), whereas the whole cells are sensitive to this antibiotic only upon EDTA treatment (Russell, 1967), suggesting that the cells present a permeability barrier to vancomycin.

(g) *Role of LPS in drug resistance.* An interesting technique has recently been described by Tamaki, Sato and Matsuhashi (1971) for isolating novobiocin-supersensitive (NS) or penicillin-supersensitive (PS) mutants of *E. coli* by treatment of the parent cells with N-methyl-N'-nitro-N-nitrosoguanidine (NTG) as described by Adelberg, Mandel and Chem (1965). Such treated cells are grown on agar to give several hundred colonies/plate at 37°C. Colonies from this master plate are replicated on plates of agar containing antibiotics. Colonies which do not grow on at least one of the replica plates at 37°C are collected from the master plates. Tamaki *et al.* (1971) also point out that a more efficient method for isolating anti-biotic-supersensitive mutants is the penicillin screening technique first described by Lederberg (1950). In this, the cells are treated with NTG and subsequently segregated for 17 h, and are then transferred to nutrient broth (to give a density of ca. 10^8 viable cells/ml) containing 300 μg/ml of penicillin and 400 μg/ml of novobiocin. After incubation at 37°C for 16 h with shaking, the cell suspension is diluted a 1000-fold with broth, and 0·1 ml samples spread on nutrient agar plates. Most of the colonies which appear in the experiments described were NS.

Sud and Feingold (1970) have recently examined the lipid composition and susceptibility to polymyxin B of liposomes (lipid spherules in aqueous suspension) prepared from the lipids isolated from wild type, highly poly-myxin-resistant *Proteus mirabilis*, and two polymyxin-sensitive mutants (one obtained by use of NTG, the other by using sulphadiazine), and have found that polymyxin B resistance is determined by a permeability barrier presented by the cell envelope. Details of the isolation of wall lipid from *Ps. aeruginosa* are given by Brown and Wood (1972).

(h) *Correlation between lipophilic character and antibacterial activity.* A relationship between lipophilic character, expressed as a chromatographic R_m value (measured by means of reversed-phase thin layer chromatography) and antibacterial activity of penicillins and cephalosporins has been demonstrated (Biagi *et al.*, 1970).

2. *Gram-positive bacteria*

The resistance of Gram-positive bacteria to antibacterial agents may also be the result of permeability factors, recent studies having shown that there is a relationship between the amount of lipids in the cell walls of staphylococci and of vegetative bacilli and their resistance to antibacterial agents (Hugo and Stretton, 1966; unpublished findings from our laboratories). This is of more than mere academic interest since, when freshly isolated, staphylococci may contain an appreciable amount of lipid in their cell walls.

The effect of cellular lipid can easily be demonstrated experimentally. Bacteria are repeatedly subcultured in nutrient broth containing 3% w/v glycerol; as a result, there is an increase in the negative mobility (see Electrophoresis, p. 123) of the cells in the presence of 10^{-4} sodium dodecyl sulphate, indicating an increased lipid content at the surface of the cells (James, 1965). The amount of cellular lipid may be quantitatively determined by extraction with chloroform : methanol from the dry cells (Folch *et al.*, 1957).

These readily extractable lipids from Gram-positive (or from Gram-negative) bacteria may be separated by thin layer chromatography on silica gel G plates, and the classes of bacterial lipid characterized by various methods (Dunnick and O'Leary, 1970): by comparison of R_f values with R_f values of standard lipid samples; and by reaction of bacterial lipids with various lipid stains applied to the plate in the form of a spray, e.g. iodine vapours, rhodamine 6G (Dittmer and Lester, 1964) or 2,7-dichloro-fluorescein for the determination of all lipid classes, and ninhydrin, molybdenum blue, periodate-schiff reagent and diphenylamine reagent for the determination of, respectively, primary and secondary amines, phosphate ester groups, lipids containing α-glycols and glycolipids.

A flow-sheet of the process is briefly given in Fig. 2, which also shows the separation of phosphatidyl ethanolamine fractions and fatty acids. The latter may be characterized by infrared spectra or by gas chromatograms.

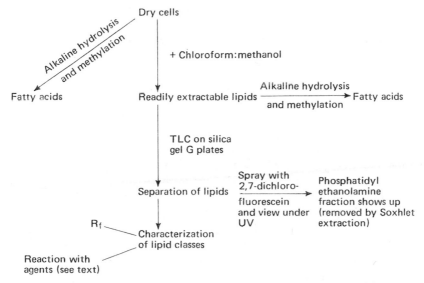

FIG. 2. Outline of scheme for isolation of lipids and fatty acids.

3. *Bacterial spores*

Sykes (1970) has postulated that the reason why several bactericidal agents are not lethal to spores is because of the impermeability of these forms to such compounds. King and Gould (1969) and Gould, Stubbs and King (1970) have recently lent support to such a hypothesis, and have described the structure and composition of resistant layers in spore coats. Treatment of spores with β-mercaptoethanol (ME) was carried out in such a way as to cause sensitization of spores to lysozyme, a spore enzyme or hydrogen peroxide, but insufficient to cause inactivation before exposure to these; further treatment with alkali, which removed a protein from the outer coats of ME-treated spores, caused greater sensitization to these lytic agents. To determine this, spores (10 mg equiv. dry wt/ml) are incubated in 7M urea (pH 2·8) containing ME (10% v/v) for 1 h at 37°C cooled, centrifuged and washed four times with cold water. For alkali treatment, the cells are resuspended in 0·1N NaOH and incubated for 15 min at 4°C before washing four times in cold water. Subsequent lysis by lysozyme, spore enzyme or H_2O_2 can be measured by the decrease in optical density.

The results from such an experiment suggested (i) that the disulphide rich protein is involved in resistance, since its removal by reagents which break disulphide bonds allows lysozyme to pass through the spore coat and reach its mucopeptide substrate, (ii) that the alkali-soluble protein also pays a role in resistance of spores to lysozyme and H_2O_2 (Gould et al., 1970).

Such a technique is obviously worthy of further consideration in relation to the resistance of spores to other agents.

C. Methicillin-resistant staphylococci

These present a special problem and hence are considered separately. The reasons for their resistance are not known; what has been ascertained, however, is the lack of evidence for a difference in the proportion of the cell mass that is mucopeptide in the cells of methicillin-resistant (MR) and methicillin-sensitive (MS) cultures; nor is there any major difference in the amino-acid composition of cell walls of MR and MS strains (Dyke, 1969). However, studies with lysostaphin have suggested that although there is no difference in amino-acid *composition*, there could (a) be differences in amino-acid *sequence* or (b) be present some non-mucopeptide component in MR cells that prevented access of lysostaphin to its substrate (glycyl-glycyl bonds) (Sabath et al., 1970).

Strains of MR staphylococci which are naturally occurring show a population heterogeneity in their response to methicillin. They also produce the enzyme penicillinase (β-lactamase), but penicillinase-less variants of MR strains may be used for studying their resistance without the complicating presence of the enzyme. The selection of penicillinase negative variants from MR strains has been described by Dyke, Jevons, and Parker (1966). In addition, Dyke (1969) has reported the isolation of an MR penicillinase negative strain which is homogeneously and stably resistant to methicillin.

Methods of detecting MR are as follows (Hewitt, Coe and Parker, 1969; Parker and Hewitt, 1970).

(a) Resistance should be suspected when a zone of inhibition (no matter what size) around a methicillin disc contains large numbers of evenly distributed colonies.

(b) If a 30°C incubator is available, a disc test with methicillin (10 μg disc) is probably the method of choice: growth up to, or within, 1 mm of such a disc on agar or blood agar denotes an MR strain. Alternatively, a spot inoculum (0·002 ml drop of culture) can be incubated at 30°C on an agar plate containing 10 μg methicillin/ml.

(c) Profuse growth of MR strains occurs on agar containing 10 μg methicillin/ml and 5% w/v sodium chloride (Barber, 1964) after 18 h at 37°C.

(d) An MR strain requires 25 μg/ml (or more) of methicillin to inhibit growth in broth after 18 h at 30°C (Annear, 1968) or 48 h at 37°C.

D. Drug inactivation

Inactivation of an antibacterial substance by a bacterial strain should mean that that compound is ineffective against that particular strain. If results are taken after a long period, e.g. 24–48 h as in experiments involving MICs, then this is the logical conclusion. However, over a much shorter period this may be incorrect, e.g. the majority of cells of some strains of *Ps. aeruginosa* are initially killed by penicillin, but there is simultaneous destruction of the antibiotic to a point where a very low drug level is reached, when re-growth of the surviving cells occurs (Sabath and Abraham, 1964). The same finding emerges with *E. coli* R+ TEM and cephaloridine and a new cephalosporin, 7-cyanoacetylaminocephalosporanic acid (Russell, *unpublished results*).

Thus, a consideration of enzymatic destruction of a compound must be balanced by the fact that the cells may, in fact, be intrinsically sensitive to the drug. A classical example occurs with penicillinase-producing strains of staphylococci, and a simple method for comparing intrinsic sensitivity (genotype) and resistance caused by destruction of the drug by the culture as a whole (phenotype) is to determine the MIC of a penicillin or cephalosporin against both a large (ca. 10^7 viable cells/ml) and a small (ca. 10^3/ml) inoculum. Reduction of day-to-day variation in results can be attained by prior standardization of the viable numbers in the culture, e.g. by adjustment to optical density (Hewitt and Parker, 1968).

1. Destruction of penicillins and cephalosporins

(a) *Detection of β-lactamase-producing strains.* Several methods have been described for detecting those strains of bacteria which produce a β-lactamase, but only four will be described here. Smith and Knox (1961) described a method in which a membrane filter on which an organism had grown overnight on agar was placed on filter papers impregnated with benzylpenicillin (or cephaloridine, although Fleming *et al.* (1970) recommended cephalosporin C for detecting "cephalosporinase" producers) and 2% Andrade's indicator. Penicillinase-producing organisms became red; however, to distinguish between β-lactamase and penicillin amidase (acylase) activity, Hamilton-Miller, Smith and Knox (1963) recommended a butanol/acetate chromatographic procedure. A membrane filter procedure has also been employed by Holt and Stewart (1963): in this, benzylpenicillin is incorporated into an agar base containing the Oxford strain of *Staph. aureus* (NCTC 6571). A membrane filter is layered on top, and heavy spot inocula of suspected β-lactamase-producing organisms added. Growth of the indicator (Oxford) strain indicated β-lactamase activity. A combined enzyme induction-enzyme detection test (methicillin-induced

N-phenyl-1-naphthylamine-azo-*o*-carboxybenzene or MI-PNCB test) has been described by Duma and Kunz (1968), in which a 5 μg methicillin disc is used for induction, and PNCB (purple when acid) is used to detect enzyme production by staphylococci. Gram-negative β-lactamase-producing bacteria produce a red/orange colour when grown in broth containing 100–250 μg/ml or more of a new cephalosporin (7-cyanoacetylamino cephalosporanic acid) and it is conceivable that *in vitro* use could be made of this finding (Russell, 1971c).

(b) *Inactivation of β-lactam drugs*. Several methods have also been described for investigating, quantitatively, the sensitivity of penicillins to β-lactamases. These methods have been well documented by Hamilton-Miller, Smith and Knox (1963) and the following is based in part on their review.

(i) Iodometric technique (Perret, 1954; Citri, 1958). This method is based on the fact that penicilloic acids but not penicillins take up iodine (8 molecules per molecule of ampicilloic or benzylpenicilloic acid); it thus cannot be used to follow hydrolysis by penicillin amidase, because 6-amino penicillanic acid (6-APA) does not reduce iodine. In Perret's method, iodine uptake is determined by sampling the reaction mixture into excess iodine and back-titrating with sodium thiosulphate. In Citri's procedure, the time taken for a standard amount of blue starch-iodine complex to be totally decolorized is the basis for determining the reaction velocity.

(ii) Micro-iodometric technique. A considerably more sensitive method for determining the rate of hydrolysis of penicillins by β-lactamases has been described by Novick (1962) who also used decolorization of the blue starch iodine complex as the chromogen, absorption at 620 nm being measured. Jack and Richmond (1970) have recently employed this technique in studying the β-lactamases synthesized by Gram-negative bacteria against benzyl-penicillin, ampicillin and cephaloridine as substrates (at 6 mM), thus obtaining what is termed a "substrate profile". One mole of cephaloridine after hydrolysis, was assumed to react with four equivalents of iodine (see Alcino, 1961).

(iii) Hydroxylamine technique. Hydroxylamine reacts with penicillins at pH 7, leading to the production of a hydroxamic acid:

$$\text{R.CO.NH}-\underset{\substack{| \\ \text{O}=\text{C}-\text{N}-\text{CH.COOH}}}{\text{CH}}-\text{CH} \overset{\text{S}}{\diagup} \text{C}-\text{Me}_2 \quad + \text{NH}_2\text{OH} \longrightarrow \quad \text{R.CO.NH}-\underset{\substack{| \\ \text{CO} \quad \text{NH}-\text{CH.COOH}}}{\text{CH}}-\text{CH} \overset{\text{S}}{\diagup} \text{C}-\text{Me}_2$$

Hamilton-Miller *et al.* (1963) state that this reaction is complete within 10 min at room temperature and at pH values 6–8, and that the hydroxamic acid is stable for 2 h. It forms a coloured complex with Fe^{+++} ions;

although this chromogen is stable for only a few minutes, extended stabilization can be achieved by extraction into *n*-butanol. Absorption is measured colorimetrically at 550 nm.

This method will not measure penicillin amidase activity, but suffers from the disadvantage of a lack of sensitivity, the lower limit for most penicillins being 400 μg/ml.

(iv) Acidimetric procedures. The rate of hydrolysis of penicillin can be measured either manometrically (Henry and Housewright, 1947) or by an alkaline titrimetric method. In the manometric assay, the volume of CO_2 liberated from a bicarbonate buffer as the antibiotic is hydrolysed to the corresponding penicilloic acid is proportional to the rate of hydrolysis. The method is time-consuming. Wise and Twigg (1950) devised an alkaline titrimetric method, used by, e.g. Selzer and Wright (1965), in which measured amounts of dilute alkali (0·1N NaOH) are added at a sufficient rate to neutralize the carboxyl groups as they are freed by enzymatic hydrolysis of the penicillin molecule.

(v) Spectrophotometric determination. O'Callaghan *et al.* (1968) followed the rate of hydrolysis of cephaloridine by its decrease in absorption at 255 nm. The advantage of this method, is that it allows a study of the hydrolysis of the antibiotic in the presence of penicillins, and other (slowly or non-hydrolysable) cephalosporins. 3 ml of a 100 μM solution of cephaloridine (initial extinction ca. 1·4 at 255 nm) was used for this study.

(vi) Microbiological. The microbiological assay of antibiotics is a procedure too well known to be described in detail here; in brief, it involves a comparison between a solution of known potency and a solution of unknown potency in their inhibitory effect on the growth of a susceptible micro-organism. The classical method of carrying this out is by the cup- or cylinder-plate technique. The difficulty is, of course, that enzyme activity may continue during the assay. A suitable procedure is to remove the bacteria by, e.g. membrane filtration, and stop the enzyme activity in the filtrate by iodine treatment. This is diluted to subinhibitory levels when dilutions are prepared for placing in the cups or cylinders, especially if a spore-former such as *Bacillus subtilis* is used as the assay organism.

2. Destruction of other drugs

(a) *Chloramphenicol*. Inactivation of chloramphenicol on incubation of the antibiotic with appropriate co-factors and extracts of *E. coli* carrying resistance (R) factors has been found (Shaw, 1967), and Sompolinsky, Ziegler-Schlomowitz and Herczog (1968) have described chloramphenicol-susceptible, inactivating and tolerant strains of *E. coli*. They examined acylation of the drug by the inactivating strain by treatment with alkaline hydroxylamine, and $FeCl_3$ to measure hydroxamate formation at 540 nm.

Holt (1967) has used an infrared spectrographic method to show that inactivation results from an attack at the amino group of the chloramphenicol molecule.

(b) *Aminoglycoside antibiotics*. Some bacteria possess R factors which confer resistance to amino-glycoside antibiotics in a host bacterium by virtue of enzymic inactivation of these drugs, e.g. inactivation of streptomycin by phosphorylation and adenylation, and of kanamycin by acetylation and phosphorylation, has been described (Ozanne *et al.*, 1969). Benveniste and Davies (1971) have found that strains of *E. coli* carrying an R factor which inactivate kanamycin by N-acetylation will inactivate other aminoglycoside antibiotics by acetylation also. Adenylating or phosphorylating activity is determined with ^{14}C-adenosine 5′-triphosphate (ATP) and μ^{32}P-ATP, respectively, using osmotically shocked cells (treatment of cells with tris-EDTA-sucrose, followed by shocking with cold water) to remove the adenylating and phosphorylating activity from the cells (Ozanne *et al.*, 1969). A somewhat similar procedure, for determining acetylating enzyme activity with (1–^{14}C) acetylcoenzyme A, is described by Benveniste and Davies (1971).

3. *Enzyme induction*

A detailed account of enzyme induction is obviously outside the scope of this Chapter. It is however, of relevance to the present Section since β-lactamase induction has been shown to occur in Gram-positive bacteria but not to such a great extent in Gram-negative organisms (a notable exception to this is *Ps. aeruginosa*). Pollock (1957) has described the activity and specificity of inducers of penicillinase production in a strain (NRRL 569) of *Bacillus cereus*, and has shown that only compounds closely related to benzylpenicillin, including various cephalosporins, could act as inducers. In Pollock's method cells were grown to a specific opacity, before being transferred to conical flasks to which suitable quantities of the substances under test were added (a control consisted of no added inducer). Samples were removed when required into chilled 8-hydroxyquinoline solution, and penicillinase activity determined manometrically (see earlier).

4. *Antibiotic combinations*

A penicillin or cephalosporin which is rapidly destroyed by a Gram-negative β-lactamase-producing organism may, in fact, be highly active against these bacteria if the enzyme activity is inhibited. Such protection of the drug can be achieved by using it in conjunction with a β-lactamase-resistant penicillin (which is itself *inactive* against that organism), e.g. methicillin, cloxacillin, flucloxacillin or nafcillin. Experiments with whole cells can be carried out in broth for determinations of MICs and viable counts, or in agar where an antibiotic diffusion technique may be used. Such experiments have recently been carried out by Hamilton-Miller (1971). An alternative procedure is to examine for spheroplast induction (p. 137) (Russell, *unpublished data*).

With crude enzyme systems of a β-lactamase, and a cephalosporin $\pm$ a "protective" penicillin, the spectrophotometric technique of O'Callaghan *et al.* (1968), may be used. Selzer and Wright (1965) have used the potentiometric method described earlier for measuring the impairment by β-lactamase-resistant penicillins of the inactivation of benzylpenicillin by *B. cereus* penicillinase.

E. Resistance (*R*) factors

Multiple drug resistance among the Enterobacteriaceae was first observed in Japan, and has been shown to be "infectious" or "transmissible" in that resistance to several drugs can be transferred from resistant (donor) strains to sensitive (recipient, acceptor) strains by conjugation (Watanabe, 1963; see also reviews by Datta, 1965; Anderson, 1968; Walton, 1968) similar to the F-factor in *E. coli* (Meynell, Meynell and Datta, 1968).

Techniques for demonstrating R-factor transfer may be made in both liquid and solid media.

1. *Liquid media*

Basically, this procedure involves growing donor and recipient strains together overnight in broth, and then plating on to a medium (the selective medium) containing an antibiotic to determine whether the recipient strain is now resistant to this drug. Examples of the methods employed by the many investigators in this field are provided below.

Anderson and Datta (1965) used *E. coli* K12 F⁻, requiring methionine, as the recipient. Mixed cultures of this and resistant *Salmonella typhi* were spread on minimal agar supplemented with 0.5% lactose, 20 μg/ml methionine and 25 μg/ml ampicillin. Colonies of the recipient strain which developed were purified by plating on nutrient agar and identified as *E. coli* K12 Met⁻. Anderson (1965) and Anderson and Lewis (1965) described a technique for screening drug-sensitive strains for the presence of transfer factors. This involves the incorporation of a strain in a mixture consisting of an intermediate recipient (containing a non-transferring R-determinant) and a final recipient which is devoid of a transfer factor and which is drug-sensitive.

Smith (1970) inoculated 0.02 ml of 24 h cultures of each of donor and recipient strains into broth, the recipient strain consisting of a nalidixic acid (NA)-resistant, antibiotic-sensitive strain of *S. typhi*, and the donor strain being a NA-sensitive antibiotic-resistant strain of *E. coli*. The mixed culture was incubated at 37°C for 24 h, and then inoculated on to a plate of McConkey agar containing NA plus one of the antibiotics (as discs) to which the donor strain was resistant and the recipient strain sensitive. The plate was incubated at 37°C for 24 h, and any colonies of the recipient strain which grew were purified by replating and determining the drug sensitivity pattern. The proportion of organisms of the recipient strain which have acquired resistance may be determined by carrying out a viable count, using the surface viable dropping method, on McConkey agar containing NA alone and with one or other of the antibiotics to which the donor strain is resistant.

A somewhat similar procedure is employed by Hinshaw *et al.* (1969) except that donors were NA-sensitive, antibiotic-resistant strains of *Klebsiella* and *Aerobacter*, and the recipient was a NA-resistant, antibiotic-sensitive *E. coli* mutant strain.

2. *Solid media*

Because of the difficulty in the above method of isolating the cells in the donor culture that contribute the R-factor in the transfer process, Lee and Richmond (1969) developed a method whereby the frequency of transfer of an R-factor could be assessed on solid media and cells of the donor type could be isolated. The method involved using a derepressed mutant of *E. coli* K-12 W3110 which is sensitive to antibiotics and which synthesizes alkaline phosphatases at a fully derepressed rate in the presence of 0·2M inorganic phosphate. This enzyme is usually produced by *E. coli* only when the concentration of phosphate in the medium becomes limiting, with repression virtually complete in the presence of 0·1M phosphate. Basically, the technique is to grow "microcolonies" of the donor strain on agar (2 h incubation), add the recipient strain, incubate for ca. 30 min and then cover with half-strength agar containing 0·2M phosphate plus the desired antibiotic. Resistant recipient colonies are detected by examining for alkaline phosphatase production with 0·1M sodium α-naphthylphosphate and 0·1M 3,3'-dimethoxybenzidine; such colonies are stained a bright purple. Care is needed because of the carcinogenic nature of the dimethoxybenzidine. See also Sykes and Richmond (1970).

V. REPAIR OF INJURY

Bacteria which have been sublethally injured may require a "convalescent" period during which the damage to the cell is repaired, e.g. ultraviolet-irradiated bacteria, in which cellular injury is presumably the result of the formation of pyrimidine dimers in DNA may be able to remove these dimers and hence repair the damage inflicted upon them. In the same way, heat-treated cells can repair permeability damage and damage to ribosomal RNA (Iandolo and Ordal, 1966; Allwood and Russell, 1969b). Iandolo and Ordal (1966) used changes in the sensitivity of *Staph. aureus* cells to NaCl as an index of repair. The repair of injury induced by freeze-drying *Salmonella anatum* occurs rapidly after rehydration (Ray, Jezeski and Busta, 1971). Repair of damage caused by various drugs may also occur.

In general terms, a suitable procedure is to transfer treated bacteria to an appropriate liquid recovery medium wherein growth, DNA, RNA, protein and cell wall (e.g. mucopeptide (peptidoglycan)) syntheses, DNA degradation, RNA degradation, metabolic pool composition and permeability controls can be assessed. Details of these techniques will appear in subsequent Sections of this Chapter. Allwood and Russell (1969b) used some of these methods when heat-treated *Staph. aureus* cells were transferred to recovery media. Tomlins and Ordal (1971a) showed that recovery of *Salmonella typhimurium* from thermal injury was dependent on RNA and protein syntheses. Tomlins and Ordal (1971b) used a technique involving polyacrylamide gel (3% in Tris acetate buffer, pH 7–7·2) electrophoresis of ribosomal (*r*) RNA, and showed that after thermal injury of these cells the 16s RNA was totally, and the 23s RNA was partially degraded; sucrose gradient analysis demonstrated that after injury the 30s ribosomal subunit was totally destroyed. During recovery of the cells from thermal injury, four species of rRNA accumulated.

VI. DETERMINATION OF BINDING OF DRUGS

The determination of the binding or uptake of a drug by bacterial cells or their components is a necessary part of any attempt to elucidate the mechanism of action of the drug. Binding studies indicate the site of action of the drug but they do not necessarily provide direct evidence for a proposed mode of action.

Quantitative and qualitative techniques are available for the determination of binding and the quantitative methods are concerned with three main problems:

(a) The addition of the drug to the potential binding materials.
(b) The separation of the bound drug from that not bound.
(c) The assay of the free and/or bound drug.

Some of the qualitative methods can be quantitatively applied also.

A. Theoretical considerations of adsorption

Comprehensive studies of adsorption processes have been described elsewhere (Giles *et al.*, 1960). A brief account of the four main classes of absorption isotherms follows.

(a) *S curves*, which indicate a vertical orientation of the adsorbed molecules at the surface.

(b) *L curves*, or "Langmuir" isotherms which usually indicate that the molecules are adsorbed flat on the surface, or sometimes, that ions with particularly strong intermolecular attraction are adsorbed vertically.

(c) *C curves*, which are linear and which indicate that the solute penetrates into the adsorbate more easily than the solvent.

(d) *H curves*, which are indicative of solutes adsorbed as ionic micelles.

B. Outline of procedure for quantitative studies

1. *Addition of drug to binding component*

When using a non-radioactive form of the drug it is often necessary to use thick suspensions of binding material in order to detect the amount bound. The amount of material used is standardized and a range of quantities are placed in contact with the drug. The concentration of the drug can also be varied and the period of contact is also controlled. It is therefore possible to estimate the rate and the extent and degree of binding. This procedure can be carried out under different conditions so that the effects of pH, temperature and competitors for the binding site can be estimated.

The sensitivity of the method is increased by use of radio labelled drug and the higher the specific activity the greater the sensitivity. The procedure adopted is as described for the non-radioactive drug and with either form the distribution of the drug within whole cells or the components of cells can be determined by utilizing a suitable separation procedure.

2. *Separation of bound and free drug*

(a) *Centrifugation.* Separation of the particulate matter from the supernatant fluid can be achieved by centrifugation at a sufficient speed to produce a clear supernatant fluid. When this procedure is chosen it complicates any studies on the rate of binding because of the time spent during centrifugation. Also if the binding is not very strong it is possible that some of the drug will be freed during the process.

Gradient centrifugation can be used to localize the area of binding to a cellular component or to determine the distribution of the drug within that component. The drug—material mixture is added to the top of a gradient such as a sucrose or caesium chloride gradient and centrifuged at high speed for sufficient time to achieve good separation. The disadvantage of centrifugation mentioned above is inherent in this method also and an indication of separation of the complex is given when trailing of radioactivity occurs when a radioactive drug is used.

(b) *Chromatography*. Depending on the properties of the drug and binding material, systems can be developed for separating drug and binding material from the complex formed between the two. Provided there are differences in the mobility of the components of the reaction mixture, separation can be achieved and the amount bound assayed. Radiolabelled drug finds greatest application for quantitative studies by this method. It is possible that the system employed will cause some bound drug to be released from the binding material, but chromatography will also provide information on the type of binding occurring.

(c) *Electrophoresis*. This method exploits the difference in mobilities of the components of the reaction mixture under the influence of an electrical field and the actual system employed will depend on the properties of the drug and material used. For bacterial cells a method has been developed specifically for measuring changes in electrophoretic mobility in the presence of drugs (see page 123).

(d) *Filtration*. When suspensions of binding material are used, this method allows rapid separation of the components provided the binding material does not pass through the filter. It can be used to gain information on the relationship of binding with time and when a radioactive drug is used accurate determinations of the amount bound and the amount free can be made. Allowances must be made for any drug that adsorbs to the filter and usually the cells are washed on the filter so that only the drug bound remains attached to the cells on the filter.

(e) *Dialysis and ultrafiltration*. The technique of dialysis utilizes the properties of a barrier which is selective in allowing solutes to diffuse through it; the driving force is a concentration gradient. Ultrafiltration differs in that solutes are forced through a barrier by applying pressure to one side of it. (The two techniques also differ in that solvent flows in the same direction as small molecules in the latter method but in the former method there is usually a flow of solvent in the opposite direction to that of the small molecules.)

The barrier normally employed is Visking tubing which is made of cellulose and has a known pore size. The apparatus consists of the tubing arranged to provide a suitable dialysing area and the mixture of drug and binding material is placed inside and the unit sealed. The outside of the tubing is covered by the diffusate solvent and temperature controls and stirrers can be used if necessary.

For ultrafiltration a similar apparatus is used except that a source of pressure is included. Separation proceeds more quickly with ultrafiltration but dialysis is probably the more discriminating method.

3. *Measurement of drug*

(a) *Absorption methods.* Some drugs possess characteristic absorption spectra and these can be assayed by constructing a reference curve with purified drug relating absorption (usually at the wavelength of maximum absorption) to concentration. Supernatant fluids can then be determined for free drug and hence the amount bound can be determined. It is also possible that the drug bound to a component could be selectively re-absorbed and assayed and whenever this is possible it would allow determinations to be made to account for all the drug used.

(b) *Chemical determinations.* The chemical character of some drugs enables chemical determinations to be carried out and supernatant fluids can be assayed by utilizing a standard curve constructed from determinations made with known amounts of the drug.

(c) *Biological assay.* The plate-cup method can be used for determining the amount of drug not bound and determinations of small quantities can be carried out by this method.

C. Other methods

1. *Difference spectroscopy*

By measuring the changes in absorption of drugs or cellular components information on their interaction can be obtained. This is described in detail later (p. 141).

2. *Chromatography*

Chromatography can be used for separating free drug from drug-binding material complexes. It can also be used directly as a measure of binding by adding the drug and binding material to the system employed and allowing separation to take place.

3. *Analytical centrifugation*

Evidence that binding has occurred can sometimes be obtained by adding a drug to a bacterial component that normally will not sediment in an analytical centrifuge. If sedimentation now occurs then it is due to the binding of the drug to the component.

4. Electrophoresis using bacteria

The basis of this technique is that bacteria carry a net charge on their surface and as such will move under the influence of an electric field. The migration rate of a particle under the influence of 1 V cm^{-1} is called its electrophoretic mobility. When a drug combines with the surface of a bacterium it is likely to alter the net charge with a consequent change in the observed mobility. The bacteria are suspended in a suitable conducting medium and placed in a cylindrical transparent cell. A current is passed through this cell via electrodes placed at each end (usually copper–copper sulphate or mercury–mercuric nitrate) and the velocity calculated by measuring the time taken for the bacteria to travel a set distance.

From the current conductivity of the buffer solution used as medium and the cross sectional area of the cell, the electric field strength can be determined and hence the electrophoretic mobility. This is repeated in the presence of the drug and the effects of the latter are thereby measured. It is essential to carry out a large number of determinations of the velocity of the bacterium and safeguards against mechanical movement of the apparatus, convection and the entrapping of air bubbles must be taken. The apparatus is designed so that emptying and filling of the cylindrical cell is easily carried out and provision is made for the use of a microscope for following any movement of the bacteria.

The theory and precise practical details of this and other aspects of electrophoresis will be found in the excellent report edited by Bier (1959).

The technique as applied to bacteria indicates binding to surface layers and the use of protoplasts will provide information on the binding to membranes.

5. Fluorescence methods

Drugs that fluoresce under light of a particular wavelength can be determined both inside the cell or cell component and in the free state. Some drugs fluoresce when they react with particular cell components and it is also possible to add a fluorescent "tag" to a drug and follow the uptake of this form.

6. Hydrated electrons method

A rather sophisticated technique has been developed for studying the binding of ions to biological material (Phillips et al., 1970). It involves pulse radiolysis of the materials used and provides information concerning the reversibility of binding tendencies of drugs.

VII. PHYSICAL AND MORPHOLOGICAL CHANGES

Changes which can be observed in whole cells during exposure to lethal agents may be subtly small or large deformations. Bearing in mind the nature of the agent, particularly its known properties concerning reactivity with biological material, it may be possible to predict certain gross changes that can occur to alter cell morphology. Observable changes include alterations to cell size or shape, light-scattering ability, lysis, changes in the cell matrix and movement.

A. Changes in morphology and size—indirect methods

1. *Electron microscopy*

Electron micrographs may indicate changes in the appearance of the cellular matrix (Allwood and Russell 1969a). Alterations in membrane structure are readily observable (Silva, 1967). Care must be taken in interpreting observable changes to allow for artefacts during the preparation of samples for microscopy. Due consideration of the fixation process should be made.

(a) *Fixation of heated bacteria*. It seems difficult at present to correlate the ultrastructural findings with real alterations in the structure of bacterial cell components. The situation during the fixation of intact bacteria, which have a normal internal pressure, is different from that existing during the fixation of heated bacteria mainly when the fixative is a slow penetrating one as is the case with the complete RK procedure.

Another point to be considered concerns the likely alteration in the environmental conditions induced by heat treatment (for instance the ionic conditions prevailing in the outside and inside of the bacterial cell). It is known that such conditions markedly influence the electron microscopic image of bacterial membranes by interfering with the fixation process.

(b) *Fixation of bacteria treated with chemical agents*. The possibility that the chemical agents under study may interfere with the fixation process has to be taken into consideration.

For instance EDTA will compete with the calcium used in the RK fixation procedure. It is known that fixation under conditions of calcium deficiency affects the preservation of bacterial membranes. Thus, appropriate controls should be used when such fixation techniques are employed.

2. *Light measurements*

Changes in cell size and density of intracellular constituents (although not their location) can be readily detected by light-scattering and turbidity measurements (Mager et al., 1956). However, there are many pitfalls and the interpretation of readings poses considerable problems since interrelated effects can add up to a final optical density change or amount of incident light scattered by cells. Relatively concentrated suspensions must be employed. Turbidimetric and light-scattering measurements should be considered separately.

(a) Optical density (O.D.). A common method for detecting changes in cell size and density of cell contents, it is rapidly and easily carried out. Measurements are sensitive to the temperature of the suspending medium and its composition. The presence of salts may significantly affect the observed O.D. of a cell suspension (Bernheim, 1971) particularly of cells exposed to certain lethal agents. As a generalization, O.D. changes are inversely related to cell size changes (Berhneim, 1963; Koch, 1961). Other factors will affect the observed O.D. Protein coagulation or other changes in the opacity of the cell constituents will increase the O.D., which in contrast is probably reduced by leakage and cell lysis, a secondary effect of many lethal agents. The refractive index of the suspending fluid may also influence readings. The most important practical consideration is the choice of the wavelength of light employed, which must not be absorbed by cell constituents. Therefore light of wavelength greater than 350 nm is necessary. Sensitivity will be reduced at very high wavelengths: see Mitchell (1950) (see also Mallette, 1969, Vol. 1 of this Series.)

(b) Light-scattering. A nephelometric method may be used to detect changes in light-scattering properties of cell suspensions. Lovett (1965) has related changes in light-scattering inversely to cell volume changes, provided the refractive index of the cell matrix and cell shape remain unchanged. Clearly, it will depend on the reflecting properties of the cell surface and the overall changes in readings may be influenced by intracellular disorganization (Allwood and Russell, 1969a). A refined technique has been developed to measure changes in cell size and shape. Measurement of the angular distribution of light scattered by bacterial cells is described in detail by Berkman and Wyatt (1970) (cf. this Volume, p. 183).

B. Measurements of changes in cell sizes

1. Electron micrographs

While it may prove difficult to measure cell size by light microscopy, the use of electron micrographs of whole cells or ultrathin sections is a convenient method of measuring the size of bacterial cells. Provided care is taken to ensure identical fixation and fixed magnification factors, changes in cell size should be quantifiable. Bayde and Williams (1971) have described the use of the scanning electron microscope for measuring the sizes of very small cells, although there are significant limits to its accuracy see Bulla *et al.*, this Volume, p. 1.

2. *Packed cell volume*

Lark and Lark (1960) described the use of the haematocrit tube and centrifuge to measure changes in the cell volume of bacteria. A concentrated suspension of cells (ca. 5×10^{11} cells/ml), and centrifugation for a fixed time, are essential. This method may be useful for the examination of volume changes in curved or filamentous micro-organisms, after drug exposure.

3. *Automatic particle counter*

The use of electronic particle size counters to measure bacterial size has been described (Harvey and Marr, 1966; Kallings *et al.*, 1969; Kubitscheck 1969, this Series, Vol. 1), and these references should be consulted for detailes. When employing the instrument to detect changes in the sizes of cells during exposure to lethal agents some precautions are necessary. The concentration of electrolyte should be minimal, preferably not more than 0.9% (w/v) sodium chloride (Allwood and Russell, 1969b). Rye and Wiseman (1967) showed that concentrations of NaCl greater than 3% (w/v) could result in cell shrinkage. Agent-induced aggregation of cells could distort cell size distributions. Also, lethal agents causing an increase in membrane leakage may increase the permeability to the electrolyte and consequently affect the conductivity of the cells. All these points should be considered in assessing results obtained with the Coulter Counter or similar instrument.

4. *Centrifugation in sucrose gradients*

Although little used, this technique may prove a successful method for measuring changes in cell size. Chatterjee *et al.* (1971) employed a 2 to 12% linear sucrose gradient centrifugation of cells at 2000 r.p.m. The rate of sedimentation will depend on species. The influence of the high concentrations of sucrose, which may cause shrinkage (particularly of cells with altered permeability or cell wall damage), limits the usefulness of this technique.

VIII. CELL WALL DAMAGE

A. Cell wall synthesis

The synthesis of mucopeptide is a multistep process and has been studied extensively by many workers (reviewed by Strominger *et al.*, 1968; Rogers and Perkins, 1968). The steps shown occur within the cell and after the formation of the subunit of GlcNAc-MurNAc-pentapeptide, the latter is transported across the membrane and inserted into existing cell wall. The final step is the cross-linking of the linear mucopeptide strands in which two linear strands are made to undergo a transpeptidation reaction with the formation of an interpeptide cross-bridge. This results in the elimination of the terminal D-alanine in some organisms mediated by a D-carboxypeptidase. Most of these steps have been elucidated with the use of cell-free systems.

1. *Total mucopeptide*

Mucopeptide can be isolated and estimated by the method of Hancock and Park (1960) and has been applied successfully for studying *B. subtilis*, *S. aureus* and *M. lysodeikticus* (Gledhill, 1967; Rogers, 1967; Garrett, 1969). Mucopeptide can be isolated from Gram-negative bacteria by processes involving a series of treatments using NaOH (0·1N), sodium dodecyl sulphate (4%), rupturing, washing and phenol (Leutgeb *et al.*, 1963). Another scheme described by Mandelstam (1962) involves treatments with ethanol-ether mixtures, acetone, ether, alkaline urea, 2-mercaptoethanol and iodoacetate, pepsin, formic acid, phenol and a copper sulphate-ethylene diamine mixture respectively.

Isolated mucopeptide can be estimated chemically. Amino nitrogen can be determined by hydrolysing a sample with HCl (6N) for about 16 h at 105°C, removing the acid *in vacuo* and applying the ninhydrin method. Amino sugars and amino-acids can also be estimated by separating these two components after hydrolysis by paper chromatography, and again applying the ninhydrin method (Hatton, 1969) (see this Series, Vol. 5B).

2. *Mucopeptide precursors*

The accumulation of precursors indicates an interruption of a synthetic pathway. Precursors of mucopeptide can be estimated by the scheme outlined in Fig. 3 which is based on the method first introduced by Strominger (1957). The method is still widely used and is based on the fact that most N-acetyl amino sugars are present as uridine nucleotide derivatives and utilizes the modification of the Elson–Morgan reaction (Elson and Morgan, 1935) introduced by Reissig *et al.* (1955) for the determination of amino sugars.

3. *Incorporation of labelled compounds*

[14]C-alanine, ^{3}H-DAP, ^{14}C-lysine, ^{14}C-glutamic acid and ^{3}H-aspartic acid are commonly used for studying mucopeptide synthesis. For specific determination of the incorporation of these compounds, a fractionation procedure is necessary and important precautions are necessary under

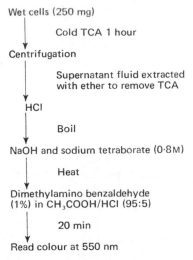

FIG. 3. Scheme for estimation of N-acetylamino sugars (Reissig *et al.*, 1955).

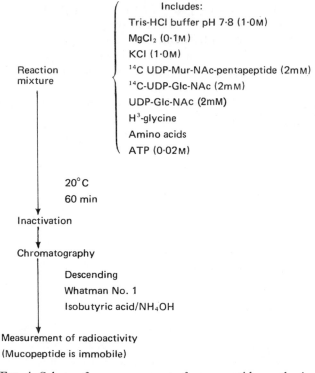

FIG. 4. Scheme for measurement of mucopeptide synthesis.

certain conditions. For example, ^{3}H-DAP is converted to lysine normally so excess lysine must be provided for the bacteria in order to inhibit the DAP decarboxylase (Smith and Davis, 1967). Similarly, aspartic acid can be converted to metabolites other than DAP (Garrett, 1969).

4. *Degree of cross-linking*

Inhibition of the final step of mucopeptide synthesis leads to a reduction in the amount of cross-linking occurring between peptide chains. This, consequently, results in an increase in the number of free amino groups and the content of alanine in the mucopeptide layer. Free amino groups can be determined using the method of Fraenkel-Conrat *et al.* (1955) in which mucopeptide (0·5–1·0 μmoles) in a 4% v/v solution of triethylamine

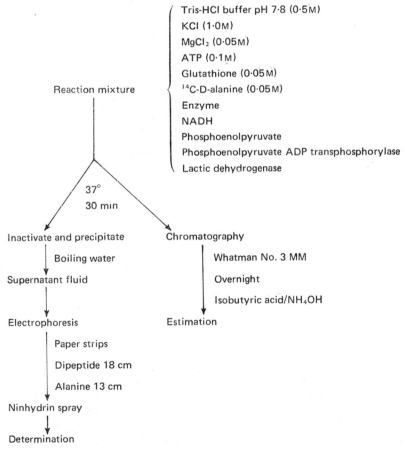

Reaction mixture

{
Tris-HCl buffer pH 7·8 (0·5M)
KCl (1·0M)
MgCl$_2$ (0·05M)
ATP (0·1M)
Glutathione (0·05M)
^{14}C-D-alanine (0·05M)
Enzyme
NADH
Phosphoenolpyruvate
Phosphoenolpyruvate ADP transphosphorylase
Lactic dehydrogenase
}

37°
30 min

Inactivate and precipitate   Chromatography
  Boiling water   Whatman No. 3 MM
Supernatant fluid   Overnight
                                 Isobutyric acid/NH$_4$OH
Electrophoresis   Estimation
  Paper strips
  Dipeptide 18 cm
  Alanine 13 cm
Ninhydrin spray
Determination

Fig. 5. Scheme for measurement of D-alanine-D-alanine synthesis.

in water : ethanol (10 : 1 v/v) is reacted with an ethanolic solution of fluorodinitrobenzene (5% v/v) for 30 min at 60°C. After evaporation, the residue is dissolved in water, extracted with ether and the aqueous phase dried under pressure. The resulting DNP-murein is hydrolysed in 4N HCl at 105°C for 14 h and amino-acids estimated by the ninhydrin method or using an amino-acid analyser.

5. *Cell-free systems*

Much of our knowledge of mucopeptide synthesis has been obtained from the use of cell-free systems developed by Strominger, Park, Neuhaus, Ghuysen and their colleagues. It does not fall within the scope of this Chapter to cover this aspect in detail and the reader is referred to the work written by Neufeld and Ginsburg (1966) for precise practical details. Instead, an outline of how some of the steps in mucopeptide synthesis can be determined are given in Figs. 4–7.

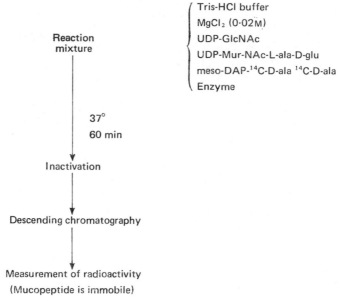

FIG. 6. Scheme for measurement of transpeptidation and carboxypeptidation.

Cell-free enzymes. The preparation of the respective enzymes involved in the various steps occurring in mucopeptide synthesis has been described in the work written by Neufeld and Ginsburg (1966). Normally, a large batch of culture is produced of the particular bacterium, the cells sonicated and particulate matter removed. The supernatant fluid is then fractionated by a process of elution and precipitation to produce

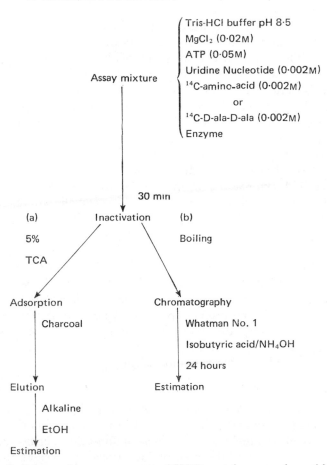

FIG. 7. Scheme for measurement of UDP-acetyl muramyl peptides.

different enzyme fractions, the conditions employed being governed by the characteristics of the individual enzymes.

6. *Inhibition of mucopeptide synthesis*

A number of drugs interfere with mucopeptide synthesis and for most of these the site of action is now known. Such drugs include penicillins, cephalosporins, D-cycloserine, vancomycin and ristocetin.

IX. MEMBRANE DAMAGE

A. Introduction

The cytoplasmic membrane is one of the most delicate components of the bacterial cell. Consequently any environmental force or chemical agent which is known to react with protein or lipid may influence the integrity of the membrane either at specific functional points or over its entire area. The membrane is very accessible, the only barrier usually being the cell wall. Although there are many indicators of membrane damage, it is difficult to measure the quantity of damage or the total area of the membrane whose functions have been influenced by a damaging agent. Antibacterial agents may influence a specific function of the membrane or cause a generalized loss of permeability control. The latter agents, at least, are usually lipophilic compounds or almost any physical exposure detrimental to cell survival. See the review by Harold (1970).

The bacterial cytoplasmic membrane controls the entry and exit of many substances, carries out a number of metabolic functions and is closely associated with the chromosome (see the review by Ryter, 1968).

B. Methods

1. Membrane synthesis

The determination of membrane protein can be carried out as discussed in this Series, Vol. 5 (see p. 168). The membrane is isolated by methods outlined earlier and total protein or the incorporation of amino-acids can be measured. Similarly, the synthesis of the lipid and lipopolysaccharide can be determined by measuring the incorporation of fatty acids and sugars, and phosphorus incorporation. (Yudkin, 1963).

2. Membrane function

(a) Leakage of intracellular materials. A change in membrane function often results in the uncontrolled release of intracellular materials from the cell. These materials include nucleotides, amino-acids, sugars, and cations and are normally part of the pool of low molecular weight metabolites present in cells. However, larger constituents are also lost from the cells under some conditions.

Purines and pyrimidines are most easily determined by measuring the absorbance of the medium used at 260 nm. In order to do this the bacteria must be removed by:

(i) Centrifugation—the suspension should be centrifuged at a suitable speed to allow maximum sedimentation of cells in a minimum time. Centrifugation at 10,000 g for 5 min is normally sufficient. Temperature should be carefully controlled.

(ii) Filtration—the cells can be removed rapidly by passing the suspension through a bacteria-proof filter (which should be washed before use). Immediate separation is obtained but it is essential to ascertain that the filter pad does not absorb material from the medium. With membrane filters, pre-washing in water is adequate.

When non-growing cells are being studied, a suitable buffer system can be used and for a growing culture a synthetic glucose-salts medium is satisfactory. If the drug itself absorbs strongly at 260 nm then it must be removed and the procedure adopted will depend on the chemical nature of the drug. Penicillins and cephalosporins can be removed by acidification and extraction with ethyl acetate and a similar procedure can be used with novobiocin (Morris and Russell, 1970; Smith and Davis, 1967). Whatever the procedure used it must be ensured that it is specific for the drug and does not remove the materials lost from the cell. This can be achieved in part by testing the procedure with purines and pyrimidines. The release of purines and pyrimidines can also be determined by allowing a culture to incorporate the radioactive form prior to treatment with the drug. The radioactivity of the supernatant fluid can then be determined.

The loss of amino-acids can be determined either chemically or by using the radioactive form. Chemical methods include those of Yemm and Cocking (1955), Moore and Stein (1948) and protein can be determined by the method of Lowry et al. (1957).

A number of methods are available for the determination of sugars, e.g. by the anthrone method (Trevelyan and Harrison, 1952). Reducing sugar can be determined by the method of Nelson (1949) and can be measured using the orcinol technique (Mejbaum, 1939). Where a growth medium is being used problems arise because a number of common constituents interfere with the procedures adopted. Phosphate and sugars will interfere with the orcinol determination (see Munro and Fleck, 1966) and these must be replaced in the medium if possible. For resting cultures there are fewer problems. Radioactive sugars can also be used (Davies et al., 1968) and the supernatant fluid examined accordingly.

Another indication of membrane damage is afforded when the supernatant fluid is tested for increased enzyme activity. For example β-lactamase activity can be assessed as described earlier and the use of a new chromogenic substrate allows determinations to be made in nutrient media also (O'Callaghan et al., 1972).

Metal ions can be determined by flame photometry or by using a radioactive form. K^+, Na^+ and Rb^+ have been determined with a flame photometer (Harold and Baarda, 1967) and radioactive forms of K^+, Rb^+, P have been determined in supernatant fluids of drug treated cultures (Harold and Baarda, 1968; Silver and Wendt, 1967). It must also be realized that once the membrane has been affected by an agent leakage may continue even if the drug is removed.

(b) *Responses to alterations in the osmotic environment.* Membrane damage may result in the increasing sensitivity of cells to the osmotic properties of the environment.

Osmotic protective substances, such as sucrose, may reduce the leakage of cell material during membrane damage (Allwood and Hugo, 1971).

(c) *Increased entry of substances.* In addition to the uncontrolled release of intracellular substances, changes in membrane function can also result in the increased entry of certain substances such as dyes, metal ions and certain substrates.

The use of dyes has proved a useful criterion for measuring changes in membrane function—commonly used dyes include 2,3,5-triphenyl tetrazolium chloride or bromide, and anilino or N-tolyl-α-naphthyl-amino-β-sulphonic acid (ANS and TNS). The tetrazolium dyes are reduced to coloured derivatives by dehydrogenases which absorb at 525 nm (Smith and Weinberg, 1962; Hugo and Freir, 1969). The dye is added to the drug-treated cells and the cell aliquots are extracted with acetone, removed and the absorbance read. ANS and TNS fluoresce when complexed with protein. They are normally well excluded from bacteria but membrane damage results in increased permeability and the resulting reaction with intracellular protein. In practice the cells are added to the dye and the fluorescence measured by using an incident light at 400 nm and the fluorescence at 470 nm using a spectrofluorimeter. Sometimes, however, the dye will fluoresce strongly when complexed with surface proteins and it is not always true to infer that membrane damage has occurred when an increase in fluorescence is observed.

Controls must be carried out to allow for light-scattering of the cells and to show that the drug or supernatant constituents do not combine with the dye.

Acriflavine has also been used to detect changes in permeability (Silver and Wendt, 1967). It fluoresces when bound to nucleic acids and although it enters cells passively, it is necessary to show that the observations made, reflect changes in permeability rather than surface binding.

The Gram stain can also be employed for demonstrating changes in permeability (Hugo and Longworth, 1964).

The methods mentioned above for determining the release of metal ions from the cell can be used for determining the entry of those ions also (Harold and Baarda, 1967).

(d) *Use of mutants.* Certain mutants are incapable of utilizing a substrate even though they possess the necessary intracellular machinery. They lack the required transport system and are termed permease negative (i^-, z^+, y^-). The increased hydrolysis of a substrate can therefore be used to indicate membrane changes and the most commonly employed mutants are those that possess a β-galactosidase but no permease. By using the chromogenic substrate o-nitrophenyl-β-D-pyranoside-galactoside (ONPG) its hydrolysis can be determined by measuring changes in absorbance at 420 nm. In practice the drug treated cells are added to the substrate and after a suitable time the reaction is stopped with sodium carbonate and the absorbance read after removal of the cells: see Brock and Brock (1959).

Mutants of this nature can also be used to demonstrate membrane action of drugs by determining changes in growth characteristics. If a non-utilizable substrate essential for growth is used and sub-inhibitory concentrations of a membrane active drug, the bacteria will be found to grow more readily.

3. Gross membrane damage

Membrane active drugs that cause gross damage will often cause lysis of bacteria, e.g. the polymyxins. Thus, the demonstration of a lysis by changes in optical density is a preliminary indication of this effect.

C. Protoplasts, spheroplasts and L-forms

Bacterial variants such as protoplasts, spheroplasts and L-forms have now become standard tools for investigating aspects of drug action and for studies on bacterial structure and function. Preparation of these forms involves the use of either a metabolic inhibitor or a muralytic enzyme (McQuillen, 1960; Hughes, Wimpenny and Lloyd, this Series, Vol. 5A).

1. Definitions

Protoplasts are defined as osmotically sensitive forms which are entirely devoid of cell wall, are unable to divide and do not revert to the parent form.

Spheroplasts are defined as osmotically sensitive forms which are not completely devoid of cell wall, do not divide, but can revert to the parent form after removal of the inducing agent.

L-Forms are osmotically sensitive forms which are devoid of, or contain very little, cell wall; they can divide but do not revert to the parent form. They are able to grow into characteristic colonies on agar and are sometimes regarded as stable, non-reverting spheroplasts (Klieneberger-Nobel, 1960).

The above classification is not rigid and there is a distinct requirement for standard nomenclature in this field. Protoplasts are described as spheroplasts and vice versa and the term spheroplast encompasses a wide spectrum of morphological variants. Also protoplasts are capable of reverting under certain physical conditions (Landman and Forman, 1969; Clive and Landman, 1970). The above definitions are based on the reports of Brenner et al. (1958), McQuillen (1960) and Martin (1967).

2. Preparations

(a) Protoplasts

(i) *Gram-positive bacteria.* Protoplasts are normally prepared from Gram-positive bacteria by the action of muralytic enzymes. Lag- or log-phase bacteria are washed and suspended in a hypertonic, buffered medium containing the muralytic enzyme. The type of buffer employed is not critical but the pH should be optimum for the particular enzyme; metal ions and cations are also sometimes necessary (see later). The solute used for providing the required tonicity should not be metabolized and should not penetrate the membrane. Sucrose, polyethylene glycol and sodium chloride are commonly used and the concentration will depend on the organism. For example, 0·1M and 1·0M sucrose is necessary for supporting protoplasts of *B. megaterium* and *Sarcina lutea* respectively. Conversion time is of the order of 30 min and determination of complete conversion can be made by microscopical examination, determination of loss of viability, measurement of the decrease in turbidity in the absence of an osmotic stabilizer, phage typing, antigenic determinations and estimation of mucopeptide. The measurement of changes in turbidity is the most convenient since some bacteria do not undergo a morphological change during conversion (Op Den Kamp, 1968).

The most commonly used enzyme is lysozyme and it has been used for preparing protoplasts of *B. megaterium* (Weibull, 1953), *Streptococcus faecalis* (Bibb and Straughn, 1962), *B. subtilis* (Van Iterson and Op Den Kamp, 1969), *Streptococcus faecium* (King and Gooder, 1970), *Sarcina lutea* and *Micrococcus lysodeikticus* (Gilby and Few, 1960) and *Listeria monocytogenes* (Ghosh and Murray, 1967). Its pH optimum lies between 6 and 7.

Other muralytic enzymes that have been used for preparing protoplasts include an enzyme isolated from *Streptomyces griseus* (Ward and Perkins, 1968), a phage associated muralysin (Fremier *et al.*, 1959) and enzymes from various bacteria (see McQuillen, 1960; Mohan *et al.*, 1965).

Inhibitors of mucopeptide synthesis are not normally used for preparing protoplasts, since cell wall material remains after treatment. However, they are employed for preparing L-forms of both Gram-positive and Gram-negative bacteria and it depends upon the individual worker's interpretation as to whether the variants formed initially are either spheroplasts or protoplasts.

(ii) *Gram-negative bacteria.* Protoplasts of Gram-negative bacteria are difficult to prepare because of the diversity of layers present in the envelope of these bacteria. Therefore, spheroplasts or L-forms of this class of organism are usually prepared although it has been reported that if *E. coli* is plasmolysed in sucrose prior to treatment with EDTA and lysozyme, true protoplasts are formed (Birdsell and Cota-Robles, 1968).

(b) *Spheroplasts*

(i) *Gram-positive bacteria.* Muralytic enzymes have been employed for preparing spheroplasts of Gram-positive bacteria, too, and include lysostaphin (Watanakunakorn *et al.*, 1969) and chalaropsis B (Allwood, 1968). Conditions used are similar to those outlined above.

(ii) *Gram-negative bacteria.* The most commonly used muralytic enzyme for the preparation of spheroplasts is lysozyme. However, the mucopeptide substrate is usually inaccessible to the lysozyme and special techniques have been developed to overcome this difficulty.

High pH. Lysozyme will convert *E. coli* to spheroplasts in pH 9·0 buffer (see McQuillen, 1960; Zinder and Arndt, 1956).

EDTA treatment. Ethylene diamine tetra-acetic acid (EDTA) is often used in conjunction with lysozyme for the preparation of spheroplasts. Tris buffer (pH 7–8) is also necessary when *E. coli* is used, since other buffers such as Tes and Bicine are not suitable, although they can be used for lysing *Ps. aeruginosa* (Gray and Wilkinson, 1965). The method of addition of the components of the system appears to be critical (Repaske, 1958) and magnesium ions are not normally necessary in addition to the stabilizing agent. Conversion can be determined by methods already described for conversion of protoplasts. Examples of concentrations used are as follows: lysozyme 20 μg/ml, EDTA 100 μg/ml and tris buffer 0·03M.

Spheroplasts of Gram-negative bacteria have been prepared using leucozyme C and phage-produced muralytic enzymes (see McQuillen, 1960). Autolytic procedures have also been employed for preparing spheroplasts (Mohan *et al.*, 1965) and spheroplasts have been prepared using lysozyme in conjunction with a complement system (Muschel, 1965).

Induction with Metabolic Inhibitors. There are a large number of steps involved in the laying down of the insoluble mucopeptide layer. If the process is inhibited, the mucopeptide loses its rigidity and lysis ensues. However, in the presence of an osmotic stabilizer conversion into spheroplasts occurs and this takes place as the bacteria grows. It is not common for metabolic inhibitors to be employed for preparing spheroplasts of Gram-positive bacteria but some workers have described the preparation of these forms (Hamburger and Carleton, 1966; Montgomerie *et al.*, 1966). Normally, the L-form is prepared by prolonging the period of incubation with the inhibitor (page 138).

A large number of antibacterial agents have been used for preparing spheroplasts of Gram-negative bacteria. The most commonly used are the β-lactam antibiotics (see McQuillen, 1960; Russell, 1962; Hirokawa, 1963; Lederberg, 1956) and spheroplasts have also been prepared using cyclo-serine (Ciak and Hahn, 1959), lithium chloride (Pitzura and Szybalski, 1959). 5-fluorouracil (Tomasz and Borek, 1960), glycine (Jeynes, 1957) and D-amino-acids. Freshly prepared cells are added to a stabilized growth medium (usual sucrose concentration 0·3M) containing the inhibitor. As the bacteria grow they are converted into spheroplasts and the latter continue to grow in size. There is a requirement for magnesium ions (approx. 0·1M) and conversion is most easily followed by phase-contrast microscopy. Magnesium ions can be replaced by other metal ions or other cations (Hugo and Russell, 1961; Tabor, 1962).

(c) L-forms

The initial stages of L-form formation require conditions described above for the preparation of protoplasts and spheroplasts. Both muralytic enzymes and metabolic inhibitors can be used and a protective medium is neces-sary. The variants produced initially are subcultured repeatedly into fresh medium containing the inducing agent until a stage is reached when no reversion to the parent form will occur in the absence of the inducer. L-forms produce characteristic colonies on solid medium and production is followed by this method. Agents used successfully include the β-lactam antibiotics (Dienes and Sharp, 1956; Dienes, 1967; Hamburger and Carle-ton, 1966) vancomycin (Roberts, 1967), bacitracin (Rotta et al., 1965; Roberts, 1967), lysozyme (Willett and Thacore, 1966; Gooder, 1968) lysostaphin (Watanakunakorn et al., 1969). See Maxted, this Series, Vol. 7A.

Apart from an osmotic stabilizer, brain heart infusion and magnesium ions are normally included in the growth medium.

4. Susceptibility to antibacterial agents

(a) Protoplasts. By virtue of the definition used above protoplasts do not divide or revert to the parent form. Hence effects of drugs on the viability of these forms cannot be assessed quantitatively. However, when placed in a suitable growth medium (e.g. Fountain and Russell, 1969) proto-plasts are capable of growing in size and will carry out metabolic functions similar to those of the parent. The effects of drugs on growth can be deter-mined by measuring changes in turbidity and more specific information can be obtained by determining the synthesis of protein, DNA and RNA in the presence of the drug. The effects of drugs on membrane synthesis and function can also be determined by methods employed for normal bacteria, and total counts are made easier by the comparatively large size of these forms. For resting protoplasts, drug action can be determined by measuring total number of cells, changes in turbidity and changes in membrane integrity (leakage). Microscopy can also be employed to study the effects of drugs on structure. For electron microscopy these forms can be fixed with glutaraldehyde (see also Munton and Russell, 1970b).

(b) *Spheroplasts.* The minimum inhibitory concentration of drugs against spheroplasts can be determined in either liquid or solid media. Spheroplasts are capable of reversion and MIC determinations are a measure of the inhibition of this process. The media are supplemented with increasing concentrations of drug and are seeded with the spheroplast which has been freed of the inducing agent. The lowest concentration preventing growth after 24 h incubation is the MIC. It is feasible that a similar procedure could be adopted to achieve an MIC against spheroplast development, but this would necessitate the presence of the inducing agent and would not always be successful because insufficient growth would occur to allow visual determination of the MIC to be made. Both methods also suffer from the disadvantage that it is difficult to achieve 100% conversion to spheroplast form during the inducing procedure. The parent cells remaining can complicate the findings particularly using liquid media.

Changes in turbidity of cultures of growing spheroplasts can be measured as for protoplasts and the concentration that produces a 50% inhibition of growth compared with the control can be determined. (This can also be applied to protoplast growth.) Changes in protein, DNA, RNA and membrane synthesis can be determined also using methods similar to those used for parent bacteria and it is also possible to measure the viability of these forms. Once more this is a means of measuring the ability of these forms to revert to the parent and serial dilutions are made in hypertonic diluting medium, e.g. a 0·3M sucrose and 0·01M Mg^{++} buffer solution and recovery is made in a hypertonic agar medium, e.g. nutrient agar containing 0·3M sucrose and 0·01M Mg^{++}. In this way the bactericidal action of a drug can be quantified, but it is necessary to account for any parent cells that may be present initially. This is achieved by carrying out a duplicate determination of viability, but using hypotonic diluting, e.g. water and, as recovery medium, nutrient agar. It is imperative to remove the inhibitory effects of the inducing agent and this is done by dilution or by using an inactivating agent (p. 103).

Similar determinations can be made with resting spheroplasts and as with protoplasts total counts can be determined and can be utilized to explain any observed changes in turbidity.

Sensitivity to drugs can also be determined in solid media using impregnated discs and by electron microscopy (Davies *et al.*, 1968).

(c) *L-forms.* As for spheroplasts, changes in turbidity, macromolecular syntheses, membrane structure and function and total numbers can be determined using L-forms. True viability can also be determined and the number of colony forming units is measured by diluting to a suitable number and plating into a suitable agar medium. Colonies develop over a period of 2–6 days and can be counted under a microscope or by eye. Total counts are somewhat more difficult because of the irregular mode of division of these forms. MIC determinations can be carried out in either liquid or solid media, the inducing agent having been removed prior to the addition of the drug under investigation (by definition, L-forms will not revert to the parent after removal of he inducing agent) (Panos, 1965).

(d) *Mycoplasma*. Strains of mycoplasma usually grow very slowly and it is therefore difficult to follow the effects of drugs on these organisms. For routine testing of susceptibility to drugs, innovations have been introduced in order to obtain results over a relatively short period of time. Measurement of turbidity is not always satisfactory and some species have a tendency to clump. MIC determinations can be made in either liquid or solid media and the media are supplemented with indicators that change colour if the organisms are growing. The most popular indicator is phenol red and depending on the species of organism is used in conjunction with arginine or glucose. The indicator changes colour long before there are visible signs of growth and the MIC is the lowest concentration that prevents colour development. Normally observations are made until the MIC is the same on two consecutive days. Another variation is to use discs saturated with different levels of drug and placing these on the surface of agar seeded with the organism. A standard zone diameter is set for the MIC and the clear zone is surrounded by an area of colour due to the indicator incorporated in the medium. The MIC is that level of drug that produces the arbitrary size of inhibition zone.

Viability can be determined using the method of most probable numbers but a high degree of replication is necessary to reduce the errors likely with this technique. The number of colony forming units can be determined by carrying out the necessary dilution and dropping the culture on to agar without spreading. Counts are made after 4–6 days of incubation using a microscope and this is facilitated by staining the colonies. In this way the minimum mycoplasmicidal concentration can be determined. Changes in turbidity of cultures can also be determined.

X. DNA DAMAGE

A. DNA synthesis

Methods of estimating DNA synthesis have been well described in Vol. 5 of this Series, and will not be repeated here. Drugs which inhibit

DNA synthesis include mitomycins, nalidixic acid, phenethyl alcohol and novobiocin.

B. Interaction of drugs with DNA

Several drugs are known to interact with DNA, with a consequent inhibition of DNA or RNA synthesis. Preliminary, but hardly quantitative, information as to the extent of binding of a drug to DNA can be obtained by washing treated bacteria free of the drug and resuspending the cell in drug-free media. A rapid resumption of growth and of DNA (or RNA) synthesis parallel to control (untreated) bacteria suggests little (or weak, reversible) binding of the drug to DNA. Thus, the antibiotic novobocin, which among its many actions inhibit DNA synthesis, is unlikely to be strongly bound to DNA (Morris and Russell, 1970).

The experimental procedures described below have, in many cases, been widely used in studying drug/DNA interactions. It must, however, be pointed out that sources of DNA, e.g. calf-thymus DNA, other than bacterial DNAs are frequently employed, and that only rarely has DNA been examined after treatment of a bacterial culture with a drug, i.e. the usual procedure has been to extract the DNA from bacteria, usually by the procedure of Marmur (1961), and to study the effects of drugs on this isolated fraction. The tendency then has been to assume that the *in vitro* interaction of a drug with DNA is the same as that which occurs inside the bacterial cell, and that this interaction effects the mode of action of the drug.

1. *Spectral changes*

(a) *Changes in the visible and/or ultraviolet spectrum.* Such studies have been made with the acridines, triphenylmethane dyes, and various antibiotics including the mitomycins (e.g. mitomycin C, porfiromycin) and the actinomycins. Experiments can be carred out in a spectrophotometer of drug + DNA against a blank of a suitable buffer; of drug +DNA against a control solution of the drug; or of drug +DNA against a control solution of DNA. The last two examples are *difference spectra*, and have been used in, e.g. studying the interaction of proflavine with DNA (Walker, 1965), between actinomycin D and guanine-containing DNAs (Cerami *et al.*, 1967) and between various antibiotics and DNA or different polynucleotides (Ward *et al.*, 1965). The procedure of Ward *et al.* (1965) for carrying out difference spectra is briefly described to examplify the method: changes in optical density (ΔO.D.) against wavelength were carried out for a drug against that drug +DNA or polynucleotide (in 0·01M Tris hydrochloride, pH 7·4 containing 0·01M NaCl). This gives a qualitative indication of whether or not binding of a drug to DNA will take place. In contrast, the difference spectra method carried out by Walker (1965), in which O.D. changes were measured for the drug +DNA against DNA, gives a quantitative measurement of the binding of that drug to the DNA. This is described more fully below.

Interaction of a drug with DNA results in a change in the visible and/or ultraviolet spectrum of that drug, e.g. proflavine shows two sharp maxima on spectrophotometric examination, one at 260 nm and the other at 445 nm. The addition of calf thymus or bacterial DNA causes a progressive displacement of the absorption maximum in the visible range to regions of higher wavelength (Walker, 1965). From a decrease in the absorption at 440 nm, a measure of the fraction of the drug bound to the DNA (moles of drug/mole of DNA phosphorus $=r$) may be obtained by the method of Peacocke and Skerret (1956), who point out that the measurement of the association of a small molecule or ion with a macromolecule (in this case DNA) involves the determination of an equilibrium concentration, c, of free ligand and of the amount (r) of ligand bound by unit amount of macromolecules. In their procedure, the ligand is proflavine.

In the spectrophotometric method (Peacocke and Skerret, 1956), if T_A and T_L represent the total concentrations (molarities) of DNA and ligand, respectively, D_1, the O.D. of the free ligand when $r=0$, and $(L) = T_L$, D_2 the O.D. of the bound ligand (when $(L) = 0$ and $rT_A = T_L$) and D the O.D. of a mixture of free and bound ligand.

$$(L) + rT_A = T_L \tag{i}$$

then
$$D = ((L)/T_L) D_1\tau + (rT_A/T_L)D_2 \tag{ii}$$

Peacocke and Skerret point out their equation (ii) applies only under the following conditions:

(i) when the macromolecule A (DNA in this case) is non-absorbing at the wavelength used.
(ii) when both free ligand and bound ligand obey Beer's law over the experimental range of concentrations.
(iii) when the extinction coefficient of the bound ligand is constant and does not vary with r.

If the fraction of total bound ligand is represented by α, then from equations (i) and (ii),

$$\alpha = rT_A/T_L = D_1 - D/D_1 - D_2$$

When the sites on DNA which bind a drug are of a single type, and behave independently of each other, the binding process can be described in simple mass action terms, giving

$$k = \frac{c(n-r)}{r} \tag{iii}$$

or

$$\frac{r}{c} = \frac{n}{k} - \frac{r}{k} \tag{iv}$$

in which k is the dissociation constant of the complex, c is the molar concentration of free drug, r is the number of drug molecules bound per nucleotide, and n is the number of binding sites per nucleotide (Waring, 1965). A plot of r/c against r gives a straight line. If, however, the binding process involves more than one single type of site, or the binding at one site affects the interaction at neighbouring sites, a plot of r/c against r gives a curvature, and the more detailed treatment, described above, of Peacocke and Skerrett (1956) must be used.

It must be noted that the amount of drug bound may depend on ionic strength (I) e.g. Walker (1965) has shown that the amount of proflavine bound to DNA at increasing sodium chloride or sodium phosphate concentrations decreases with increasing I.

It must also be pointed out here, that the absence of changes in optical density of a drug in the presence of DNA or of a polynucleotide need not necessarily mean the absence of binding of that drug, e.g. the antibiotic chromomycin forms complexes with Mg^{++} and other cations, and it is only this chromomycin Mg^{++} complex which interacts with DNA.

A useful spectrophotometric technique which may be employed is to use pairs of matched cells in tandem, i.e. the pair in the reference beam of light will contain separate solutions of the two main components, and the pair in the measuring beam will contain a mixture of identical amounts of the two components and a solvent blank. If the "difference" curve is non-horizontal, then interaction is present. It must also be added that unmatched cells will give a horizontal line displaced from zero.

For a discussion of the uses and pitfalls of this method, and of spectrophotometric methods in general, the excellent book by Donbrow (1967) should be consulted. In particular, pH changes and DNA, sensitivity of the instrument and stray light should be considered.

(b) *Base specificity.* Considerable information may be obtained as to the nature of the reaction by studying the effect of base specificity of DNA, e.g. spectral changes of the drug in the presence of polynucleotides such as poly dGdC, poly dAdT, poly dIdC and poly dAT should be made. In the experiments carried out by O'Brien *et al.* (1966), solutions contained

5×10^{-5}M quinacrine (an antimalarial drug which also shows antibacterial activity), $\pm 1 \cdot 6 \times 10^{-4}$M polynucleotide phosphorus and 5×10^{-3}M Tris buffer, pH 7·5.

(c) *Use of urea*. The stability of drug-DNA complexes can be examined by measuring the absorption spectra of the drug in the presence of 6M urea in the presence and absence of DNA. A suitable method of showing this is the one described by O'Brien *et al.* (1966) for quinacrine: this involves the difference spectra of a 10^{-4}M solution of the drug, $\pm$DNA (10^{-3}M as phosphorus), in 6M urea and 5×10^{-3} Tris buffer, pH 7·5. The dissolution of a DNA-drug complex can then be measured by plotting Δ absorbancy against wavelength.

Abolishment of the drug-DNA complex by 6M urea suggests that the complex is originally formed by hydrogen bonding.

(d) *Use of acid-denatured DNA*. This can be produced by adding 0·1N HCl to DNA to give a pH of 3·3, and then carrying out all spectral studies at this pH. Alternatively, an acid spectrophotometric titration of DNA in the presence of a drug can be carried out. In this procedure (Gellert *et al.*, 1965), varying amounts of HCl are added to a spectrophotometric cell containing fixed amounts of DNA and the drug under test, and the pH is measured via semimicro electrodes inserted in the cell. This type of experiment indicates whether or not measurable binding of the drug occurs to disordered DNA.

(e) *Use of apurinic acid*. When DNA is treated at pH ≤ 3 at $\geq 60°$C, the phosphodiester backbone is unaffected, whereas the sugar purine bonds are broken, giving the apurinic acids.

Apurinic acid is a useful substance to use in these studies, since there is no increase in absorption in the ultraviolet range when it is heated to 100°C. This absence of hyperchromicity suggests that there is a complete lack of secondary structure in this polymer (Walker, 1965). Walker (1965) has carried out difference spectra of proflavine ($1 \cdot 2 \times 10^{-5}$M) in the presence of apurinic acid (0·2 mg/ml), and has shown that spectral changes were similar to those obtained with native DNA.

(f) *Interaction of drugs with other polymers*. Waring (1966) has made the pertinent point that only a small proportion of the mitomycin C taken up by bacterial cells can be involved in the cross-linking of DNA (see p. 146), and that this must be taken into account in assessing its mode of action, especially as another mitomycin (labelled ^{14}C-porfiromycin) is bound to protein and to the ribosomal fraction. Thus, spectrophotometric studies should also be made with bacterial RNA and with polyribonucleotides. These are of the difference spectra type, involving a solution of the drug against a solution of the drug containing RNA, poly A, poly I, poly U or poly C. Measurements with various drugs have been made (Ward et al., 1965) in 0·1M Tris hydrochloride, pH 7·9, with a drug concentration of 40 μg/ml and a polynucleotide concentration of 400 μg/ml.

2. Thermal denaturation studies

High temperatures bring about a collapse of the helical structure of DNA by a dissociation of hydrogen bonds, a complex helix-coil transition giving an increase of ca. 40% in the O.D. at 260 nm. Renaturation is temperature dependent, and can be prevented if the thermally-denatured DNA is rapidly cooled. The effects of drugs on both the melting profile of DNA and the renaturation process have yielded information as to their modes of action.

(a) *Melting profile and drugs.* The binding of a drug to DNA will stabilize the macromolecule towards thermal denaturation. The effect of a compound on the melting profile of DNA can be investigated in a spectrophotometer, fitted with an electrically heated cell compartment, whereby a temperature range of 20–100°C may be employed. The transition temperature T_m of DNA (the temperature corresponding to the mid-point of the transition) in the presence or absence of the drug can be obtained, as shown in Fig. 8. This is carried out at 260 nm with DNA+drug in the standard cell, and drug (or buffer) in the blank cell. In addition, the absorption at the maximum wavelength of the same drug-DNA solution relative to a phosphate buffer blank can be studied at increasing temperatures.

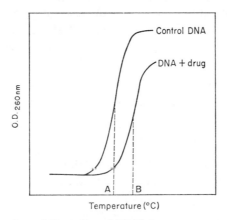

FIG. 8. Determination of T_m value of DNA in presence and absence of a drug. A: T_m of DNA; B: T_m of DNA in the presence of a drug, e.g. ethidium (Waring, 1966).

An increase in absorption at 260 nm results from destruction of the DNA helix; an increase at 420 nm (with actinomycin D: Gellert *et al.*, 1965) or 440 nm (proflavine: Walker, 1965) arises from dissociation of the drug-DNA complex.

(b) *Renaturation.* In this procedure, DNA extracted from drug (e.g. mitomycin C)-treated organisms is compared with DNA from control cells. The DNA from both sources is heated, and the O.D. at 260 nm determined. Next both DNAs are rapidly cooled (quenching) and the O.D. at 260 nm again measured. If the drug forms cross-links between the complementary DNA strands, thereby preventing the melted strands from separating completely during rapid cooling, a much larger decrease in O.D. will occur during the quenching process of this DNA in comparison to normal DNA (Iyer and Szybalski, 1963, 1964).

3. *Fluorescent complexes*

At high salt concentrations, some drugs form a fluorescent complex with helix polynucleotides (Le Pecq and Paoletti, 1967; Chan and van Winkle, 1969).

Fluorescence measurements may be made.

  (i) in an Aminco Bowman spectrofluorimeter: see the section dealing with membrane damage.

 (ii) by means of a fluorescence attachment, ZFM4, of the Zeiss spectrophotometer PMQ11. In this apparatus, a mercury lamp and a filter provide monochromatic excitation light, and the monochromator and the photomultiplier of the spectrophotometer are used to measure emitted light. In the experiments described by Le Pecq and Paoletti (1967), a slit of 0·2 mm was used at the entrance of the monochromator, the wavelength of excitation was 546 nm and of emission 590 nm.

(a) *Evaluation of amount of bound dye.* The fluorescent intensity (I_0) of pure drug solution equals the linear function of drug concentration, c_0, i.e.

$$I_0 = kc_0 \qquad\qquad \text{(v)}$$

If I_1 represents the total fluorescence intensity when DNA is added, and I_b and I_f are respectively the contributions to fluorescence due to the bound and free dye, with c_b and c_f representing the respective concentrations,

$$I_1 = I_b + I_f \qquad\qquad \text{(vi)}$$

and

$$c_0 = c_b + c_f \qquad\qquad \text{(vii)}$$

If V is the ratio between the fluorescence intensity emitted by bound and free dye when excitation is produced under the same conditions of wavelength, concentration temperature and solvent, then

$$I_b = kVc_b \tag{viii}$$

$$I_f = I_0 - I_b/V$$

therefore

$$I_b = I_1 - I_0/1 - 1/V$$

$$c_b = \frac{I_b}{Vk} = \frac{I_1 - I_0}{1 - 1/V} \times \frac{1}{Vk} = \frac{I_1 - I_0}{(V-1)k} \tag{ix}$$

Thus c_b can be determined by measuring the fluorescence intensities under appropriate conditions. The above calculation assumes that the ratio V is constant; the validity of this has been confirmed by Le Pecq and Paoletti (1967).

(b) *Effect of pH.* It would be expected that pH changes would affect the fluorescence intensity, and abrupt changes of fluorescence will occur at the pHs of acid and of alkaline denaturation of native DNA, which implies that for binding to occur, a double-stranded structure is required.

4. *Analytical ultracentrifuge*

A decrease in sedimentation coefficient occurs when the DNA helix is intercalated with a drug, the helix + intercalated drug then behaving as a stiffer, more slender rod in solution. Sedimentation coefficients have been determined (Waring, 1970) by boundary sedimentation in a Beckman model E ultracentrifuge equipped with ultraviolet absorption optics. Films are scanned with a Joyce–Loebl recording microdensitometer, and the positions of the boundaries taken as the 50% concentration point. Sedimentation coefficients may be calculated by the method of Markham (1960); see also Crawford and Waring (1967). Le Pecq and Paoletti (1967) measured buoyant densities in caesium chloride in an analytical ultracentrifuge using an ultraviolet absorption optical system, photographs being taken after 20 h at ca. 45,000 g. See also Bauer and Vinograd (1968, 1970), and Kersten *et al.* (1966).

5. *Viscosity measurements*

An understanding of the nature of drug binding to DNA can be obtained from a study of the viscosity of DNA in the presence and absence of that drug. An increase in viscosity occurs because the DNA helix plus an intercalated drug behaves as a stiffer, more slender rod in solution (Waring,

1970), e.g. the intrinsic viscosity of DNA increases when it complexes with proflavine (Gittelson and Walker, 1967). A pertinent discussion of the effects of dye intercalation on viscosity has been given by Lerman (1961).

A suitable apparatus for measuring viscosity is a concentric cylinder viscometer, which consists essentially of two parts separated by the material under test. The two parts can rotate relative to each other about the same axis. As one part rotates, the other tends to be dragged round with it, because the test material transmits a torque to the second part.

6. Equilibrium dialysis

The principle of this method is that the unbound ligand is allowed to equilibrate across a membrane which is impermeable to the macromolecule (Peacocke and Skerrett, 1956). DNA solution is placed inside Visking dialysis tubing (the membrane) and the unbound ligand concentration in the outer solution is determined. Peacocke and Skerrett used a spectrophotometric technique for this determination; Wells and Larson (1970) used a tritiated drug, and carried out radio-active measurements after 72 h. Peacocke and Skerrett (1956) made the important point that adsorption of proflavine to the membrane could occur, and thus made an appropriate allowance for this via adsorption isotherms. A variation on this procedure is described by Gellert *et al.* (1965), who use buffer one side and DNA plus tritiated actinomycin in various ratios on the other side of the membrane. The cells are shaken for several days to ensure equilibration, samples from both sides of the membrane are removed, diluted, and counted in a scintillation counter. However, Gellert *et al.* (1965) also use the technique described earlier to check their equilibration procedure.

Peacocke and Skerrett (1956) describe the following equation for measuring the amount r of ligand bound by unit amount of macromolecule (in this case DNA) at equilibrium:

$$r = \frac{c^1 V_0 - c V_t}{T_A V_i} = \frac{c^1 - c(x+1)}{T_A x} \tag{x}$$

where V_0 is the volume of outer solution, V_i the volume of inner solution, V_t the total volume, T_A the total molar concentration of macromolecule (A) inside the bag, c^1 and c the initial and final concentrations of unbound ligand, and x is V_i/V_0.

7. Other procedures

Various other techniques for studying drug-DNA interaction have been described. Examples of these are listed below.

(a) *X-ray study.* Suwalsky *et al.* (1969) have made an X-ray study of the interaction of DNA with spermine. A solution of DNA (2 mg/ml) in

0·005M sodium chloride is added dropwise to a 0·1M solution of spermine, and fibres of the DNA-spermine complex are pulled from the resulting precipitate with a fine needle. The fibre specimens are photographed in a specially constructed cell in which they are kept under tension, by means of a spring, and in equilibrium with saturated salt solutions of known relative humidities.

(b) *Infrared spectra.* A method for studying the interaction of DNA and phleomycin is provided by Pietsch and Garett (1968). In this procedure, DNA was dissolved in water and divided into two aliquots. Cu^{++} phleomycin was added to one, thereby precipitating the DNA fibres as robin's egg blue, spoolable threads. This precipitate was washed briefly in several changes of water to remove excess antibiotic and then placed in ethanol. The second aliquot, after precipitation in ethanol, was spooled untreated. Mineral oil mulls were prepared of the fibres and of the phleomycin, and infrared spectra recorded at $1670–1690$ cm^{-1}.

(c) *Electron microscopy.* Friefelder (1971) has carried out an electron microscope study of the DNA-ethidium bromide complex and has found that the DNA increases in length, as a result of drug intercalation, by as much as 27% at saturation. The electron microscope study is carried out by the method described by Klenschmidt *et al.* (1965), in which molecules are spread in a monomolecule film of a basic protein floating on water. The basic molecules adsorb to the primary phosphate acid groups of the DNA, so that both its thickness and visibility are increased. The complexes are collected on a membrane and examined.

(d) *Temperature-jump relaxation kinetic studies.* Such studies have been carried out recently (Li and Crothers, 1969) to study the proflavine-DNA complex. The principle of the method is that the drug is mixed with DNA until binding equilibrium is reached; this is then perturbed by a rapid temperature jump, which is brought about by discharging a high voltage capacitator through the solution. The temperature rise takes only a very short period (ca. 1 micro-second) and if the restoration of equilibrium is longer than this, the "relaxation time" of the system to its new equilibrium can be determined from the variation of absorbance with time.

(e) *Interaction with supercoiled DNA.* Closed circular duplex DNA is different from other types of DNA in that the number of rotations of one strand about the other remains constant, which is responsible for the supercoiling which has been observed in all naturally occurring closed DNAs (Bauer and Vinograd, 1970). Superhelix density is defined as the number of superhelical turns per 10 base pairs. Supercoiled DNA from OX 174 RF (obtained from infected cells of *E. coli*) (Waring, 1970; Bauer and Vinograd, 1970) and polyoma virus (Crawford and Waring, 1967) have been used in studies with intercalative drugs. Exposure of super-coiled DNA to a denaturation process, e.g. heat with formaldehyde, or high pH, converts it into a form which has a sedimentation velocity similar to that of unsupercoiled DNA.

Intercalative drugs, e.g. ethidium, acridines, duanomycin, cause a local uncoiling of the double helix of OX 174 RF DNA, whereas drugs which interact with DNA by a method other than intercalation, e.g. spermine, mithramycin and chromomycin, do not show this local uncoiling (Waring, 1970).

(f) *Effect on RNA polymerase reactions*. In addition to studying the binding of actinomycin D to DNA, Wells and Larson (1970) also investigated the effect of the antibiotic on RNA polymerase reactions. RNA formation was followed by the incorporation of radioactive ribonucleoside triphosphates into acid-insoluble polynucleotide. The reaction mixtures contained per 0·05 ml: 40 mM Tris HCl, pH 8; 4 mM $MgCl_2$, 1 mM $MnCl_2$, 12 mM mercaptoethanol, 500 nmol of each ribonucleotide triphosphate complementary to both strands of DNA used as template (one of the triphosphates bearing a ^{14}C-label), then *E. coli* RNA polymerase was added. 20 μl samples were removed after a 20 min incubation, and assayed for acid-insoluble radioactive material.

C. Mutagenic effects

Several drugs which affect DNA synthesis exert mutagenic effects, and a method for measuring such effects has been described by Cook, Goss and Deitz (1966), using the streptomycin-dependent (Sm^D) strain of *E. coli* ATCC 11143. The principle of this method is to treat non-growing cells of this organism with the drug under test and then determine the increase in frequency of Sm-independent cells among the survivors when these are placed on Sm-containing and Sm-free agar. A long period (7 days) of incubation at 37°C is required for colony development. An alternative procedure is to carry out tests for mutagenicity with proliferating cultures.

D. Photoproducts in ultraviolet irradiated bacteria

As will be shown below, u.v. light induces the formation of photo-products (PS) in sporing and in non-sporing bacteria. An understanding of the nature of experiments designed to show PS production and removal in terms of sensitivity and resistance of bacteria to u.v. means that an initial consideration of the theoretical implications is essential. For this reason, theoretical as well as practical details are dealt with where appropriate.

1. *Dose-survivor curves, sensitivity and resistance*

A preliminary assessment of u.v. sensitivity or resistance of bacteria or their spores is made by carrying out viable counts for the enumeration of survivors at various u.v. dose levels, as described in Section II.B, 3. A plot of the surviving fraction against dose will then give responses depicted in Fig. 9 (a, b, c). Note that the shape of the dose-survivor curve may be more apparent than real, e.g. depending on the abscissa scale, a response may appear to be concave down (Fig. 9a) or exponential (Fig. 9b).

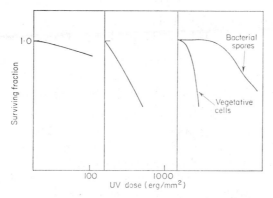

Fig. 9. (a) Sensitivity to ultraviolet irradiation (abscissa 0–100 ergs/mm^2). (b) Sensitivity to ultraviolet irradiation (abscissa 0–1000 ergs/mm^2). (c) Comparative sensitivities to ultraviolet of vegetative bacteria and bacterial spores.

Ultraviolet-resistant vegetative cells (uvr^+) may be resistant at low u.v. doses and killed at higher doses, so that the dose-survivor curve shows an initial shoulder followed by exponential death. *M. radiodurans* is particularly resistant to u.v. as well as to ionizing, radiations, since it possesses efficient mechanisms of dark repair (see below) of both processes; however, mutants of this organism which are very u.v.-sensitive have been described (Moseley, 1968) and these will obviously be of importance in comparing effects of u.v. on wild-type and mutant cells.

Bacterial spores are considerably more resistant than vegetative cells to u.v., and this is depicted in Fig. 9(c).

2. *Theoretical aspects of u.v. damage*

(a) *Formation of PS*. Ultraviolet light induces dimer formation (PS) between any two adjacent pyrimidine bases (cytosine (C), thymine (T)) in a DNA strand, but $\widehat{TT}$ homodimers are more readily induced than $\widehat{CT}$ or $\widehat{CC}$ dimers (see Howard-Flanders, 1968; Witkin, 1969, for excellent reviews). In bacterial spores, cyclobutane-type thymine dimers are not produced, but other thymine PS are formed (Donnellan and Stafford, 1968; Stafford and Donnellan, 1968).

Thymine   Thymine $\widehat{TT}$ Homodimer

(b) *Photoreactivation* (PR). This is defined (Jagger, 1958) as being the reversal with near u.v. light, or visible light, of u.v. radiation damage. A photoreactivating enzyme monomerizes $\widehat{TT}$ *in situ*, thereby restoring normal DNA function. PR occurs in vegetative bacteria, in vegetative cells of some, but not all bacilli, but *not* in spores (Stuy, 1956).

(c) *Excision repair*. This is a dark repair process, and is an alternative mechanism for removing dimers from bacterial DNA. In contrast to PR, however, the dimers are not chemically altered, but are removed physically form the DNA of *uvr*+ strains. This may involve the introduction of two single-strand breaks (by an endonuclease) from either side of the dimer, with the subsequent release (by an exonuclease) of a single stranded oligonucleotide. This includes the pyrimidine dimer and a small number of bases on either side of it. The excision of these dimers is accompanied by extensive DNA degradation of neighbouring nucleotides, thus releasing these PS into the cold acid-soluble fraction of the cell (see below) and into the medium. This excised material is then replaced by normal DNA, i.e. by insertion of nucleotides, by means of a localized resynthesis, or repair replication, the template consisting of the undamaged region of the complementary DNA strand, with a rejoining of the 3′,5′-phosphodiester linkage by the action of the enzyme DNA ligase. Thus, the process overall is a 2-step one, involving (i) the sensing and removal of the defective region; (ii) the subsequent replacement of the excised nucleotide sequence by bases complementary to the removed strand.

Both $\widehat{TT}$ dimer excision and DNA degradation occur in wild-type *uvr*+ *E. coli*, but both are greatly reduced in certain u.v.-sensitive (*uvr*−) mutants, notably strains B_{s-1} and K-12 *uvr*− (Aoki *et al.*, 1966; Boyce, 1966; Howard-Flanders, 1968; Moseley, 1969).

(d) *Recombinational repair*. This is responsible, at least partly, for the greater u.v. resistance of normal bacteria in comparison to recombination-deficient (*rec*−) mutants. *Rec*-mediated repair occurs independently of *uvr* functions, but depends on the product of the *recA* gene which is also required for genetic recombination. Rec^- strains show a decreased capacity for genetic recombination and increased sensitivity to u.v. and X-irradiation (Smith and Meun, 1970; Radman *et al.*, 1970; Rupp *et al.*, 1971; Monk *et al.*, 1971).

Recombinational repair is active in excision-deficient mutants, and thus enables survival and colony formation to take place after u.v. exposure even though the DNA contains several pyrimidine dimers, e.g. *E. coli* K-12 *uvrA* 6 (Rupp and Howard-Flanders, 1968).

Other theoretical points will come to light during a consideration of the practical methods outlined below.

3. *Practical aspects of u.v. damage*

(a) *Presence of PS.* The techniques of Donnellan and Setlow (1965) and Jagger, Stafford and Snow (1969) may be used to demonstrate the presence of PS in u.v.-irradiated bacteria. The principle of this method is that overnight cultures of the organisms are labelled with ^{3}H-thymidine before being exposed to u.v. After exposure, the suspensions are hydrolysed with 98% formic acid at 175°C, and the PS separated by paper chromatography using *n*-butanol : water (86 : 14) in one direction and a saturated ammonium sulphate, M sodium acetate and isopropyl alcohol (80 : 18 : 2) solvent in a second direction. Regions of the paper containing thymine (1st direction) or T̂T dimer (2nd direction) are then cut into strips, eluted with water, placed in a scintillation counter and counted. Alternatively (Donnellan and Stafford, 1968), acid soluble material may be removed with 5% cold TCA prior to hydrolysis, and paper chromatographic separation of PS after hydrolysis may then be made with a butanol : acetic acid : water (80 : 12 : 30) solvent system. Some 5–7% of the total radioactivity in unirradiated or u.v.-treated spores occurs in compounds other than thymine. Phenol extraction of DNA prior to hydrolysis gave no significant difference in the amounts of PS recovered as compared with unextracted spores, but does eliminate the 5–7% of the radioactive non-thymine material in unirradiated spores.

At certain times in their germination, spores of various bacilli become much more resistant to u.v. as measured by viable counting (Irie *et al.*, 1965; Donnellan and Stafford, 1968; Stafford and Donnellan, 1968), and at this point, the amount of thymine-containing PS is only a fraction of that found in vegetative cells or dormant spores. This phase is then followed by one in which an increase in sensitivity of the germinating spores to u.v. takes place, these forms eventually becoming more sensitive than the dormant spores, and the population approaches the sensitivity of vegetative cells.

(b) *Photoreactivation.* After u.v. exposure, photoreactivating light may be obtained from a large quartz-prism Hilger monochromator illuminated with a 500 W high pressure mercury arc lamp (Jagger *et al.*, 1969). In many experiments, however, PR is unwanted, as in dark repair studies, the u.v.-irradiated cells can then be handled under yellow light to avoid PR.

Muhammed (1966) has described the isolation of a PR enzyme from yeast.

To determine, quantitatively, the effect of PR, viable counts are made on the initial suspension and on u.v. irradiated suspensions with and without exposure to PR. Then (Jagger, 1958) if N_O is the number of viable cells before u.v., N_D the number after u.v. (dark survival) and N_L (light survival) the number after PR,

$$\% \text{ light survival} = \frac{N_L}{N_O} \times 100 \qquad \text{(xi)}$$

$$\% \text{ of PR} = 100 \frac{N_L - N_D}{N_O - N_D} \qquad \text{(xii)}$$

(c) *Excision repair, etc.* A measure of single-strand breaks in DNA can be obtained by using the technique of McGrath and Williams (1966) in which there is a decrease in sedimentation velocity of labelled DNA in an alkaline sucrose gradient. The method is described in the Section dealing with DNA damage caused by ionizing radiation, and is explained diagrammatically in Fig. 10.

The principle of the methods for measuring the excision of pyrimidine dimers is to determine the *decrease* of dimers in the acid-insoluble fraction

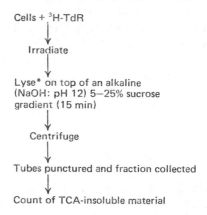

Cells + ³H-TdR
↓
Irradiate
↓
Lyse* on top of an alkaline
(NaOH: pH 12) 5–25% sucrose
gradient (15 min)
↓
Centrifuge
↓
Tubes punctured and fraction collected
↓
Count of TCA-insoluble material

* Usually by lysozyme, followed by exposure to detergent or alkali. With *M. radiodurans*, use R1 enzyme (from *Streptomyces albus*) then, 5 min later, treat with SDS.

FIG. 10. Scheme for measuring DNA strand breakage.

of the cells and their appearance in the acid-soluble fraction. The procedure described by Setlow *et al.* (1968) illustrates this method. Note that these authors also examined the supernatant fraction after removal of the cell fraction by centrifugation, thereby obtaining also a measure of DNA degradation.

DNA degradation after u.v. may also be studied by determining the changes in the amount of ^{3}H-thymidine remaining in the TCA-insoluble fraction. Basically the method (Howard-Flanders and Theriot, 1966; Walker, 1970; Paterson *et al.*, 1971) is to grow the organisms in media containing ^{3}H-thymidine to label the DNA uniformly before irradiation. After irradiation, the bacteria are resuspended in unlabelled medium (Howard-Flanders and Theriot, 1966) supplemented this with 20 μg/ml thymine to minimize re-incorporation of any radioactive nucleotides released) and the extent of degradation from cold TCA-insoluble to TCA-soluble fragments determined; this is usually expressed as the percentage of ^{3}H-thymidine remaining in the TCA-insoluble fraction. Such degradation could, or course, occur in both dead and living cells. A technique for "classifying" DNA degradation is described by Reiter (1970) based on the autoradiographic method of Eberle and Lark (1967). In this, the number of grains/cell is a direct measure of the amount of radioactive label (^{3}H-thymidine) in cell DNA. The number of grains in cells in each of three classes (single cells—not recovered, unable to grow or divide; long forms or "snakes" with no visible septa; cells divided several times to give "microcolonies") in an u.v.-irradiated suspension is compared with an unirradiated control suspension to give an estimate of the relative loss of DNA from each of the three categories of irradiated cells.

DNA synthesis after u.v. may be determined by transferring the cells to a suitable minimal medium containing deoxyadenosine and ^{3}H-thymidine and measuring the incorporation of label into the cold TCA-precipitable material. In *E. coli* able to excise $\widehat{TT}$, exposure of the cells to moderate u.v. doses causes a lag in DNA synthesis, after which there is a resumption in DNA synthesis at a rate almost equal to a control. Not all the cells are necessarily viable in such a population, since colony-forming ability may be quite low, whereas processes such as respiration are found to be more resistant to u.v. (Hamakalo and Swenson, 1969). After irradiation of *uvr*$^-$ mutants of *E. coli*, inhibition of DNA may be permanent, or such synthesis may certainly not be as much as 10% (of the control (Aoki *et al.*, 1966)).

Repair replication is the ability of an organism to fill the gap left by pyrimidine dimer excision. Walker (1970) used thymine-requiring *ras*$^+$ and *ras*$^-$ strains which were grown for ca. 4 generations in ^{3}H-thymidine medium, washed, u.v.-irradiated and shifted to low-phosphate minimal medium containing BUdR and ^{32}P. The DNA was extracted and subjected to equilibrium density gradient centrifugation. Billen *et al.* (1967) used D_2O–^{15}N–^{13}C as a density label for studying DNA repair replication after u.v. or X-ray exposure of *E. coli* strains. In this procedure, cells were grown in a medium containing D_2O, ^{15}NH$_4$Cl and ^{13}C-glucose, then transferred to a similar medium (H_2O, ^{14}NH$_4$Cl and ^{12}C-glucose) and subsequently u.v. or X-irradiated. After incubation of the irradiated cells in medium containing ^{3}H-thymine, cell lysates were obtained by a lysozyme-pronase procedure and subjected to CsCl density gradient analysis. X-ray irradiation of cells did not lead to a repair process similar to that of u.v.-irradiated cells.

(d) *Recombinational repair.* As pointed out above, this mechanism is active in certain excision-deficient mutants and is thought to occur after the replication of dimer-containing DNA. Newly synthesized DNA from u.v.-irradiated cells will sediment more slowly in CsCl gradients than DNA from unirradiated cells, but with continued incubation of the cells the sedimentation rate of DNA from the former cells approaches that of control DNA (Rupp and Howard-Flanders, 1968). Howard-Flanders and Theriot (1966) investigated the ability of Rec$^-$ mutants of *E. coli* K-12 to form recombinants with Hfr donor strains by mating for 2 h with a Hfr strain and then plating on agar selective for Thr$^+$Leu$^+$Str^R or Ile$^+$ His$^+$ recombinants.

(e) *Host cell reactivation* (Hcr). This is the ability of bacterial strains to propagate u.v.-irradiated phage. Three genetic loci (*uvrA, uvrB* and *uvrC*) control the reactivation of phage. T1 or λ phage irradiated with u.v. form more plaques when plated on wild-type cells than when plated on radiosensitive mutants which are unable to excise pyrimidine dimers in the dark.

In Howard-Flanders and Theriot's (1966) method T1 bacteriophage irradiated in phosphate buffer (pH 7) is then plated in soft agar seeded with various strains of bacteria poured over YET (yeast extract +tryptone) agar plates. The plaques are counted after incubation overnight at 37°C. The numbers of u.v.-irradiated phage forming plaques are then expressed as a fraction of the numbers formed by unirradiated phage at different u.v. dose levels. A similar type of technique has recently been carried out by Paterson *et al.* (1971) and by Walker (1969). Bacterial strains which can propagate u.v.-irradiated phage are then referred to as Hcr$^+$, and those which cannot as Hcr$^-$.

(f) *Transformation.* The transforming ability of DNA falls after u.v. treatment, and use has been made of this to show the presence of PS in the irradiated DNA. Moseley and Setlow (1968) have shown that *Micrococcus radiodurans* can undergo genetic transformation and can repair u.v.-irradiated transforming DNA with the same high frequency that it repairs its own DNA.

An example of the transformation procedure is provided in a recent paper by Moseley and Mattingly (1971). Transforming DNA, in their technique, is prepared from a streptomycin-resistant strain of *M. radiodurans* by a lysozyme + sodium dodecyl sulphate treatment, with subsequent purification of the DNA by the method of Marmur (1961). The procedure for transformation is as follows: to 0·2 ml of a streptomycin-sensitive strain of *M. radiodurans* is added 0·05 ml of transforming DNA *or* 0·05 ml of 0·067M phosphate buffer and 0·05 ml of a crude extract of wild-type bacteria (obtained by French press disruption and subsequent removal of vegetative cell and cell wall debris), which enhances the frequency of transformation in *M. radiodurans* (Moseley and Setlow, 1968). The resulting mixtures are shaken gently at 30°C for 3 h, appropriately diluted with chilled medium, and 1 ml samples covered with molten agar at ca. 40°C. Incubation is carried out for 8 h at 30°C, and then 10 ml of molten agar containing 200 μg streptomycin/ml poured on top. The colonies derived from transformed bacteria are counted after incubation at 30°C for at least 4 days.

Streptomycin is a frequently used marker, but other drugs, e.g. cathomycin (novobiocin), have also been employed (Rahn *et al.*, 1969, in studies with *Haemophilus influenzae*).

The survival of biological activity in u.v.-irradiated transforming DNA can be determined by loss of transforming activity with increasing radiation dose, i.e. fewer colonies of streptomycin-sensitive *M. radiodurans* will develop (after the above transformation procedure) in streptomycin-containing agar.

Temperature may have an important role in studies on transforming DNA. At very low temperatures, there is only a relatively low yield of pyrimidine dimers (measured as described earlier in this Section) in u.v.-irradiated transforming DNA prepared from *H. influenzae*, and only a small inactivation by u.v. of this transforming DNA (Rahn *et al.*, 1969). This method may, in fact, be used to study u.v. inactivation and dimer formation, since there is a close relationship between inactivation and dimers in *H. influenzae* transforming DNA irradiated at temperatures between 25°C and −196°C. This method assumes further importance when it is realized that an additional photoproduct, chromatographically indistinguishable from the PS obtained from u.v.-irradiated bacterial spores, appears at low temperatures which is not photoreactivable. It may thus be concluded that the non-photoreactivable damage by u.v. treatment at low temperatures is to a large extent accounted for by spore-type PS (see earlier).

(g) *Bromouracil-containing DNA*. Bacteria containing 5-bromouracil (BU) in DNA instead of thymine are very sensitive to u.v. light. Hutchinson and Hales (1970) grew *B. subtilis* for 2·5 generation times in a defined medium containing 50 μg/ml of 5-bromo-2′-deoxyuridine. Double labelled, hybrid and unlabelled DNAs were separated from the extracted DNA by CsCl density gradient centrifugation. They made the important practical point that, when used, BU–DNA should be handled in the dark as far as possible, to minimize photochemical effects from sunlight or light from fluorescent fixtures. DNA in which all the thymine is replaced by BU shows a loss of transforming ability, as determined by the method described above, and this can be quantitatively accounted for by single-strand breaks induced by u.v., since there are additional sites of degradation in DNA containing BU; this does not depend on the action of the excision because DNA degradation studies with *uvr+* and *uvr−* strains of *E. coli* indicate that it occurs to approximately the same extent when these are exposed to u.v.

Boyce (1966) prepared cells containing BU and labelled with ^{14}C-thymine by growing them in a salts-glucose medium containing Casamino acids, 5 μg/ml ^{14}C-thymine and 50 μg/ml BU.

(h) *Recent developments with mutant strains*. An additional u.v.-sensitive X-ray-resistant mutant of *E. coli* K12, designated *ras−*, has been isolated by Walker (1969, 1970). The *ras−* mutant and *ras+* have normal recombinational activity (method as earlier) and Hcr+ activity as measured by the reactivation of u.v.-irradiated bacteriophages T1 and λ. After u.v., there is an excessive amount of DNA degradation in *ras−* (decrease in ^{3}H-thymidine in cold TCA-insoluble fraction) and a delay in DNA synthesis (incorporation of ^{3}H-thymidine into cold TCA-insoluble fraction). However, pyrimidine dimers are excised at the normal rate by *ras−*, and PR at 405 nm reverses the effect of u.v. Walker (1969, 1970) thus presumed that the *ras* locus is involved in pyrimidine dimer repair, participating at a step after pyrimidine dimer excision.

Monk, Peacey and Gross (1971) have recently investigated the repair of u.v. damage in DNA polymerase-defective *E. coli* cells (*pol A*1); viable counts indicated that cells of this organism were four times as sensitive to u.v. as wild-type cells. Cells of the *E. coli* mutant *uvr A*6 (which are unable to excise dimers) were 12 times as sensitive as wild-type cells, whereas the double mutant *pol A*1 *uvr A*6 was only slightly more u.v.-sensitive than the *uvrA*6 single mutant. It was thus concluded that the u.v. sensitivity associated with a defect in DNA polymerase was primarily the result of a reduction in the efficiency of the excision-repair pathway, and that the *recA* repair system which is involved in excision repair in *pol A*1 cells, could substitute for DNA polymerase in repairing the gaps produced by dimer excision. Somewhat similar studies with *pol A*1 have been made by Paterson, Boyle and Setlow (1971).

(i) *Preparation of endonuclease.* Recently, studies have been carried out with endonuclease both *in vitro* (Nakayama, Okubo and Takagi, 1971) and *in vivo* (Okubo, Nakayama and Takagi, 1971). Nakayama *et al.* (1971) have described methods for purifying about 750-fold on endonuclease from crude extracts of *M. lysodeikticus,* using phase partition, TEAE-cellulose, and phosphocellulose column chromatography and isoelectric focusing. The endonuclease induces single-strand breaks in u.v.-irradiated (but not non-irradiated) double- or single-stranded DNA. Ultraviolet endonuclease activity can be assayed by measuring the degradation of ^{32}P-labelled, u.v.-irradiated DNA from *E. coli,* i.e. by an increase of ^{32}P in the acid-soluble fraction.

B. Strand breakage

The detection of strand breaks in DNA using sucrose density gradients was introduced by McGrath and Williams (1966). This elegant technique overcame the problem of introducing strand breaks during the manipulation of the isolated chromosome prior to centrifugation, by lysing the cells, preformed into spheroplasts, directly on top of the sucrose gradient. Using prelabelled samples, changes in the molecular weight as a result of strand shearing can be followed by denaturation in alkali (pH 12·0) which separates the two strands of the DNA. Single or double strand breaks will cause a lowering of the molecular weight of the DNA fragments and consequently a reduced rate of sedimentation through sucrose gradients. For a general discussion of this technique consult Sykes, this series, Vol. VB.

1. *Strand breaks in denatured DNA*

(a) *Methods.* The method described by McGrath and Williams (1966) is as follows (Fig. 10); cells in the logarithmic phase of growth are labelled with ^{3}H-thymidine. After washing and exposure to the lethal agent, cells of *E. coli* are formed into spheroplasts by the lysozyme-EDTA method. A sucrose gradient containing 4·8 ml of 5–25% sucrose in 0·3M sodium hydroxide in prepared. For *E. coli* 0·1 ml of the spheroplast suspension (containing ca. 5×10^6 cells) is added to 0·1 ml 1·0M sodium hydroxide placed on top of the gradient. Cells of *Micrococcus radiodurans* are treated with sodium dodecyl sulphate (SDS) +RI enzyme fraction of *Streptomyces albus* 9 in 0·04M veronal buffer containing 0·01M EDTA pH 8·6 (Dean *et al.,* 1969). 0·1 ml of the spheroplast suspension is placed in 0·1 ml of 5% w/v SDS on top of the alkaline sucrose gradient. Tubes are centrifuged at 30,000 r.p.m. for 90 min of 20°C in a Spinco Model centrifuge with swing-out head, or equivalent. Two drop samples are taken and collected on paper discs after piercing the base of the tube, and assayed for radio-activity.

(b) *Calculation of molecular weight.* The average molecular weight of a sample of DNA sedimenting through a sucrose gradient may be calculated from the average distance D travelled by the material in the gradient. The sedimentation coefficient for any segment of DNA

$$S°_{20,w} = \frac{\beta.D}{rpm^2.t} \qquad \text{(xiii)}$$

(Burgi and Hershey, 1963). β is a constant and t is the centrifugation period (hours). At low concentrations of DNA individual rates of sedimentation are constant. Thus,

$$\frac{D2}{D1} = \frac{(M2)^k}{(M1)} \qquad \text{(xiv)}$$

where M is the molecular weight of the fraction. The two constants, β and k, can be calculated using alkaline DNA of known molecular weight, obtainable from bacteriophage (Burgi and Hershey, 1963); β is dependent on such experimental conditions as temperature and ionic strength and should be determined with standard DNA from bacteriophage isolated by the method of Thomas and Abelson (1966).

Assuming that the sedimentation coefficient $S°_{20.w}$ is directly proportional to molecular weight, Studier (1965) derived the empirical relationship

$$S°_{20,w} = KM^a \qquad \text{(xv)}$$

where K and a are constants.

Using DNA isolated from bacteriophage T_2, $S°_{20,w} = 73$ and $M = 6.7 \times 10^7$, then in the alkaline gradient $S°_{20,w} = 0.0528 \, M^{0.400}$ which may be employed for DNA of molecular weight up to 1×10^9.

Results from McGrath and Williams (1966) suggest that the molecular weight of unirradiated DNA obtained in alkaline sucrose gradients by their method is that of the single strand of the genome. In measuring the number of single strand breaks, it was assumed that the mean peak sedimentation value was valid for calculating strand breaks. Hagan (1967) has shown this to be incorrect and suggests that the number average molecular weight Mn should be employed in the equation

$$Mn = \frac{\Sigma \, Wi}{\Sigma \, (Wi/Mi)} \qquad \text{(xvi)}$$

Mi is the mean molecular weight of the fraction i (di is the distance between centres of starting fraction and the ith fraction); Wi is the weight of DNA in fraction i (proportional to the amount of radioactivity). However, the calculation of Mn is critically dependant on the accuracy of the sedimentation coefficients of the slowly sedimenting species. Small errors in Wi or di for the top few fractions can invalidate the calculation of Mn. The value of Mw (the weight average molecular weight) is insensitive to these small errors and should be used in preference to calculate Mn (Lett et al., 1970):

$$Mw = \frac{\Sigma\ Wi.Mi}{\Sigma\ Wi} \tag{xvii}$$

The relationship $Mw = 2Mn$ holds true provided that the distribution of molecular weight is random (for a discussion of this point see Lett et al., 1970), which may be confirmed according to the method of Dean et al. (1969). A plot of $\log_n (C/M . \Delta M)$ against M will be linear if the distribution of particles is random (M is the mean molecular weight of the fraction; C is the radioactivity in each fraction and ΔM the molecular weight range covered by that fraction). The equation $Mw = 2\ Mn$ holds true provided that the molecular weights are not too high, equivalent in bacterial samples to at least 5–10 breaks per genome (Lett et al., 1970). For DNA of molecular weight greater than 1×10^8, a slower speed of centrifugation (less than 10,000 r.p.m.) may provide for a random distribution of DNA fragments (Lehmann and Ormerod, 1970) since the sedimentation behaviour of large DNA fragments is dependent on the speed of centrifugation. A recent report suggests that the method cannot be applied to very high molecular weight DNA (Ormerod and Lehmann, 1971).

To calculate the number of breaks per strand, the following relationship may be used:

$$\text{number of breaks per gram DNA}(n) = N\left(\frac{1}{M_I} - \frac{1}{M_0}\right) \tag{xviii}$$

N is Avogadro's number; M_0 is the number average molecular weight of DNA before irradiation and M_I after irradiation with dose I. Where n is directly proportional to D (distance moved by the DNA peak in the gradient)

$$\frac{N}{M_I} = KI + C \tag{xix}$$

K being a measure of the efficiency of strand breakage.

Certain doubts have been expressed concerning the accuracy of the McGrath–Williams technique to calculate the molecular weights of DNA over wide variations in size. Ginsberg and Webster (1969) suggest that the method is quantitatively reliable particularly if comparative and no absolute data are derived. However, Friefelder (1968) doubts if the quantitative results hold true for large molecular weight DNA or at high DNA concentrations. If the initial molecular weight distribution is heterogeneous as is invariably true, and the molecular weight measured from the sedimentation peak for small doses of irradiation (i.e. small number of strand breaks), the weight will be underestimated since the breaks are more likely to occur in the large molecules before the average-sized ones. This error may be excessive when estimating the relationship between single strand breaks and inactivation when small doses of irradiation are employed.

2. *The detection of double-strand breaks*

(a) *Methods.* Double-strand breaks in DNA should be detectable by means of a sucrose gradient in the absence of strand-splitting. This is achieved in a neutral gradient. However, the presence of alkali-labile cell components can lead to spurious results and consequently modifications are necessary in the cell preparation procedures to detach these cell components from the genome. Lehmann and Ormerod (1970) suggest that, to be meaningful, the assay for double strand breaks should fulfil the following conditions:

(i) The sedimenting DNA is not contaminated by other cellular materials.
(ii) The DNA sediments according to theory.
(iii) All the radioactivity is recovered from the gradient.

A method has been described by Burrell *et al.* (1971) suitable for the study of *M. radiodurans.* Cells are labelled with ³H-thymidine and harvested in late log or early stationary phase. Cells are suspended in 0·04M Veronal buffer pH 8·6 +0·01M EDTA, centrifuged and washed three times in the Veronal buffer +EDTA solution saturated with *n*-butanol. After one further washing in buffer +EDTA, the cells are suspended in two volumes of Veronal buffer +1 volume of *Streptomyces RI* fraction (or lysozyme—see Driedger and Grayston (1970)). After 30 min at 20°C, spheroplast formation should be complete. After slow speed centrifugation, spheroplasts are lysed in 0·1 ml SDS on top of the sucrose gradient. The neutral gradient (5–20% sucrose) is prepared in 0·01M Tris buffer pH 7·5 + 0·01M EDTA and sodium chloride (0·01–1·0M). After adding the spheroplasts, the gradients are maintained at 20°C for 30 min prior to centrifugation.

(b) *Calculation of molecular weight.* According to Burrell *et al.* (1971) the sedimentation coefficients are related directly to molecular weight over the range of rotor speeds 10,000–40,000 r.p.m. provided that the molecular weight does not exceed 2×10^8. With large DNA fragments, speeds below 20,000 r.p.m. should be used. Sedimentation rates are unchanged in gradients varying in ionic strength between 0·02 and 1·0M. Employing the preparation technique described, DNA peaks were found not to be contaminated with protein, lipid or RNA.

The sedimentation coefficient for natural DNA is calculated from equation (xiii), the constant β derived from bacteriophage T_2 DNA sedimenting in neutral gradients. Molecular weights can then be calculated from Studier's equation:

$$S°_{20,w} = 0·0882M^{0·346}$$

Number average molecular weights are calculated as previously described after assessing that DNA fragments are randomly distributed in the neutral gradient. Burrell et al. (1971) reported that such is the case at least after exposure of M. radiodurans to X-rays over the range 50–700 krads. The rate of double-strand breaks was directly proportional to X-ray dose over this range and may be calculated from the slope of the graph of Mn^{-1} against X-ray dose, or as previously described. The DNA from cells exposed to less than 50 krads sedimented anomalously at rotor speeds above 15,000 g and the distribution in the gradient was non-random.

Double-strand breaks appear to be introduced into the DNA backbone as single events during exposure to ionizing radiation. The introduction of two single strand breaks in opposite strands in close proximity to each other would result in a non-linear relationship between Mn^{-1} and dose of exposure (but would vary as the square of the dose with respect to Mn values in neutral gradients). Such "double-event" breaks have also been found to depend on the ionic strength of the gradient (Corry and Cole, 1968). It is therefore essential to examine both of these parameters before inferring numerical values to double-strand breaks as determined in neutral sucrose gradients.

XI. RNA DAMAGE

For a general discussion of methods for the detection and quantitative analysis of nucleic acids see Herbert et al., this Series, Vol. 3B. This Section will be concerned with those methods which are applicable to detecting damage or degradation of ribonucleic acids (RNAs). Nucleic acid degradation can be measured by the increase in the nucleotide content of the cell metabolic pool (cold TCA extract) and leakage of nucleotides from the cell in relatively large quantities. It may be confirmed by the measurement of the RNA fraction of the cell by extraction (this Series, Vol. VB) or by the use of prelabelled cells (Leive, 1965).

A. Ribosome breakdown and loss of activity

1. *Release of small molecular weight nucleotide material from isolated ribosomes*

The isolation of ribosomes from bacterial cells has been described (this Series, Vol. VB). The breakdown of rRNA may be detected by separating the supernatant fluid from ribosomes after intervals of exposure to the lethal agent. Any degradative activity is stopped by the addition of an equal volume of 10% trichloroacetic acid (TCA) followed by cooling to 0°C for 30 min. The mixture is centrifuged at 10,000 *g* for 10 min and the supernatant fluid examined for RNA material. The reaction mixture held at 37°C should contain 0·01M Tris buffer pH 7·4 and 0·01M magnesium acetate to reduce the degradative activity of RNAse present in the ribosomal particles. Alternatively, if suitable, a strain of *E. coli* can be employed with low RNAse activity. A control consisting of ribosomes not exposed to the agent should be incorporated into the experiment to determine endogenous RNAse activity, which may also be heat-activated (Haight and Ordal, 1969).

2. *Viscosity measurements*

Changes in the viscosity of ribosome suspensions and rRNA will be indicative of alterations in the shape or size of the RNA particles. This may be measured in an Ostwald or Ostwald–Fenske Viscometer (Tal, 1969). Concentrations of 2 mg/ml of ribosomal particles or 0·25 mg/ml rRNA in Tris buffer have been employed.

3. *Changes in the ability of ribosomes to function in protein synthesis*

The ability of ribosomes to incorporate amino-acids into protein can be determined using Poly U-directed incorporation of ^{14}C-phenylalanine into compounds insoluble in hot TCA. The influence of a lethal agent on this process may be estimated in isolated ribosomes or ribosomes separated from cells exposed to the agent. The requirements for ribosomal protein synthesis in cell-free systems have been summarized by Ciferro and Parisi (1970). The following incubation mixture has proved successful for poly U-directed protein synthesis by heat-treated ribosomes isolated from *B. stearothermophilus* (quantities in micro-Moles unless otherwise stated): Tris chloride buffer pH 7·8, 4·0; magnesium acetate, 4·0; potassium chloride, 24·0; β-mercaptoethanol (as source of -SH groups), 1·4; adenosine triphosphate, 0·25; guanosine triphosphate, 0·01; phosphoenol pyruvate, 1·25; phosphoenol pyruvate kinase, 12 μg; polyuridylic acid (Poly U), 100 μg; ^{14}C-phenylalanine, 0·76M Moles; washed ribosomes, 0·5 mg RNA; activating enzyme preparation (a source of transfer enzymes, RNA and phenylalanine tRNA synthetase), 0·2 mg protein (obtained as a super-natant after centrifugation of the ribosome fraction at 105,000 g for 90 min). Total volume of the system is 0·4 ml and this mixture is incubated at 37°C for 20–30 min. The reaction is then stopped by adding 1 ml of 10% TCA containing 4 mg/ml ^{14}C-phenylalanine, the pellet harvested by centrifugation, washed in cold 5% TCA containing ^{14}C-phenyl-alanine and then in hot 5% TCA for 20 min at 100°C. After a final cold rinse in 5% TCA, the pellet is dissolved in 1 ml of 0·1N sodium hydroxide and dried on a planchet before measuring the radioactivity of the sample.

Poly U-directed protein synthesis is satisfactory for detecting the effects of lethal agents on the normal functioning of ribosomes. This technique should also operate for the translation of natural mRNA or a heteropoly-ribonucleotide chain provided that chain initiators (N-formylmethionyl tRNA) together with initiator and terminator factors are present in the activating enzyme preparation. A mixture of L-amino-acids is added to the reaction mixture. However, the cell-free biosynthesis of complex poly-peptides may prove more difficult in practice.

4. *Sucrose density centrifugation*

This method for separating ribosomal praticles has been described in detail by Sykes, this Series, Volume 5B. It may be used to measure changes in the molecular weight of ribosomes resulting from exposure to lethal agents.

B. Changes induced in RNA

1. *RNA chain scission*

Pollard and Weller (1967) describe a technique for the quantitative assay of changes in the molecular weight of nucleic acids using a turbi-dimetric measurement for the precipitation of large molecules in 10% TCA. Macromolecules of RNA in high concentration will form a colloidal suspension in TCA causing increases in turbidity relative to the quantity of large molecules present, whilst small molecules (less than about mono-mers) will remain in true solution. The process of nucleic acid breakdown by strand scission can be followed by measuring the optical density of a mixture of RNA after the addition of TCA. For calibration purposes, a series of concentrations of RNA in buffer is prepared, one part added to an equal volume of 10% TCA and the precipitate allowed to form at room temperature for 10 min. The optical density (O.D.) is then read against a suitable blank at 425 nm and used to construct a calibration curve of O.D. *vs* RNA concentration (0–100 μg/ml). Test samples, after exposure to the lethal agent, are treated identically and the amount of large molecular weight RNA determined from the calibration curve. This method has been found to be sensitive for RNA but the technique is less satisfactory for DNA.

2. *Hypochromic effects*

Alterations in the helical structure of rRNA may be indicated by hypochromic effects after treatment with urea, thermal denaturation or hydrolysis (Suzuki and Kilgore, 1967). Thus, rRNA or ribosomes from treated and untreated cells are suspended in Tris buffer containing 0·01M Mg^{++}, diluted to produce a suitable O.D. at 260 nm and treated as follows:

(1) Equal volumes of 8M urea are added at 20°C for 30 min;
(2) Thermally denatured in a water-bath at 90°C for 60 min;
(3) Hydrolyzed in alkali by the addition of one part of 1N potassium hydroxide to two parts of sample at 37°C for 20 h, and finally neutralizing the mixture with hydrochloric acid. After these processes, drug-induced changes may be detected by comparing the O.D. of control and test samples at 260 nm.

3. *Changes in Tm*

The thermal denaturation profiles of ribonucleic acids can be influenced by lethal agents (for details of the method see p. 145).

C. RNA synthesis

Methods of estimating RNA are described in detail in this Series, Vol. 5, and will thus not be considered further here.

XII. PROTEIN DAMAGE

A. Protein synthesis

Methods of assessing protein levels can be determined in a number of ways: see this Series, Vol. 5, for details.

1. *Cell-free systems*

Procedures for utilizing cell-free systems have been described in detail by Nirenberg (1964) and involve lysing the bacteria, removing remaining intact cells and debris by low-speed centrifugation and small molecules by dialysis. A number of factors are necessary for the systems to operate properly including Mg^{++}, ATP and messenger RNA, which can be of natural origin (Nathans *et al.*, 1962) or be a synthetic polyribonucleotide (Lengyell *et al.*, 1961; Nirenberg and Matthaei, 1961). The various components of the protein synthesizing system can be fractionated further (Traub *et al.*, 1966; Likeover and Kurlard, 1967; Traub and Nomura, 1968).

A number of well-characterized systems have been developed for studying particular steps involved in protein biosynthesis.

(a) *Binding of m-RNA and aminoacyl t-RNA to ribosomes.* In many bacteria, initiation of protein synthesis involves the binding of m-RNA to the 30S subunit followed by the binding of f Met t-RNA$_F$ (Okomota and Takanami, 1963; Kaji *et al.*, 1966; Anderson *et al.*, 1967; Nomura and Lowry, 1967). Evidence for complexation can be obtained by two main methods—filtration of the reaction mixture through nitro- cellulose filters (Nirenberg, 1964) and gradient centrifugation (Kondo *et al.*, 1968). The basis of the filtration technique is that any complex formed with the ribosome or ribosomal subunit will be retained on the filter and the free aminoacyl t-RNA and m-RNA will not. This method is much more rapid and is advantageous because a complex may dissociate during centrifugation (see Lengyell and Soll, 1968). Labelled derivatives are used for determining binding.

(b) *Puromycin-dependent release of peptide chains.* Peptide bond formation and translocation. Puromycin inhibits protein synthesis by binding to peptide chains and causing the release of incomplete peptides from the ribosomes (Yarmolinsky and de la Haba, 1959). It was realized, therefore, that this antibiotic would be useful for studying peptide bond formation (Gilbert, 1963; Nathans, 1964; Traut and Monro, 1964) and translocation (Cundliffe and McQuillen, 1967; Pestka, 1968, 1970; Igarishi *et al.*, 1969). Ribosomes to which peptidyl t-RNA is bound can exist in two states. If the peptidyl t-RNA is attached to the P site puromycin can react to form peptidyl puromycin. If the peptidyl t-RNA is bound to the A site, puromycin will not react unless GTP and high speed supernatant fraction is added. The latter catalyse the translocation from site A to site P. Thus using ribosomes in the first state peptide bond formation can be determined, whereas when in the second state, both peptide bond formation and translocation can be followed. Inhibition of the puromycin reaction by a drug suggests that the drug inhibits peptide bond formation, some other function of the 50S subunit or possibly both. If no inhibition occurs then the drug interferes with the 30S subunit if it inhibits protein synthesis *in vivo* (Cundliffe and McQuillen, 1967). The reaction is followed using labelled derivatives of aminoacyl t-RNAs, and the technique is summarized in Fig. 11.

(c) *Reconstitution of functional ribosomes.* Under suitable conditions ribosomal components will reassociate to produce functional ribosomes. If complementary components derived from resistant and sensitive bacteria are reassociated, the determination of the effects of a drug on the synthetic

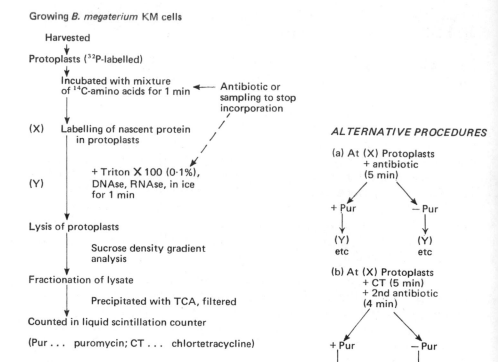

FIG. 11. Determination of the effect of antibiotics on the puromycin reaction.

capabilities of the ribosomes will indicate the site of action of the drug (Davies, 1964; Nomura *et al.*, 1968).

(d) *Specific binding of the drug.* Methods for determining binding have been described earlier (p. 119). It remains only to be mentioned, therefore, that such studies with inhibitors of protein synthesis have indicated whether binding occurs to the 50S subunit, the 30S subunit, or both (Vasquez, 1964; Chang and Weisblum, 1966; Kaji and Tanaka, 1968; Maxwell, 1968) and to what component of these subunits (Okura *et al.*, 1970).

B. Substances inducing protein misreading

Streptomycin (Sm) has for many years occupied an important place in antibacterial therapy. Nevertheless, despite extensive experimentation, its exact site of action remains in doubt. Anand and Davis (1960), for example, showed that Sm caused membrane damage in *E. coli*. More recent studies have shown that Sm has a highly specific effect in protein synthesis in being able to cause an inhibition or misreading (miscoding), depending upon the amino-acid, or amino-acid sequences in growing polypeptide chains.

The subject of the effect of Sm and of other aminoglycosidic antibiotics on protein synthesis has been well reviewed by Jacoby and Gorini (1966). Spotts and Stanier (1961) postulated that Sm sensitivity, resistance and dependence was a function in each case of the same cellular unit, the ribosome, and Flaks et al. (1962) found experimentally that the difference between sensitivity and resistance to, and dependence upon, Sm was caused by a difference in the ribosomes obtained from the different bacterial strans. In particular, ribosomal sensitivity to Sm is associated with the 30S ribosomal subunit, as will be described in the various methods below.

1. Binding of aminoacyl t-RNA and of oligonucleotides to ribosomes

(a) Use of homopolynucleotide template. Homopolymers which can be used as homopolynucleotide templates are poly U, poly A, poly C and poly I. Poly G is a poor template. The action of an antibiotic on the specificity of RNA codon recognition, i.e. prior to peptide bond synthesis, can be studied by measuring its effect on polynucleotide-directed binding of ^{14}C-aminoacyl t-RNAs to ribosomes. Ribosomes should be used from both Sm^S and Sm^R bacteria. For the assay (Pestka, Marshall and Nirenberg, 1969) 50 μl reaction mixtures are used containing 0·03M magnesium acetate and 1–2 A_{260} units of ribosomes, and ^{14}C-aminoacyl t-RNA (as specified by the authors) added last to initiate the binding. The incubation period is usually 20 min at 24°C, and the extent of binding determined after washing the ribosomes on nitrocellulose filters.

(b) Trinucleotide template. A similar technique may be used involving the effect of Sm, or other drugs, on the recognition of RNA codons prior to peptide bond synthesis by directing the binding of ^{14}C-aminoacyl t-RNAs to Sm^S and Sm^R ribosomes with trinucleotide templates. The trinucleotides used are pCpCpC, pApApA, ApApA, UpUpU and UpUpC, where p to the left of the nucleoside initial represents a 5′-phosphate and p to the right a 3′-phosphate.

(c) Use of dissociated and reassociated ribosomes. Ribosomal sub-units have been extensively employed in studying the localization of the action of Sm and dihydrostreptomycin (DHSM) The preparation of 30S and 50S units from 70S ribosomes, e.g. by dialysis at low Mg concentrations, has been described earlier. Ribosomes from Sm^S, Sm^R and Sm^D bacteria can be used.

(d) Binding of m-RNA to ribosomes. The effect of Sm on the attachment of poly U to ribosomes may be studied by the sucrose density gradient method as described by Davies (1964). In this, ^{14}C-poly U is mixed with a pre-incubated crude bacterial extract at 0°C and sedimented through a gradient; fractions are assayed for optical density (260 nm), TCA-precipitable poly U and ability to incorporate phenylalanine. In similar experiments involving Sm, the antibiotic (10^{-4}M) is added to the extract and incubated prior to addition of the poly U and running the gradient.

2. *Polypeptide synthesis*

(a) *Use of homopolymers.* The effects of antibiotics on polypeptide synthesis directed by various polyribonucleotides (poly U, poly A, poly C and poly I) can be studied by the method of Davies, Gorini and Davis (1965) and Nishimura *et al.* (1965). Here, the *in vitro* amino-acid incorporating system contained, in a total volume of 1 ml: 100 μmol Tris HCl, pH 7·8; 10 μmol magnesium acetate; 50 μmol KCl; 6 μmol β-mercaptoethanol; 1 μmol ATP, 5 μmol phosphoenolpyruvate, 20 μg phosphoenolpyruvate kinase, 0·5–1 μC of ^{14}C-amino-acid, 0·25 μmol GTP, 20 O.D. units of ribosomes, 200 μg of 100,000 g supernatant fraction, 30 O.D. units of *E. coli* t-RNA and the polynucleotide as specified. Incubation was usually carried out at 37°C, and aliquots (0·01–0·02 ml) taken and analysed for different amino-acids as specified.

(b) *Use of ribopolynucleotides containing two nucleotides in alternating sequence as templates.* The ribopolynucleotides poly UG, poly AG, poly UC, and poly AC are efficient templates in the cell-free protein synthesizing system (Nishimura, Jones and Khorana, 1965; Jones, Nishimura and Khorana, 1966; Davies, Jones and Khorana, 1966). As two of these poly-nucleotides contain G, misreading of this base can be tested (compare above); also, the position of a base in all three positions of a triplet can be studied in its susceptibility to misreading.

The first step in this study involves the synthesis of poly UG, poly AC, poly UC and poly AG from poly d-TC : AG and poly d-TG : AC. For poly UC, for example, poly d-TC : AG is used as template in the presence of RNA polymerase, UTP and CTP.

The second step utilizes step 1 in polypeptide synthesis in the presence and absence of the drug. In the procedure described by Nishimura, Jones and Khorana (1965), the reaction mixture contained/ml: 60 μmol Tris hydrochloride, pH 7·8, 9 μmol of magnesium acetate, 2 μmol of magnesium chloride, 12 μmol of β-mercaptoethanol, 0·5 μmol of manganese chloride, 50 μmol of potassium chloride, 0·25 μmol of GTP, 2 μmol of ATP, 5 μmol of phosphoenolpyruvate, 20 μg of phosphoenolpyruvate kinase, 20 O.D. units of ribosomes, 16 O.D. units of t-RNA, 0·5–2 μC of ^{14}C-amino-acid (as specified), 63 nmol of ^{12}C-amino-acid where indicated, and poly d-TC : AG, poly UC, excess nucleoside triphosphates and RNA polymerase as introduced from step 1. This reaction mixture was incubated at 0°C for 10 min, and to it was then added 200 μg of 100,000 g supernatant fraction, with subsequent incubation at 37°C. For routine measurement of amino-acid incorporation, portions of the reaction mixture were taken at intervals, and a radio-active counting procedure employing Whatman 3MM filter paper discs (ca. 1 cm^2 in area) used as described in detail by these authors. An alternative procedure was to measure the incorporation of radio-active material from ^{14}C-amino-acids into polypeptidic material by applying portions of the reaction mixture, after an alkaline treatment, to paper chromatograms. The appropriate areas were then cut out, and counted for radioactivity.

(c) *Use of ribosomal sub-units.* The effect of Sm and DHSM can be studied on poly U-directed polyphenylalanine synthesis with hybrid and with reconstituted parental ribosomes. 30S and 50S subunits are preincubated at 0°C for 30 min in the absence of poly U to allow 70S hybrid ribosome formation. Note that the Mg concentration in this system must be carefully controlled, as the degree of inhibition by Sm and DHSM of polypeptide synthesis directed by various ribopolynucleotides varies with this cation concentration. Cox, White and Flaks (1964) and Davies (1964) have shown that only those hybrids containing 30S ribosomes from Sm^S strains are susceptible to Sm.

Van Knippenberg *et al.* (1965) observed varying effects on ribosomes from Sm^S cells with messengers of viral origin and endogenous messengers, and showed that, depending on Mg concentration, stimulation or inhibition could be achieved.

(d) *Double-labelling technique.* Old and Gorini (1965) have described an interesting method for showing a simultaneous effect of Sm on protein synthesis (phenylalanine incorporation) and protein misreading (isoleucine incorporation) in a poly U-directed incorporating system. The technique is a double-labelling one involving ^{3}H-phenylalanine and ^{14}C-isoleucine. In the absence of Sm, the polypeptide contained only phenylalanine, and in the presence of Sm both phenylalanine (although in a greatly reduced amount) and isoleucine. The incorporation of these amino-acids into polypeptides was measured by a radio-active counting procedure after extraction with TCA at 90°C and Millipore filtration.

(e) *Use of a subunit of the 30S ribosome.* As described above, the determinant of Sm sensitivity resides on the 30S ribosomal unit. When 30S or 50S ribosomes are centrifuged to equilibrium in 5·2M caesium chloride solution containing 0·04M Mg^{++}, they dissociate into free protein and protein-deficient ribonucleoprotein cores, which have sedimentation coefficients of 23S and 42S, respectively. The dissociated protein accumulates at the meniscus, whereas the cores give a band in the gradient. Poly U-directed polyphenylalanine synthesis *in vitro* is not supported by the cores, but only takes place when the cores are combined with the corresponding meniscus fraction and dialysed to remove the caesium chloride. Use has been made of this procedure by Staehelin and Meselson (1966) in studying the *in vitro* incorporation of phenylalanine and isoleucine in the presence and absence of Sm.

3. *Ribosomal changes*

The experiments described above have postuated that Sm and Nm combine with the ribosome, the conformation of which is thereby altered, leading in turn to improper codon-anticodon alignment. Leon and Brock (1967) thus examined the direct effects of Sm and of Nm on the physical properties of the ribosomes from Sm^S and Sm^R strains of *E. coli* with the aim of obtaining information on alterations in ribosomal conformation.

The experiments described by Leon and Brock (1967) are of interest and will thus be described briefly. A part of their study is based upon the fact that purified 70S ribosomes show a marked hyperchromicity on heating, and the melting profile of 70S ribosomes in the presence and absence of Sm or Nm was carried out. Other experiments, below, gave more useful information.

(a) *High-temperature ultracentrifugation.* The RNA component of the ribosomes contributes mainly to the hyperchromicity observed during thermal denaturation, and Leon and Brock studied the sequence of events during this denaturation to ascertain whether RNA melted within the ribosome, or whether separation into ribosomal subunits was also involved. This was carried out by analysing the 70S ribosomes, in the presence and absence of Sm or Nm, in the ultracentrifuge at different temperatures (full practical details are provided in the original paper). The Schlieren optical system was used.

(b) *Protection against ribosomal dissociation.* The principle of this experiment is to ascertain whether drugs can protect 70S ribosomes from dissociating when placed in an environment of low Mg^{++} concentration. To carry out this experiment, the antibiotics are mixed with preparations of 70S ribosomes from Sm^S and Sm^R strains, the mixture diluted into low Mg^{++} (0·001M)-Tris buffer and analysed in the analytical ultracentrifuge, and the percentage of the 70S component calculated.

4. *Binding to ribosomes*

To study the binding of DHSM to bacterial ribosomal subunits, Kaji and Tanaka (1968) used the following typical reaction mixture: 20 μg of

30S subunits (there was no binding to 50S), 10 μg of poly U, ^{3}H-drug, and (in μmol/0·05 ml of total reaction mixture) Tris hydrochloride (pH 7·2) 3, KCl 2, magnesium acetate 1. The binding process was carried out for 20 min at 24°C, and the mixture then appropriately diluted. Millipore filters were used to retain ribosomal subunits containing any bound drug, the latter being counted by means of a scintillation counter.

XIII. CONCLUSIONS

In this Chapter, we have described and discussed some of the ways in which the mechanism of action of certain chemical and physical processes on bacteria can be assessed. We feel that the following points are of considerable importance in this assessment:

(a) the role of mutant strains of bacteria in determining the type of damage inflicted has been considered under various Sections, and

(b) useful though they are, techniques with cell-free systems must not be taken in isolation, but must be considered in relation to the bacterial cell as a whole;

(c) as many different techniques as possible should be used to measure damage to the bacterial cell, and an attempt made to correlate the results. It must be emphasized that damage to the cell might result from the inactivation of several sites in the organism and that the earliest measurable inhibition of some metabolic process need not necessarily in fact be responsible for loss of viability.

REFERENCES

Adelberg, E. A., Mandel, M., and Chen, G. C. C. (1965). *Biochem. biophys. Res. Commun.*, **18**, 788.

Alcino, J. F. (1961). *Analyt. Chem.*, **33**, 648.

Allwood, M. C. (1968). Ph.D. Thesis. University of Wales.

Allwood, M. C., and Hugo, W. B. (1971). *J. appl. Bact.* **34**, 369.

Allwood, M. C., and Russell, A. D. (1966). *Can. J. Microbiol.*, **12**, 1295.

Allwood, M. C., and Russell, A. D. (1968). *J. Bact.*, **95**, 345.

Allwood, M. C., and Russell, A. D. (1969a). *J. appl. Bact.*, **32**, 68.

Allwood, M. C., and Russell, A. D. (1969b). *J. appl. Bact.*, **32**, 79.

Alper, T., and Gillies, N. E. (1958). *J. gen. Microbiol.*, **18**, 461.

Alper, T., and Gillies, N. E. (1960). *J. gen. Microbiol.*, **22**, 113.

Anand, N., and Davies, B. D. (1960). *Nature, Lond.*, **185**, 22.

Anderson, E. S. (1968). *Ann. Rev. Microbiol.*, **22**, 131.

Anderson, E. S., and Datta, N. (1965). *Lancet*, i, 407.

Anderson, E. S., and Lewis, M. J. (1965). *Nature, Lond.*, **206**, 579.

Anderson, J. S., Matsuhashi, M., Haskin, M. A., and Strominger, J. L. (1967). *J. biol. Chem.*, **242**, 3180.

Annear, D. I. (1968). *Med. J. Austral.*, **1**, 444.
Aoki, S., Boyce, R. P., and Howard-Flanders, P. (1966). *Nature, Lond.*, **209**, 686
Araki, Y., Shimada, A., and Ito, E. (1966). *Biochem. biophys. Res. Commun.*, **23**, 518.
Baird-Parker, A. C., and Davenport, E. (1965). *J. appl. Bact.*, **28**, 390.
Barber, M. (1964). *J. gen. Microbiol.*, **35**, 183.
Bauer, W., and Vinograd, J. (1968). *J. molec. Biol.*, **33**, 141.
Bauer, W., and Vinograd, J. (1970). *J. molec. Biol.*, **54**, 281.
Bayde, A., and Williams, R. A. D. (1971). *Arch. oral Biol.*, **16**, 259.
Benveniste, B., and Davies, J. (1971). *Biochemistry*, **10**, 1787.
Berkman, R. M., and Wyatt, P. J. (1970). *Appl. Microbiol.*, **20**, 510.
Bernheim, F. (1963). *J. gen. Microbiol.*, **30**, 53.
Berhnheim, F. (1971). *Microbios.*, **4**, 49.
Best, G. K., and Durham, N. N. (1964). *Archs Biochem. Biophys.*, **105**, 120.
Best, G. K., and Durham, N. N. (1965). *Archs Biochem. Biophys.* **111**, 685.
Biagi, G. L., Guerra, M. C., Barbaro, A. M., and Gamba, M. F. (1970). *J. med. Chem.*, **13**, 511.
Bibb, W. R., and Straugnh, W. R. (1962). *J. Bact.*, **84**, 1094.
Bier, M. (1959). "Electrophoresis". Academic Press, New York and London.
Billen, D., Hewitt, R. R., Lapthisophon, T., and Achey, P. M. (1967). *J. Bact.*, **94**, 1538.
Birdsell, D. C., and Cota-Robles, E. H. (1967). *J. Bact.*, **93**, 427.
Birdsell, D. C., and Cota-Robles, E. H. (1968). *Biochem. biophys. Res. Commun.*, **31**, 438.
Boyce, R. P. (1966). *Nature, Lond.*, **209**, 688.
Boyce, R. P., and Setlow, R. B. (1962). *Biochim. biophys. Acta*, **61**, 618.
Brenner, S., Dark, F. A., Gerhardt, P., Jeynes, M. H., Kandler, O., Kellenberger, F., Klieneberger-Nobel, E., McQuillen, K., Rubio-Huertos, M., Salton, M. R. J., Strange, R. E., Tomcsik, J., and Weibull, C. (1958). *Nature, Lond.*, **181**, 1713.
Bridges, B. A. (1963). *Radiat. Res.*, **17**, 801.
"British Pharmacopoeia" (1968). Pharmaceutical Press, London.
Brock, T. D., and Brock, M. L. (1959). *Archs. Biochem. Biophys.*, **85**, 176.
Brown, M. R. W., and Wood, S. M. (1972). *J. Pharm. Pharmac.*, **24**, 215.
Burgi, E., and Hershey, A. D. (1963). *Biophys. J.*, **3**, 309.
Burrell, A. D., Feldschrieber, P., and Dean, C. J. (1971). *Biochim. biophys. Acta*, **247**, 38.
Cerami, A., Reich, E., Ward, D. C., and Goldberg, I. H. (1967). *Proc. natn. Acad. Sci. U.S.A.*, **57**, 1036.
Chan, L. M., and van Winkle, Q. (1969). *J. molec. Biol.*, **40**, 491.
Chang, F. N., and Weisblum, B. (1967). *Biochemistry*, **6**, 836.
Chatterjee, A. N., Taber, H., and Young, F. E. (1971). *Biochem. biophys. Res. Commun.*, **44**, 1125.
Ciak, J., and Hahn, F. E. (1959). *Antibiot. Chemother.*, **9**, 47.
Ciferro, O., and Parisi, B. (1960). *Progress in nucleic acid research and molecular biology*, **10**, 121.
Citri, N. (1958). *Biochim. biophys. Acta*, **27**, 277.
Clive, D., and Landman, O. E. (1970). *J. gen. Microbiol.*, **61**, 233.
Cook, A. M., and Brown, M. R. W. (1970). *J. Pharm. Pharmac.*, **12**, 116T.
Cook, T. M., Goss, W. A., and Deitz, W. H. (1966). *J. Bact.*, **91**, 780.
Corry, P. M., and Cole, A. (1968). *Radiat. Res.*, **36**, 528.

Cox, E. C., White, J. R., and Flaks, J. G. (1964). *Proc. natn. Acad. Sci, U.S.A.*, **51**, 703.

Crawford, L. V., and Waring, M. J. (1967). *J. molec. Biol.*, **54**, 247.

Cundliffe, E., and McQuillen, K. (1967). *J. molec. Biol.*, **30**, 137.

Curran, H. R., and Evans, F. R. (1937). *J. Bact.*, **34**, 179.

Datta, N. (1965). *Br. med. Bull.*, **21**, 254.

Davies, A., Bentley, M., and Field, B. S. (1968). *J. appl. Bact.*, **31**, 448.

Davies, J. E. (1964). *Proc. natn. Acad. Sci. U.S.A.*, **51**, 659.

Davies, J. E., Gorini, L., and Davies, B. D. (1965). *Molec. Pharmac.*, **1**, 93.

Davies, J. E., Jones, D. S., and Khorana, H. G. (1966). *J. molec. Biol.*, **18**, 48.

Dean, C. J., Ormerod, M. G., Serianni, R. W., and Alexander, P. (1969). *Nature, Lond.*, **222**, 1042.

Dienes, L. (1967). *J. Bact.*, **93**, 693.

Dienes, L., and Sharp, J. T. (1956). *J. Bact.*, **71**, 208.

Dittmer, J. C., and Lester, R. L. (1964). *J. Lipid Res.*, **5**, 126.

Donbrow, M. (1967). "Instrumental Methods in Analytical Chemistry; Their Principles and Practice. Vol 2—Optical Methods." Pitman & Sons, Ltd., London.

Donnellan, J. E., and Stafford, R. B. (1968). *Biophys. J.*, **8**, 17.

Driedger, A. A., and Grayston, M. J. (1970). *Can. J. Microbiol.*, **16**, 889.

Duma, R. J., and Kunz, L. J. (1968). *Appl. Microbiol.*, **16**, 1261.

Dunnick, J. E., and O'Leary, W. M. (1970). *J. Bact.*, **101**, 892.

Dyke, K. G. H. (1969). *J. med. Microbiol.*, **2**, 261.

Dyke, K. G. H., Jevons, M. P., and Parker, M. T. (1966). *Lancet*, i, 835.

Eberle, H., and Lark, K. G. (1967). *Proc. natn. Acad. Sci. U.S.A.*, **57**, 95.

Elson, L. A., and Morgan, W. T. J. (1933). *Biochem. J.*, **27**, 1824.

Ernst, R. R. (1968). *In* "Disinfection, Sterilization and Preservation" (Ed. C. A. Lawrence and S. S. Block), p. 703. Lea and Febiger, Philadelphia.

Flaks, J. G., Cox, E. C., Witting, M. L., and White, J. R. (1962). *Biochem. biophys. Res. Commun.*, **7**, 390.

Fleming, P. C., Charlebois, M., and Dunmore, R. T. (1970). *Postgrad. med. J.*, *Suppl.*, **43**, 51.

Folch, J., Lees, M., and Sloane-Stanley, G. H. (1957). *J. biol. Chem.*, **226**, 497.

Forage, A. J., and Gillies, N. E. (1964). *J. gen. Microbiol.*, **37**, 33.

Fountain, R. H., and Russell, A. D. (1969). *J. appl. Bact.*, **32**, 312.

Fraenkel-Conrat, H., Harris, J. I., and Levy, A. L. (1955). *In* "Methods in Biochemical Analysis" (Ed. D. Glick), Vol. 2, p. 359. Interscience Publ., New York.

Freeman, B. M., and Bridges, B. A. (1960). *Int. J. appl. Radiat. Isotopes*, **8**, 136.

Friefelder, D. (1968). *J. molec. Biol.*, **35**, 303.

Friefelder, D. (1971). *J. molec. Biol.*, **60**, 401.

Garrett, A. J. (1969). *Biochem. J.*, **115**, 419.

Garrod, L. P., and Waterworth, P. M. (1969). *J. clin. Path.*, **22**, 534.

Gellert, M., Smith, C. E., Neville, D., and Felsenfeld, G. (1965). *J. molec. Biol.*, **11**, 445.

Ghosh, B. K., and Murray, R. G. E. (1967). *J. Bact.*, **93**, 411.

Gilbert, W. (1963). *J. molec. Biol.*, **6**, 389.

Gilby, A. R., and Few, A. V. (1960). *J. gen. Microbiol.* **23**, 719.

Giles, C. H., MacEwan, T. H., Nakhura, S. N., and Smith, D. (1960). *J. chem. Soc.*, **304**, 3973.

Ginsburgh, D. M., and Webster, H. K. (1969). *Radiat. Res.*, **39**, 421.

Gittelson, B. L., and Walker, I. O. (1967). *Biochim. biophys. Acta*, **138**, 619.

Gledhill, W. E. (1967). *Can. J. Microbiol.*, **13**, 1615.
Godtfredsen, W. O. (1967). "Fusidic Acid and Some Related Antibiotics." Aarhuus Stiftsbogtrykkerrie, Copenhagen.
Gooder, H. (1968). *In* "Microbial Protoplasts, Spheroplasts and L-Forms" (Ed. L. B. Guze), p. 40. Williams and Wilkins Co., Baltimore, U.S.A.
Gould, G. W. (1964). 4th International Symposium on Food Microbiology, SIK, Goteburg, Sweden.
Gould, G. W., Stubbs, J. M., and King, W. L. (1970). *J. gen. Microbiol.*, **60**, 347.
Gray, G. W., and Wilkinson, S. G. (1965). *J. gen. Microbiol.*, **39**, 395.
Hagan, U. (1967). *Biochim. biophys. Acta*, **134**, 45.
Haight, R. D., and Ordal, Z. J. (1969). *Can. J. Microbiol.*, **15**, 15.
Hamburger, M., and Carleton, J. (1966). *J. infect. Dis.*, **116**, 543.
Hamkalo, B. A., and Swenson, P. A. (1969). *J. Bact.*, **99**, 815.
Hamilton-Miller, J. M. T. (1971). *J. med. Microbiol.*, **4**, 227.
Hamilton-Miller, M. J. T., Smith, J. T., and Knox, R. (1963). *J. Pharm. Pharmac.*, **15**, 81.
Hancock, R., and Park, J. T. (1960). *J. gen. Microbiol.* **22**, 249.
Harold, F. M. (1970). *In* "Advances in Microbiol Physiology" (Ed. A. H. Rose and J. F. Wilkinson), Vol. 4, p. 45. Academic Press, London and New York.
Harold, F. M., and Baarda, J. R. (1967). *J. Bact.*, **94**, 53.
Harold, F. M., and Baarda, J. R. (1968). *J. Bact.*, **96**, 45
Harris, N. D. (1963). *J. appl. Bact.*, **26**, 387.
Harvey, R. J., and Marr, A. G. (1966). *J. Bact.*, **92**, 805.
Hatton, M. P. (1969). *Can. J. Microbiol.*, **15**, 891.
Henry, R. J., and Housewright, R. D. (1947). *J. biol. Chem.*, **167**, 559.
Heppel, A. L. (1965). *Science*, **156**, 145.
Hewitt, J. H., and Parker, M. T. (1968). *J. clin. Path.*, **21**, 75.
Hewitt, J. H., Coe, A. W., and Parker, M. T. (1969). *J. med. Microbiol.*, **2**, 443.
Hinshaw, V., Punch, J., Allison, M. J., and Dalton, H. P. (1969). *Appl. Microbiol.*, **17**, 214.
Hirokawa, H. (1962). *J. Bact.*, **84**, 1161.
Hitchins, A. D., Gould, G. W., and Hurst, A. (1963). *J. gen. Microbiol.*, **30**, 445.
Hollaender, A., Stapleton, G. E., and Billen, D. (1953). *Science*, **117**, 468.
Holt, R. (1967). *Lancet*, i, 1259.
Holt, R. J., and Stewart, G. T. (1963). *J. clin. Path.*, **16**, 263.
Hopwood, D. A. (1970). *In* "Methods in Microbiology" (Ed. J. R. Norris and D. W. Ribbons), Vol. 3A, pp. 363–433. Academic Press, London and New York.
Howard-Flanders, P. (1968). *Ann. Rev. Biochem.*, **37**, 175.
Howard-Flanders, P., and Theriot, L. (1966). *Genetics*, **53**, 1137.
Howard-Flanders, P., Boyce, R. P., and Theriot, L. (1966). *Genetics*, **53**, 1119.
Hugo, W. B. (1971). Editor, "Inhibition and Destruction of the Microbial Cell". Academic Press, London and New York.
Hugo, W. B., and Frier, M. (1969). *Appl. Microbiol.*, **17**, 118.
Hugo, W. B., and Longworth, A. R. (1964). *J. Pharm. Pharmac.*, **16**, 655.
Hugo, W. B., and Russell, A. D. (1961). *J. Bact.*, **82**, 411.
Hugo, W. B., and Stretton, R. J. (1966). *J. gen. Microbiol.*, **42**, 133.
Hutchinson, F., and Hales, H. B. (1970). *J. molec. Biol.*, **50**, 59.
Iandolo, J. J., and Ordal, Z. J. (1966). *J. Bact.*, **91**, 134.
Igarashi, K., Ishitsuka, H., and Kaji, A. (1969). *Biochem. biophys. Res. Commun.*, **37**, 499.

Irie, R. N., Yano, N., Morichi, T., and Kembo, H. (1965). *Biochem. biophys. Res. Commun.*, **20**, 389.

Iyer, V. N., and Szybalski, W., (1963). *Proc. natn. Acad. Sci. U.S.A.*, **50**, 355.

Iyer, V. N., and Szybalski, W. (1964). *Science*, **145**, 55.

Jack, G. W., and Richmond, M. H. (1970). *J. gen. Microbiol.*, **61**, 43.

Jacoby, G. A., and Gorini, L. (1966). In "Antibiotics. Vol. I: Mechanism of Action" (Ed. D. Gottlieb and P. D. Shaw). pp. 726–747. Springer-Verlag, Berlin.

Jagger, J. (1958). *Bact. Rev.*, **22**, 99.

Jagger, J. (1961). *Rad. Res.*, **14**, 394.

Jagger, J., Stafford, R. S., and Snow, J. M. (1969). *Photochem. Photobiol.*, **10**, 383.

James, A. M. (1965). "Surface Activity and the Microbiol Cell." Society of Chemical Industry Monograph.

Jeynes, M. H. (1957). *Nature, Lond.*, **180**, 227.

Jones, D. S., Nishimura, S., and Khorana, H. G. (1966). *J. molec. Biol.*, **16**, 454.

Kaji, H., and Tanaka, Y. (1969). *J. molec. Biol.*, **32**, 281.

Kaji, H., Suzuka, I., and Kaji, A. (1966). *J. biol. Chem.*, **241**, 1251.

Kallings, L. O., Lantorpe, K., and Gunne, I. (1969). *Acta. path. Microbiol. Scand.*, **76**, 447.

Kersten, W., Kersten, H., and Szybalski, W. (1966). *Biochemistry*, **5**, 236.

King, J. R., and Gooder, H. (1970). *J. Bact.*, **103**, 686.

King, L. W., and Gould, G. W. (1969). *J. appl. Bact.*, **32**, 480.

Kleinschmidt, A. K., Lang, D., Jacherts, D., and Zahn, R. K. (1965). *Biochim. biophys. Acta*, **61**, 857.

Klieneberger-Nobel, E. (1960). In "The Bacteria" (Ed. I. C. Gunsalus and R. Y. Stanier), Vol. 1, p. 363. Academic Press, New York and London.

Koch, A. L. (1961). *Biochim. biophys. Acta*, **51**, 429.

Kondo, M., Eggertson, G., Eisenstadt, J., and Lengyel, P. (1968). *Nature, Lond.*, **220**, 368.

Kushner, D. J., and Khan, S. R. (1968). *J. Bact.*, **96**, 1103.

Lacey, B. W. (1958). *Symp. Soc. gen. Microbiol.*, **8**, 247

Landman, O. E., and Forman, A. (1969). *J. Bact.*, **99**, 576.

Lark, K. G., and Lark, C. (1960). *Biochim. biophys. Acta*, **43**, 420.

Latarjet, R., Morenne, P., and Berger, R. (1953). *Ann. Inst. Pasteur*, **85**, 174.

Lederberg, J. (1950). *Methods Med. Res.*, **3**, 5.

Lederberg, J., and St. Clair, J. (1955). *J. Bact.*, **75**, 143.

Lederberg, J. (1956). *Proc. natn. Acad. Sci. U.S.A.*, **42**, 574.

Lee, P. A., and Richmond, M. H. (1969). *J. Bact.*, **100**, 1131.

Lehmann, A. R., and Ormerod, M. G. (1970). *Biochim. biophys. Acta*, **217**, 268.

Leive, L. (1965). *J. molec. Biol.*, **13**, 862.

Leive, L. (1968). *J. biol. Chem.*, **243**, 2373.

Leive, L., and Kollin, V. (1967). *Biochem. biophys. Res. Commun.*, **28**, 229.

Lengyell, P., and Soll, D. (1968). *Bact. Rev.*, **33**, 264.

Lengyell, P., Speyer, J. F., and Ochoa, S. (1961). *Proc. natn. Acad. Sci. U.S.A.*, **47**, 1936.

Leon, S. A., and Brock, T. D. (1967). *J. molec. Biol.*, **24**, 391.

LePecq, J. B., and Paoletti, C. (1967). *J. molec. Biol.*, **27**, 87.

Lerman, L. S. (1961). *J. molec. Biol.*, **3**, 18.

Lett, J. T., Caldwell, I., and Little, J. G. (1970). *J. molec. Biol.*, **48**, 395.

Leutgeb, W., Maass, D., and Weidel, W. (1963). *Z. Naturforsch.*, **186**, 1062.

Levinson, H. S., and Hyatt, M. T. (1956). *J. Bact.*, **72**, 176.
Li, H. J., and Crothers, D. M. (1969). *J. molec. Biol.*, **39**, 461.
Likeover, T. E., and Kurland, C. G. (1967). *J. molec. Biol.*, **25**, 497.
Loosemore, M., and Russell, A. D. (1964). *J. Pharm. Pharmac.*, **16**, 817.
Lowry, O. H., Rosebrough, N. J., Farr, A. L., and Randall, R. J. (1951). *J. biol. Chem.*, **193**, 265.
Lund, B. M. (1962). Ph.D. Thesis. University of London.
Mach, B., and Tatum, E. L. (1963). *Science*, **139**, 1051.
MacLeod, R. A., Smith, L. D. H., and Galinas, R. (1966). *Can. J. Microbiol.*, **12**, 61.
McGrath, R. A., and Williams, R. W. (1966). *Nature, Lond.*, **212**, 534.
Mager, J., Kuczynski, M., Scharzberg, M., and Avi-Dor, Y. (1956). *J. gen. Microbiol.*, **14**, 69.
Mahler, H. R., and Fraser, D. (1956). *Biochim. biophys. Acta*, **22**, 197.
Mandelstam, J. (1962). *Biochem. J.*, **84**, 294.
Markham, R. (1960). *Biochem. J.*, **77**, 516.
Marmur, J. (1961). *J. molec. Biol.*, **3**, 208.
Martin, H. H. (1967). *Folia microbiol.*, **12**, 234.
Maxwell, H. (1968). *Molec. Pharmac.*, **4**, 25.
Mazur, P. (1966). *In* "Cryobiology" (Ed. T. H. Merryman). Academic Press, London and New York.
Mazur, P., and Schmidt, J. J. (1968). *Cryobiology*, **5**, 1.
McQuillen, K. (1960). *In* "The Bacteria" (Ed. I. C. Gunsalus and R. Y. Stanier), Vol. I, p. 249. Academic Press, New York and London.
Mejbaum, W. (1939). *Z. physiol. Chem.*, **258**, 117.
Meynell, G. G., and Meynell, E. (1965). "Theory and Practice in Experimental Bacteriology". University Press, Cambridge.
Meynell, E., Meynell, G. G., and Datta, N. (1968). *Bact. Rev.*, **32**, 55.
Mitchell, P. (1950). *J. gen. Microbiol.*, **4**, 399.
Mitchell, P., and Moyle, J. (1967). *Biochem. J.*, **104**, 588.
Mohan, R. R., Kronish, D. P., Pianotti, R. S., Epstein, R. L., and Schwartz, B. S. (1965). *J. Bact.*, **90**, 1355.
Monk, M., Peacey, M., and Gross, J. D. (1971). *J. molec. Biol.*, **58**, 623.
Montgomerie, J. K., Kalmanson, G. M., and Guze, L. B. (1966). *J. Lab. Clin. Med.*, **68**, 543.
Moore, S., and Stein, W. H. (1948). *J. biol. Chem.*, **176**, 367.
Morris, A., and Russell, A. D. (1968). *Biochem. Pharmac.*, **17**, 1923.
Morris, A., and Russell, A. D. (1970). *Microbios.*, **2**, 241.
Morrison, E. W., and Rettger, L. F. (1930). *J. Bact.*, **20**, 299.
Moseley, B. E. B. (1968). *In* "Advances in Microbiol Physiology" (Ed. A. H. Rose and J. F. Williamson), Vol. 2, pp. 173–194. Academic Press, London and New York.
Moseley, B. E. B. (1969). *J. Bact.*, **97**, 647.
Moseley, B. E. B., and Setlow, J. K. (1968). *Proc. natn. Acad. Sci. U.S.A.*, **61**, 176.
Moseley, B. E. B., and Mattingly, A. (1971). *J. Bact.*, **105**, 976.
Moss, C. W., and Speck, M. L. (1966). *J. Bact.*, **91**, 1098.
Mossel, D. A. A., and Beerens, H. (1968). *J. Hyg., Camb.*, **66**, 269.
Muhammed, A. (1966). *J. biol. Chem.*, **241**, 516.
Munro, H. N., and Fleck, A. (1960). *In* "Methods of Biochemical Analysis" (Ed. D. Glick), Vol. 14, p. 113. Academic Press, New York.

Munton, T. J., and Russell, A. D. (1970a). *J. appl. Bact.*, **33**, 410.

Munton, T. J., and Russell, A. D. (1970b). *J. gen. Microbiol.*, **63**, 367.

Murray, R. G. E. (1968). *In* "Microbial Protoplasts, Spheroplasts and L-Forms" (Ed. L. B. Guze), pp. 1–18. Williams and Wilkins Co., Baltimore, U.S.A.

Murrell, W. G. (1967). *In* "Advances in Microbial Physiology" (Ed. A. H. Rose and J. F. Wilkinson), Vol. 1, pp. 133–251. Academic Press, London and New York.

Murrell, W. G., and Warth, A. D. (1965). *In* "Spores III" (Ed. L. L. Campbell and H. O. Halvorson), pp. 1–24. American Society for Microbiology.

Murrell, W. G., Olsen, M. A. and Scott, W. J. (1950). *Aust. J. Sci. Res.*, **3**, 234.

Muschel, L. H. (1965). Ciba. Found. Symp. Complement. pp. 155–169.

Muschel, L. H., and Gustafson, L (1968). *J. Bact.*, **95**, 2010.

Nakamura, M., and Ramage, C. M. (1963). *J. Hyg., Camb.*, **61**, 77

Nakayama, H., Okubo, S., and Takagi, Y. (1971). *Biochim. biophys. Acta*, **228**, 67.

Nathans, D. (1964). *Proc. natn. Acad. Sci U.S.A.*, **51**, 585.

Nathans, D., van Ehrenstein, G., Monro, R., and Lipmann, F. (1962). *Fed. Proc.*, **21**, 127.

Nelson, F. E. (1956). *Bact. Proc.*, p. 40, number G-13.

Neu, H. C., and Winshell, E. B. (1970). *Nature, Lond.*, **225**, 763.

Neu, H. C., Ashman, D. F., and Price, T. D. (1967). *J. Bact.*, **93**, 1360.

Neufeld, E. G., and Ginsberg, V. (1966). *In* "Methods in Enzymology" (Ed. S. P. Colowick and N. O. Kaplan), Vol. VIII. Academic Press, New York and London.

Nirenberg, M. W. (1964). *In* "Methods in Enzymology" (Ed. S. P. Colowick and N. O. Kaplan), Vol. VI, pp. 17–23. Academic Press, New York and London.

Nirenberg, M. W., and Leder, P. (1964). *Science*, **145**, 1399.

Nirenberg, M. W., and Matthei, H. (1961). *Proc. natn. Acad. Sci. U.S.A.*, **47**, 1588.

Nishimura, S., Jones, D. S., and Khorana, H. G. (1965). *J. molec. Biol.*, **13**, 302.

Nishimura, S., Jones, D. S., Ohtsuka, E., Hazatsu, H., Jacob, T. M. and Khorana, H. G. (1965). *J. molec. Biol.*, **13**, 283.

Nomura, M. (1970). *Bact. Rev.*, **34**, 228.

Nomura, M., and Lowry, C. V. (1967). *Proc. natn. Acad. Sci. U.S.A.*, **58**, 946.

Nomura, M., Traub, P., and Beckmann, H. (1968). *Nature, Lond.*, **219**, 793.

Novick, R. P. (1962). *Biochem. J.*, **83**, 236.

O'Brien, R. L., Olenick, J. G., and Hahn, F. E. (1966). *Proc. natn. Acad. Sci. U.S.A.*, **55**, 1511.

O'Callaghan, C. H., and Muggleton, P. W. (1967). *J. gen. Microbiol.*, **48**, 449.

O'Callaghan, C. H., Kirby, S. M., and Wishart, D. R. (1968). *Antimic. Ag. Chemother.*, 1967, 716.

O'Callaghan, C. H., Morris, A., Kirby, S. M., and Shingler, A. H., (1972). *Antimic. Ag. Chemother.*, **1**, 283.

Okomota, T., and Takanami, M. (1963). *Biochim. biophys. Acta*, **68**, 325.

Okubo, S., Nakayama, H., and Takagi, Y. (1971). *Biochim. biophys. Acta*, **228**, 83.

Okura, A., Kinoshita, T., and Tanaka, N. (1970). *Biochem. biophys. Res. Commun.*, **41**, 1545.

Old, D., and Gorini, L. (1965). *Science*, **150**, 1290.

Olsen, A. M., and Scott, W. J. (1950). *Aust. J. Sci. Res.*, **3**, 219.

Op Den Kamp, J. A. F., van Iterson, W., and van Deenen, L. L. M. (1967). *Biochim. biophys. Acta*, **135**, 862.

Ormerod, M. G., and Lehmann, A. R. (1971). *Biochim. biophys. Acta*, **247**, 369.

Ozanne, B., Benveniste, R., Tipper, D., and Davies, J. (1969). *J. Bact.*, **100**, 1144.
Panos, C. (1965). *J. gen. Microbiol.*, **39**, 181.
Parker, M. S. (1969). *J. appl. Bact.*, **32**, 322.
Parker, M. T., and Hewitt, J. H. (1970). *Lancet*, i, 800.
Paterson, M. C., Boyle, J. M., and Setlow, R. B. (1971). *J. Bact.*, **107**, 61.
Peacock, A. R., and Skerret, J. N. H. (1956). *Trans. Farad. Soc.*, **52**, 261.
Perret, C. J. (1954). *Nature, Lond.*, **174**, 1012.
Pestka, S. (1968). *J. biol. Chem.*, **243**, 4038.
Pestka, S. (1970). *Arch. biochem. biophys.*, **136**, 80.
Pestka, S. (1971). *Ann. Rev. Microbiol.*, **25**, 487.
Pestka, S., Marshall, R., and Nirenberg, M. (1965). *Proc. natn. Acad. Sci. U.S.A.*, **53**, 639.
Pethica, B. A., and Schulman, J. H. (1953). *Biochem. J.*, **53**, 177.
de Petris, S. (1967). *J. ultrastruct. Res.*, **19**, 45.
Pietsch, P., and Garett, H. (1968). *Nature, Lond.*, **219**, 488.
Pitzurra, M., and Szybalksi, W. (1959). *J. Bact.*, **77**, 614.
Pollard, E. C., and Weller, P. K. (1967). *Radiat. Res.*, **32**, 417.
Pollock, M. R. (1957). *Biochem. J.*, **66**, 419.
Postgate, J. R. (1969). *In* 'Methods in Microbiology" (Ed. J. R. Norris and D. W. Ribbons), Vol. 1, pp. 611–628. Academic Press, London and New York.
Postgate, J. R., and Hunter, J. R. (1963). *J. appl. Bact.*, **26**, 405.
Postgate, J. R., Crumpton, J. E., and Hunter, J. R. (1961). *J. gen. Microbiol.*, **26**, 367.
Powell, E. O. (1957). *J. appl. Bact.*, **20**, 342.
Powell, J. F. (1957). *J. appl. Bact.*, **20**, 349.
Powell, J. F., and Hunter, J. R. (1955). *J. gen. Microbiol.*, **13**, 59.
Powell, J. F., and Strange, R. E. (1953). *Biochem. J.*, **54**, 205.
Radman, M., and Errera, M. (1970). *Mutation Res.*, **9**, 553.
Radman, M., Cordone, L., Krsmanovic-Simic, D., and Errera, M. (1970). *J. molec. Biol.*, **49**, 203.
Rahn, R. O., Setlow, J. K., and Hosszu, J. L. (1969). *Biophys. J.*, **9**, 510.
Ray, B., Jezeski, J. J., and Busta, F. F. (1971). *Appl. Microbiol.*, **22**, 401.
Reissig, J. L., Strominger, J. L., and Leloir, L. F. (1955). *J. biol. Chem.*, **217**, 959.
Reiter, H. (1970). *Mutation Res.*, **10**, 7.
Repaske, R. (1956). *Biochim. biophys. Acta*, **22**, 189.
Repaske, R. (1958). *Biochim. biophys. Acta*, **30**, 225.
Roberts, N. A., Gray, G. W., and Wilkinson, S. G. (1970). *Microbios.*, **2**, 189.
Roberts, R. B. (1967). *Proc. Soc. exp. Biol. Med.*, **124**, 611.
Roberts, R. B., and Aldous, E. (1949). *J. Bact.*, **57**, 363.
Roberts, T. A. (1970). *J. appl. Bact.*, **33**, 74.
Roberts, T. A., and Hitchins, A. D. (1969). *In* "The Bacterial Spore" (Ed. G. W. Gould and A. Hurst), pp. 611–670. Academic Press, London and New York.
Rode, L. J., and Foster, J. W. (1962a). *Arch. Mikrobiol.*, **43**, 183.
Rode, L. J., and Foster, J. W. (1962b). *Arch. Mikrobiol.*, **43**, 201.
Rogers, H. J. (1967). *Biochem. J.*, **103**, 90.
Rogers, H. J., and Perkins, H. R. (1968). "Cell Walls and Membranes". E. and F. N. Spon, London.
Rondle, C. J. M., and Morgan, W. T. J. (1955). *Biochem. J.*, **61**, 586.
Rotta, J., Karakawa, W. W., and Krause, R. M. (1965). *J. Bact.*, **89**, 581.
Rubbo, R. B., Gardner, J. F., and Webb, R. L. (1967). *J. appl. Bact.*, **30**, 78.

Rupp, W. D., and Howard-Flanders, P. (1968). *J. molec. Biol.*, **31**, 291.
Rupp, W. D., Wilde, C. E., Reno, D. L., and Howard-Flanders, P. (1971). *J. molec. Biol.*, **61**, 25.
Russell, A. D. (1962). *J. Pharm. Pharmac.*, **14**, 390.
Russell, A. D. (1964). *Lab. Pract.*, **13**, 114.
Russell, A. D. (1967). *J. appl. Bact.*, **30**, 395.
Russell, A. D. (1971a). *In* "Inhibition and Destruction of the Microbial Cell" (Ed. W. B. Hugo) pp. 451–612. Academic Press, London and New York.
Russell, A. D. (1971b). *In* "Inhibition and Destruction of the Microbial Cell" (Ed. W. B. Hugo) pp. 209–225. Academic Press, London and New York.
Russell, A. D. (1971c). *Proc. 7th Int. Congr. Chemother.* (Prague), in the press.
Rye, R. M., and Wiseman, D. (1966). *J. Pharm. Pharmac.*, **18**, Suppl. 114.
Ryter, A. (1968). *Bact. Rev.*, **32**, 39
Sabath, L. D., and Abraham, E. P. (1964). *Nature, Lond.*, **204**, 1066.
Sabath, L. D., Leaf, C. D., Gerstein, D. A., and Finland, M. (1970). *Nature, Lond.*, **225**, 1074.
Sato, M., and Takahashi, H. (1968). *J. gen. Appl. Microbiol.*, **14**, 417.
Selzer, G. B., and Wright, W. W. (1965). *Antimicrob. Ag. Chemother.*, 1964, 311.
Setlow, J. K., Randolph, M. L., Boling, M. E., Mattingley, A., Price, G., and Gordon, M. P. (1968). *Cold Spring Harb. quant. Biol. Symp.* **33**, 208.
Shaw, W. V. (1967). *J. biol. Chem.*, **242**, 687.
Silva, M. T. (1967). *Expl Cell Res.*, **46**, 245.
Silver, S., and Wendt, L. (1967). *J. Bact.*, **93**, 73.
Smith, D. H., and Davis, B. D. (1967). *J. Bact.*, **93**, 560.
Smith, H. W. (1970). *J. med. Microbiol.*, **3**, 165.
Smith, J. L., and Weinberg, E. D. (1962). *J. gen. Microbiol.*, **28**, 559.
Smith, J. T., and Knox, R. (1961). *Nature, Lond.*, **191**, 926.
Smith, K. C., and Hanawalt, P. C. (1969). "Molecular Photobiology". Academic Press, New York and London.
Smith, K. C., and Meun, D. C. (1970). *J. molec. Biol.*, **51**, 549.
Sompolinsky, D., Ziegler-Schlomowitz, R., and Herczog, D. (1968). *Can. J. Microbiol.*, **14**, 891.
Staehelin, T., and Meselson, M. (1966). *J. molec. Biol.*, **19**, 207.
Stafford, R. S., and Donnellan, J. E. (1968). *Proc. natn. Acad. Sci. U.S.A.*, **59**, 822.
Stapleton, G. E., Sbarra, A. J., and Hollaender, A. (1955). *J. Bact.*, **70**, 7.
Straka, R. P., and Stokes, J. L. (1959). *J. Bact.*, **78**, 181.
Strange, R. E., and Dark, F. A. (1962). *J. gen. Microbiol.*, **29**, 719.
Strange, R. E., and Postgate, J. R. (1964). *J. gen. Microbiol.*, **36**, 393.
Strominger, J. L. (1957). *J. Biol. Chem.*, **224**, 509.
Strominger, J. L. (1971). Cited by M. Niete and H. R. Perkins, *Biochem. J.*, **123**, 789.
Strominger, J. L., Izaki, K., Matsuhashi, M., and Tipper, D. J. (1968). *In* "Topics in Pharmaceutical Sciences" (Ed. D. Perlman), Vol. 1, p. 53. Wiley, New York.
Studier, F. W. (1965). *J. molec. Biol.*, **11**, 373.
Stuy, J. H. (1956). *Biochim. biophys. Acta*, **22**, 241.
Sud, I. J., and Feingold, D. S. (1970). *J. Bact.*, **104**, 289.
Suwalsky, M., Trabu, W., Schmueli, U., and Subirana, J. A. (1969). *J. molec. Biol.*, **42**, 363.
Suzuki, H., and Kilgore, W. W. (1967). *J. Bact.*, **94**, 666.
Sykes, G. (1970). *J. appl. Bact.*, **33**, 147.

Sykes, R. B., and Richmond, M. H. (1970). *Nature, Lond.*, **226**, 952.
Tabor, C. W. (1962). *J. Bact.*, **83**, 1101.
Takanami, M. (1967). *In* "Methods in Enzymology" (Ed. L. Grossman and K. Moldave), Vol. XII, pp. 491–494. Academic Press, New York and London.
Tal, M. (1969). *Biochemistry*, **8**, 424.
Tamaki, S., Sato, T., and Matsuhashi, M. (1971). *J. Bact.*, **105**, 968.
Thomas, C. A., and Abelson, J. (1966). *In* "Procedures in Nucleic Acid Research" (Ed. G. L. Cantoni and D. R. Davies), p. 553.
Tomasz, A., and Borek, E. (1960). *Proc. natn. Acad. Sci. U.S.A.*, **46**, 324.
Tomlins, R. I., and Ordal, Z. J. (1971a). *J. Bact.*, **105**, 512.
Tomlins, R. I., and Ordal, Z. J. (1971b). *J. Bact.*, **107**, 134.
Town, C. D., Smith, K. C., and Kaplan, H. S. (1970). *J. Bact.*, **105**, 127.
Traub, P., Hosokawa, K., and Nomura, M. (1966). *Biochim. biophys. Acta*, **123**, 438.
Traub, P., and Nomura, H. (1968). *Proc. natn. Acad. Sci. U.S.A.*, **59**, 777.
Trant, R. R., and Monro, R. E. (1964). *J. molec. Biol.*, **10**, 63.
Trevelyan, W. E., and Harrison, J. S. (1952). *Biochem. J.*, **50**, 298.
Van Knippenberg, P. H., van Ravenswaay Claasen, J. C. Grijm-Vos, M., Vedstron, H., and Bosch, L. (1965). *Biochim. biophys. Acta*, **95**, 461.
Van Iterson, W., and Op Den Kamp, J. A. (1969). *J. Bact.*, **99**, 304.
Vasquez, D. (1966). *In* "Biochemical Studies of Antimicrobial Drugs" (Ed. B. A. Newton and P. E. Reynolds), pp. 169–191. University Press, Cambridge.
Vinter, V. (1964). *Folia microbiol.*, **9**, 58.
Voll, M. J., and Leive, L. (1970). *J. Bact.*, **102**, 600.
Voss, J. G. (1967). *J. gen. Microbiol.*, **48**, 391.
Walker, I. O. (1965). *Biochim. biophys. Acta*, **101**, 588.
Walker, J. R. (1969). *J. Bact.*, **99**, 713.
Walker, J. R. (1970). *J. Bact.*, **103**, 552.
Walton, J. R. (1968). *Vet. Rec.*, 448.
Ward, D. C., Reich, E., and Goldberg, I. H. (1965). *Science*, **149**, 1259.
Waring, M. J. (1965). *J. molec. Biol.*, **13**, 269.
Waring, M. J. (1966). *Symp. Soc. gen. Microbiol.*, **16**, 235.
Waring, M. J. (1970). *J. molec. Biol.*, **54**, 247.
Watanabe, T. (1963). *Bact. Rev.*, **27**, 87.
Watarakunakorn, C., Goldberg, L. M., Carleton, J., and Hamburger, M. (1969). *J. Infect. Diseases*, **119**, 67.
Weatherwax, R. S. (1956). *J. Bact.*, **72**, 329.
Webb, M. (1949). *J. gen. Microbiol.*, **3**, 418.
Weibull, C. (1953). *J. Bact.*, **66**, 888.
Weisblum, B., and Davies, J. (1968). *Bact. Rev.*, **32**, 493.
Weiser, R., Wimpenny, J., and Asscher, A. W. (1969). *Lancet*, ii, 619.
Wells, R. D., and Larson, J. E. (1970). *J. molec. Biol.*, **49**, 319.
Willett, H. P., and Thacore, H. (1966). *Can. J. Microbiol.*, **12**, 11.
Wise, W. S., and Twigg, G. H. (1950). *Analyst*, **75**, 106.
Witkin, E. (1969). *Ann. Rev. Genet.*, **3**, 525.
Woese, C. R. (1958). *J. Bact.*, **75**, 5.
Yarmolinsky, M. B., and de la Haba, G. L. (1959). *Proc. natn. Acad. Sci. U.S.A.*, **45**, 1721.
Yemm, E. W., and Cocking, E. L. (1955). *Analyst*, **80**, 209.
Yudkin, M. D. (1963). *Biochem. J.*, **89**, 290.
Zinder, W. D., and Arndt, W. F. (1956). *Proc. natn. Acad. Sci. U.S.A.*, **42**, 586.

CHAPTER VI

Differential Light Scattering Techniques for Microbiology

PHILIP J. WYATT

Science Spectrum Incorporated, P.O. Box 3003, Santa Barbara, California 93105

I.	Introduction	183
	A. Background	183
	B. New tools	185
	C. Objectives of the Chapter	185
II.	The Physical Basis of Differential Light Scattering as Applied to Bacterial Systems	186
	A. Classical light scattering and polarization	186
	B. Small and very large particles	188
	C. Particles in the resonance region	188
III.	Experimental Procedures, Data, and Interpretations	220
	A. Bacterial suspensions	220
	B. Single bacteria and spores	246
	C. Data representations	251
IV.	Further Applications of Differential Light Scattering	255
	Appendix: Mathematical Formulation	257
	A. Spherically symmetric particles	258
	B. The Rayleigh–Debye approximation	259
	Acknowledgments	261
	References	262

I. INTRODUCTION

A. Background

One of the strange coincidences of nature is that the size of bacterial cells and the wavelength of visible light are approximately the same. Typically, bacteria have an average diameter from 500 to 1000 nm, whereas green light has a wavelength of about 520 nm. As a consequence of this closeness of size, bacterial cells will scatter visible radiation in a rather complicated manner since they are in resonance with the incident waves. Pijper (1919, 1931) originally interpreted these phenomena as surface diffraction effects and used them somewhat successfully to determine the mean size of bacterial cells. Actually, of course, the scattering phenomena in the resonance region arise mainly because of more complex interference effects; the contributions at the surface playing a secondary role. Ponder (1934, 1944) and Cox and Ponder (1941) extended the work of Pijper considerably, again explaining the phenomena in terms of surface diffraction. On the basis of some elementary theoretical calculations, they were able to get a better estimate for bacterial size using some features of *differential light scattering* by which we mean the variation of scattered light intensity with respect to the angle of scattering (the direction of the incident beam taken as 0°).

In related work, Lewis and Lothian (1954), Fikhman (1959, 1963), Koga and Fujita (1961), and Petukhov (1965) applied various aspects of theoretical light scattering to the determination of bacterial size and average refractive index. Barer (1952, 1954), Ross and Billing (1957), and others (Barer *et al.*, 1953; Davis *et al.*, 1954) used methods of immersion refractometry to determine further the average refractive index and size characteristics of bacteria in solutions. Although these refractometry methods are somewhat inapplicable in the resonance region, they do nevertheless yield results that agree with more recent determinations.

Much of our theoretical understanding of light scattering by these so-called resonance particles came from the theory that explains the manner by which small homogeneous spheres scatter light. This theory is often referred to as Mie (1908) scattering theory but was in fact developed by Ludvig Lorenz (1890) 18 years before Mie. The calculations based upon this complete theory were most difficult to perform until digital computers became readily available. Various approximation techniques were developed during the interim, primarily the so-called Rayleigh–Gans–Debye theory (cf. Kerker, 1969) that permits simplification in the calculations yet allows the scattering characteristics of complex structures to be approximated equally well. Several papers by Koch (1961, 1968a, b) were devoted to the exposition of many of these approximation methods together with possible applications of the exact theory. Discussions by Oster (1955) and Kratovhil (1964, 1966) provide extensive bibliographies on various applications of light scattering including bacterial systems. Gotterer *et al.* (1961) interpreted various measurements in terms of the appropriate theoretical background. Some papers by Packer (1963) and others (Packer and Perry, 1961; Packer *et al.*, 1963) contain interesting and related measurements on chloroplasts and mitochondria. Studies on photo-phosphorylation (Packer, 1963; Dilley and Vernon, 1964; Hind and Jagendorf, 1965) using light scattering techniques are also of interest. Wyatt (1968, 1970) extended the earlier work considerably and established many of the analytical bases for deducing structure from experimental measurements.

B. New tools

Three technological developments of the past decade have rekindled considerable interest in the further applications of light scattering techniques to the study of bacterial systems. In particular, we refer to lasers, microelectronics and digital computers. Lasers represent an almost ideal means for illuminating specimens for they are in general highly monochromatic, exceedingly well collimated, easily polarized, coherent (though this feature is not of primary importance for bacterial scattering measurements), available at various wavelengths and powers, and relatively inexpensive. The power of analytical instruments has been enormously enhanced in recent years by miniaturization and the incorporation of various signal processing features. Microelectronics have simplified the basic operation of many of these instruments and permitted some to be virtually automatic in their performance of certain routine analytical functions. Light scattering instrumentation for the study of bacterial systems has developed rapidly by incorporating such electronic features for both automation and control.

The interpretation and understanding of the complex resonance scattering phenomena have been made considerably more tractible and simple with the advent of improved digital computers. Large scale computers now routinely calculate in seconds the scattering characteristics of complex bacterial structures that but a few decades ago might not have been completed in a lifetime. More important perhaps than the ability to predict light scattering features of potential experimental significance is the capability (using appropriately programmed computers) to deduce structural features of bacterial systems from differential light scattering measurements. Without digital computers, the existing potential of light scattering measurements on bacterial systems might have remained in a relatively dormant state.

C. Objectives of the Chapter

This Chapter is not concerned with the detailed mathematical analysis of light scattering phenomena, references to which are appropriately noted with some discussion in the brief appendix which follows. It is intended primarily to familiarize the reader with the basic techniques of measurement and the general features of their interpretation.

As will be readily apparent in the Sections which follow, the experimental procedures are for the most part simple and easily performed. Not surprisingly, there are very few experiments relating to any facet of bacterial growth and metabolism or their interaction with various chemicals and biological agents that are not readily accessible to light scattering techniques. Indeed, such techniques are in many cases far more sensitive for monitoring subtle morphological changes than any of the more conventional methods. Recent applications of such methods to antibiotic susceptibility testing (Berkman *et al.*, 1970; Wyatt *et al.*, 1972), for example, have resulted in methods and instrumentation whose speed for determination of such effects is unequalled by the conventional approaches. As an example, the susceptibility of mycobacteria to antibiotic agents can be determined from an exponential phase culture within a matter of minutes (Reich, 1973).

Light scattering techniques, especially those relating to resonance scattering phenomena, will no doubt play an increasingly important role in the microbiology laboratory for many years to come. Although this Chapter will allude to many of these applications in detail, there are many others that have not been presented nor for that matter attempted. Section II is concerned with a detailed explanation of the meaning of differential light scattering and includes various theoretical results that can be used as a basis for interpretation. Experimental procedures and means by which interpretations are achieved are discussed in Section III together with selected applications and measurements on bacterial systems using differential light scattering. Section IV is concerned with further applications that extend the methods to areas somewhat outside of general microbiology. A brief mathematical appendix summarizes the more important mathematical theories used in interpreting and predicting various results.

The main purpose of this Chapter, of course, is to familiarize the reader with the techniques of measurement and hopefully to erase the mistaken concept that light scattering measurements are difficult to understand and perform. Although much quantitative analysis still remains to be completed on many of the measurements performed to date, many of the qualitative features of light scattering measurements should provide a useful means for rapidly understanding the biophysical phenomena affecting the bacterial system being studied.

II. THE PHYSICAL BASIS OF DIFFERENTIAL LIGHT SCATTERING AS APPLIED TO BACTERIAL SYSTEMS

A. Classical light scattering and polarization

In the classical sense, electromagnetic radiation is generated when charged particles (e.g. electrons) are accelerated, i.e. when their velocity changes with time. The scattering of electromagnetic radiation (light) is most easily thought of as a two-step process: first, the incident light waves accelerate the electrons that are bound in the molecules of the illuminated particle; these accelerating electrons then *reradiate* light, in general at the same wavelength as the incident light. (For some materials, at particular frequencies, part of the incident radiation is selectively *absorbed* by pro-moting the electrons to a higher energy state during excitation.) In some substances the induced motion of the electrons is damped by collision and energy is lost. (This is equivalent to electrical "resistance".) Although the electrons oscillate at the same frequency (when no absorption is present), the radiated waves emanating from each will not in general be in phase since the electrons of the scatterer are spatially displaced from one another. In addition, if the scatterer is inhomogeneous, the radiating electrons contained therein will be bound differently corresponding to the different chemical bonds involved. Such differences in chemical bonding produce additional phase differences in the reradiated waves.

The intensity of the scattered light is a superposition of all the reradiated waves from the bound accelerating electrons. Because of the aforementioned phase differences, some of these reradiated waves will interfere destruc-tively in certain directions and constructively in others. These "inter-ference" effects result in variations of the scattered light intensity with respect to the angle of observation (or detection). Restricting ourselves to measurements in a plane, Fig. 1 shows a typical scattering geometry.

FIG. 1. Schematic set-up of a scattering measurement. Radiation (light) source (S) illuminates scatterer (O), and detector (D) records scattered intensity at angle (θ) as it rotates about (O) at a fixed distance from it.

An incident beam of light illuminates a particle (or ensemble) while a detector rotates about it. The variations in scattered light intensity are measured and recorded. The recorded scattering pattern is called the *differential scattered light intensity* or *differential light scattering pattern*. (The term "differential" refers to the incremental light flux dF collected by the detector that intercepts scattered light within a very small solid angle, $d\Omega$.) Note that the detector is usually restrained to rotate in a circular arc about the scatterer. At all angular locations the detector will be at the same distance from the scatterer. This is necessary since the scattered energy falls off inversely as the square of the distance from the scattering particles. The recorded scattering pattern will therefore depend only on the angular position of the detector.

In much of the discussion which follows, we shall assume that the incident light is monochromatic and polarized and that the scattering particles are isotropic (i.e. non-crystalline). By *vertical* polarization we mean that the electric field of the incident light waves is perpendicular to the plane in which the scattering measurements will be made. Thus all the accelerating electrons of the scattering particle will be forced by such a polarized incident field to oscillate perpendicularly to the scattering plane. Similar remarks apply to *horizontally* polarized incident light.

B. Small and very large particles

Extremely small particles, i.e. particles whose spatial dimensions are of the order of a hundreth of the wavelength of the incident light or less, will scatter vertically polarized light isotropically. A detector rotating about such a particle per Fig. 1 would record the same intensity of scattered light at all scattering angles. Since the size of such a particle is so small, no appreciable phase difference exists between the reradiating electrons and thus the scattering pattern would be devoid of interference effects. Once the size of the particle approaches dimensions of the order of a tenth of the incident wavelength, the scattering pattern becomes slightly peaked in the forward direction due to the onset of interference effects. The relative amount of light scattered, of course, depends upon the chemical composition of the particles manifest in terms of their index of refraction, or variations thereof. Figure 2 illustrates the pronounced peaking in the forward direction for spherical homogeneous particles of different refractive indices whose radius is 100 nm. All of these scattering curves have been normalized at 30°. The incident light is vertically polarized at a wavelength of 514·5 nm. Figure 3 shows similar scattering data for horizontally polarized incident light. Note how these latter curves (normalized at 60°) could be used to differentiate (and thereby identify) the refractive index by the ratio of scattered light intensity at a large scattering angle (say, 140°) to the intensity of 60° (Figs 2 and 3 are from the *Atlas of Light Scattering Curves*, 1971).

Particles very large compared with the incident wavelength scatter light predominantly via diffraction of light passing near their surface, most of the scattered energy being directed forward. Many experimental results may be interpreted in terms of geometrical optics combined with diffraction theory (cf. Kerker, 1969, Van de Hulst, 1956). Some experimental results for such large particles may be found in the recent work of Blau *et al.* (1970).

C. Particles in the resonance region

1. *A dehydrated bacterium in air*

The particles of prime interest for this Chapter are bacteria and bacterial spores, i.e. scatterers in the so-called resonance region. Let us now examine their scattering characteristics in greater detail and begin with an

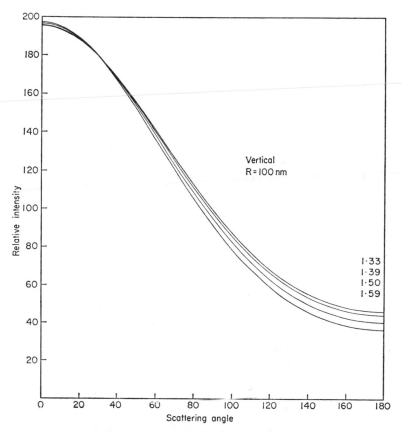

FIG. 2. Differential light scattering patterns for homogeneous spherical particles of radius 100 nm. The incident light is of wavelength 514·5 nm (argon-ion laser green line) and is vertically polarized. The particles (in air) are of refractive indices corresponding to water (1·33), hydrated protein (1·39), glass (1·50), and polystyrene latex (1·59).

individual airborne cell. Although experimental measurements of such individual air-suspended cells require specialized instrumentation, the theoretical interpretation of their differential light scattering characteristics is somewhat simpler than for liquid-borne suspensions. In a recent paper, Wyatt and Phillips (1972b) analysed the light scattering characteristics of individual cells of *Staphylococcus epidermidis*. These airborne cells were found to have an average refractive index of $1·52 \pm 0·02$; a value corresponding to almost completely dehydrated protein (cf. Ross and Billing, 1957). The average cell wall thickness was 25 ± 8 nm and the refractive index of the dehydrated cytoplasm and cell wall were found to be $1·50 \pm$

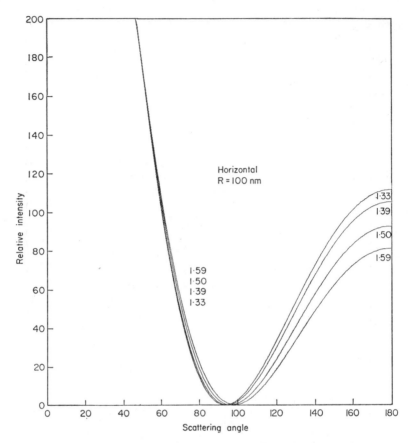

FIG. 3. Same as Fig. 2, but horizontally polarized incident light.

0·02 and 1·54 ± 0·02, respectively. Choosing these values as representative
of airborne Gram-positive organisms, a variety of theoretical curves may
be generated (see Appendix) as a function of radius to illustrate the effects
of size within the resonance region. Figs 4 through 11 present the differential light scattering patterns (*Atlas of Light Scattering Curves*, 1972) for
both vertically and horizontally polarized incident light at a wavelength
of 514·5 nm. The bacterial size varies from an overall radius of 270 nm
to 420 nm. Note how more scattering peaks occur in the patterns with
increasing bacterial size.

Table I presents the angular positions (in degrees) of the scattering
extrema as a function of overall radius for the aforementioned theoretical
parameters. The principal sequence differences (the difference between
the angular positions of the last maxima and the first minima) are listed

TABLE I

Extrema angular positions (in degrees) of the theoretical vertical differential scattering patterns of dehydrated spherical bacterial cells

R (nm)	min	max	min	max	min	max	min	max	min	max	min	max	min
200	100												
220	77	108	160										
240	75	106	145										
260	72	98	140										
270	66	79	142										
280	58	77	107	126	148								
290	56	76	105	128	153								
300	55	76	105	129	157								
310	55	76	104	130	157								
320	55	74	104	130	156								
330	55	68	104	131	154								
340	48	59	108	132	154								
350	44	60	83	100	117	124	153						
360	43	60	83	101	121	139	155						
370	43	60	83	102	122	140	158						
380	43	60	83	103	122	141	161						
390	43	58	84	102	121	141	161						
400	40	49	87	103	121	142	161						
410	35	47	69	80	97	108	122	142	160				
420	34	47	68	82	101	113	126	143	159				
430	34	48	69	83	101	115	129	145	158				
440	33	48	70	84	102	117	132	147	160				
450	33	48	70	85	102	117	132	147	162				
460	32	45	71	85	102	117	133	148	164				
470	28	39	60	65	82	87	102	117	132	148	164		
480	27	39	57	69	86	95	108	120	131	148	164		
490	26	39	57	70	86	98	112	122	130	148	163		
500	26	39	58	71	87	100	116	125	135	150	162		
510	27	40	58	72	88	100	115	126	137	151	163		
520	26	39	59	72	88	101	116	127	139	152	163		
530	23	35	66	72	88	101	114	127	139	152	164		
540	21	33	49	59	75	83	94	103	114	127	139	153	165

in Table II together with the number of secondary maxima and the intensity ratios of the last maximum to the first minimum. Such curves and tables have been shown to be useful for the rapid characterization of bacterial size. (Stull 1972). Note how the principal sequence difference is an essentially monotonically *increasing* function of cell size.

Another representation of the differential light scattering characteristics of individual cells is by means of a polar plot. Fig. 12 presents a polar plot of the predicted light scattering characteristics of the 380 nm-radius cell

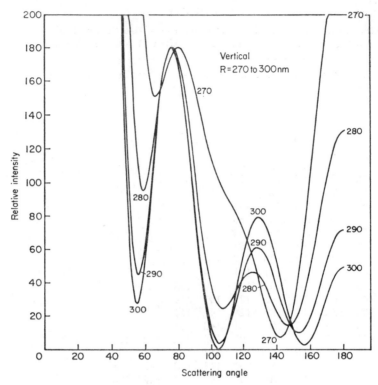

FIG. 4. The differential light scattering patterns for bacterial cells in air illuminated by vertically polarized light of wavelength 514·5 nm. The model chosen consists of a concentric structure with a cell wall 25 nm thick. The refractive indices of cell wall and cytoplasm were 1·54 and 1·50, respectively, corresponding to dehydrated cells. Cell radii 270 nm to 300 nm.

of Fig. 8. The bacterium is illuminated from the left with a vertically polarized plane wave. The relative intensity of scattered light in a particular direction is proportional to the distance from the origin to the intersection with the plotted curve. Thus were we to "walk around" such an illuminated particle, we would observe the scattered light intensity to fluctuate considerably as we observed it in our excursion from 0° (looking head-on into the illuminating beam) to 180° (the back of the bacterium). The arrow indicates the direction of the incident beam. Note that the scattering pattern is symmetric on either side of the beam. Such symmetry is typical of spherically symmetric cells or cells exhibiting axial symmetry with respect to the incident beam. The detector of Fig. 1 records the relative intensity of the scattered light as it "walks around" the illuminated bacterium. Referring again to Fig. 12, we note (for example) that when the

TABLE II

Principal sequence differences, $\triangle$ (last max − first min)

R (nm)	$\triangle$ (degrees)	No. sec max.	$X(I_{max}/I_{min})$
200			
220	31	1	
240	31	1	
260	26	1	
270	23	1	
280	68	2	0·495
290	72	2	1·355
300	74	2	2·928
310	75	2	4·172
320	75	2	1·646
330	76	2	0·788
340	84	2	0·428
350	91	3	0·374
360	96	3	0·500
370	97	3	0·750
380	98	3	1·352
390	98	3	0·758
400	101	3	0·555
410	107	4	0·534
420	109	4	0·600
430	111	4	0·500
400	114	4	0·500
450	114	4	0·578
460	116	4	0·505
470	120	5	0·667
480	121	5	1·270
490	122	5	1·823
500	124	5	1·538
510	124	5	1·000
520	126	5	0·686
530	129	5	0·956
540	132	6	4·300

detector (or observer) looks toward the bacterium from about 40°, a sharp decrease in its apparent brightness is seen. Increasing the angular position to about 60° results in an appearance of brightness, then again another null near 85°, etc. Most of the total scattered energy appears in the forward direction, as indicated. (The forward lobe is truncated by the right hand margin of the figure.)

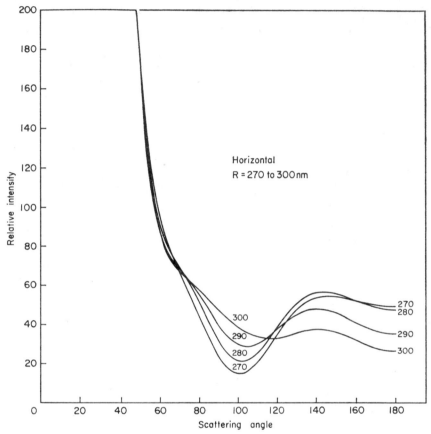

FIG. 5. Same as Fig. 4, horizontally polarized incident light.

2. Bacteria in liquids

(i) *Predicted characteristics of individual cells.* Bacterial systems are most easily examined in a liquid medium since this is most similar to their natural environment. In a liquid (such as water), however, the structural characteristics of the cells are quite different from corresponding values in an airborne, dehydrated state. Wyatt (1970) has shown, for example, that the cell wall is considerably thicker which confirms an earlier assumption of Knaysi (1951). In its fully hydrated state, the cell wall of *S. aureus* would be expected to be almost three to four times as thick as when dehydrated. The refractive indices of the cytoplasm and cell wall are found for such hydrated cells to be about 1·37 and 1·42, respectively. These values are quite close to the refractive index of water, viz. 1·33. Accordingly, such waterborne cells scatter light weakly; the intensity of light

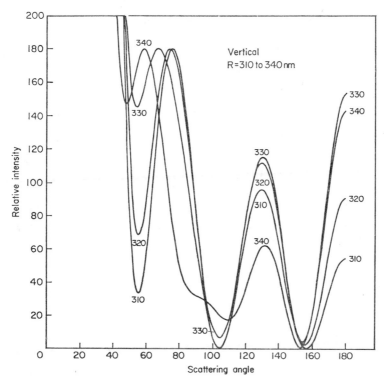

FIG. 6. Same as Fig. 4, vertically polarized incident light. Radii 310 nm to 340 nm.

scattered being proportional to the square of the difference between the average refractive index of the cell and that of water. A single dehydrated airborne cell will thus scatter many thousands of times as much light as its waterborne counterpart (see Appendix). Not only is the amount of light scattered by waterborne cells quite different, but the qualitative features of the differential light scattering patterns are changed as well.

The effects of size on the differential light scattering characteristics for waterborne cells of the type described above is shown in Figs. 13 through 18. (Contrast the differential light scattering patterns for the airborne cells of Figs. 4, 6, 8 and 10.) The incident light is polarized at 514·5 nm and all cells have a fixed wall thickness of 80 nm; the refractive indices of cytoplasm and cell wall are 1·37 and 1·42, respectively (Wyatt, 1970). Note the monotonic shift towards *smaller* angles of the first maximum as the cell size increases. (The first maximum here is defined as the first maximum beyond the forward 0° scattering lobe.) If the average cell size changes (and all other features remain constant), then an estimate of this

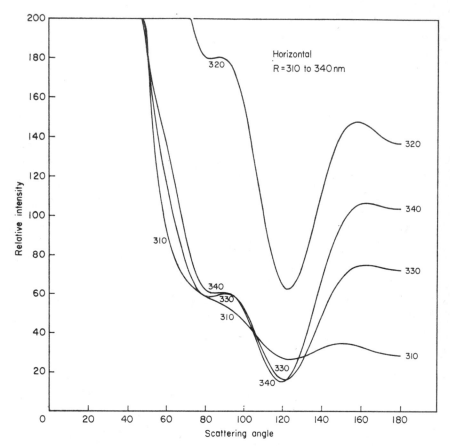

FIG. 7. Same as FIG. 6, horizontally polarized incident light.

change may be obtained from the expression

$$2\,kR \sin \theta/2 = \text{constant,} \tag{1}$$

where R is the average radius of the cell, $k = 2\pi n_0/\lambda_0$ and θ is the angle of the first maximum or any of the angular extrema (see Appendix B). The refractive index of water and the wavelength of the incident vertically polarized light are n_0 and λ_0, respectively. Whenever all the measurements are performed at the same wavelength and in the same medium (i.e. k is constant), Eqn. (1) may be simplified to

$$R \sin \theta/2 = \text{constant.} \tag{2}$$

As an example, consider a measurement made on a suspension of cells that yields a light scattering pattern (for vertically polarized incident light)

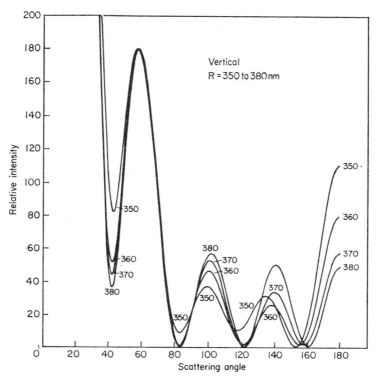

Fɪɢ. 8. Radii 350 nm to 380 nm, vertical polarization.

with a maximum at 55° (cf. Fig. 15). After adding a certain chemical to the suspension, say the recorded light scattering pattern has shifted slightly such that this same maximum feature is now at 50°. We can now easily estimate that the average size change that occurred by using Eqn. (2) as follows: if the initial average cell radius was R and after the addition of the chemical, the final average cell radius is R'; then

$$R \sin \theta/2 \quad = R \sin 55°/2 = R \sin 27\cdot5° = \text{const.}$$

$$R' \sin \theta'/2 \quad = R' \sin 50°/2 = R' \sin 25° = \text{const.}$$

or $R' \sin 25° \quad = R \sin 27\cdot5°.$

Hence $(R' - R)/R = \left(\dfrac{R \sin 27\cdot5°}{\sin 25°} - R \right)/R$

$$= \left(\frac{0\cdot520}{0\cdot467} - 1 \right) = (1\cdot114 - 1) = 0\cdot114 = \Delta R/R,$$

i.e. we may conclude that the average cell radius increased by about 11%.

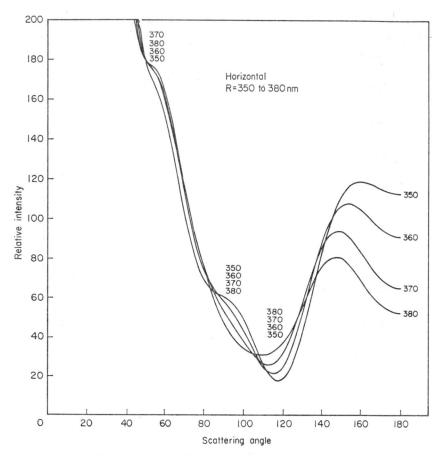

FIG. 9. Same as Fig. 8, horizontal polarization.

If the differential light scattering characteristics of the same bacterial system are measured at different wavelengths, specific extrema will shift to different angles more or less in accordance with Eqn. (1). The differential light scattering patterns are always a function of the ratio of size to incident wavelength ($kR \propto R/\lambda$). Thus *decreasing* the wavelength of the incident light will produce an effect equivalent to *increasing* the particle size. Theoretical curves may therefore be scaled as follows: a calculation at wavelength λ_1 and size R_1 will correspond exactly to a size R_2 for incident wavelength λ_2 (providing that the refractive index is the *same* at the two wavelengths), where

$$R_2 = R_1 \lambda_2 / \lambda_1. \tag{3}$$

Thus, for example, a measurement on a bacterial suspension with, say,

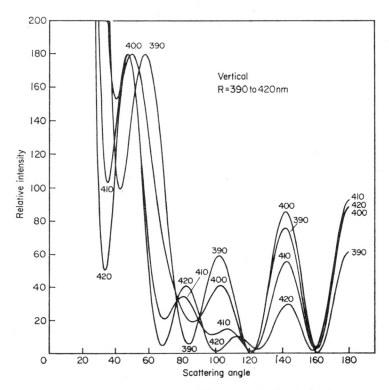

FIG. 10. Radii 390 nm to 420 nm, vertical polarization.

an average radius of 340 nm at a wavelength of 514·5 (Argon-ion laser) will produce a light scattering pattern almost identical to that obtained from a suspension of larger cells (average radius R) for a measurement performed at 632·8 nm (He-Ne laser red line), if

$$R = 340 \times 632\cdot8/514\cdot5 \simeq 418 \text{ nm.}$$

This latter result is a direct consequence of Eqn. (3) and assumes that the refractive index structure of the two bacterial suspensions are almost identical at the two different wavelengths.

If the curves of Figs. 13, 15 and 17 (vertically polarized incident light) were all multiplied by $\cos^2 \theta$ (where θ is the scattering angle), the results shown for the horizontally polarized cases (Figs. 14, 16 18) would be rather well reproduced except for very large or small scattering angles. (The curves of Fig. 14 would be in very poor agreement beyond 110°.) This proportionality between vertically and horizontally-polarized scattering data is a consequence of the weakly scattering nature (cf. Kerker,

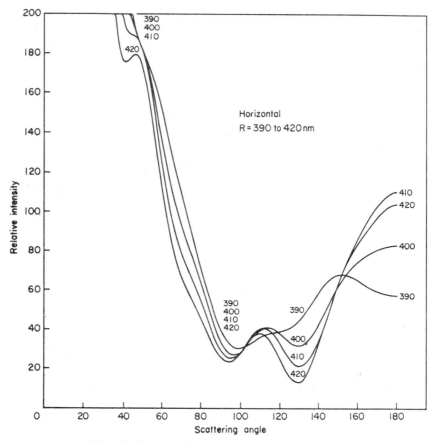

FIG. 11. Same as Fig. 10, horizontal polarization.

1969) of liquid suspended cells (see Appendix). Since little additional structural information is thereby derivable from measurements of these horizontal data, most measurements of the light scattering characteristics of liquid-borne bacterial cells are usually performed only for vertically polarized incident light.

Figure 19 presents differential light scattering patterns illustrating the effect of cell wall thickness variation. The incident radiation (light) is vertically polarized at 514·5 nm. All the cells have the same overall radius (350 nm), the same cytoplasm and cell wall refractive indices (1·37 and 1·42, respectively), and are assumed to be immersed in water ($n_0 = 1·33$). The four curves shown correspond to the four different cell wall thicknesses 40, 60, 80 and 100 nm, respectively. All curves have been normalized at their first peaks. Note that the major effect of increasing cell wall

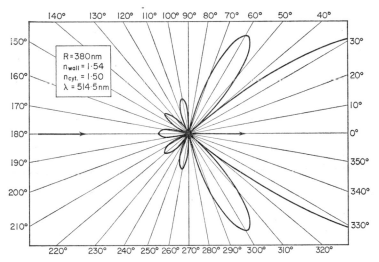

FIG. 12. Polar plot of differential light scattering pattern of 380 nm-radius cell of Fig. 8.

thickness is to *decrease* (slightly) the relative intensity of light scattered at the larger scattering angles. Referring to the second peak near 100° in Fig. 19, we note that the effect of increasing the cell wall thickness is to move this peak very slightly toward larger angles.

Although the effects of changing cell wall thickness upon the differential light scattering patterns (Fig. 19) are not particularly vivid, slight changes in the refractive indices of the cytoplasm and cell wall produce considerably greater shifts in the patterns. Figure 20 shows the effects produced as the cytoplasm refractive index varies from 1·33 (water) to 1·44. The refractive index and thickness of the cell wall are fixed at 1·42 and 80 nm, respectively. The cells are all of the same size, viz. radius of 350 nm. The shift of the first maximum as in Fig. 20 might tend to be confused with a change in average cell size per Figs. 13, 15 and 17. Fortunately, this confusion will not occur since the cytoplasm refractive index of most waterborne bacterial cells will lie in the very restricted range 1·36–1·39. Such a restriction is a natural consequence of the relatively high water content of bacteria.

Because of the occurrence of capsules and slime layers on certain bacteria grown under various conditions, we would expect that the refractive index of the "cell wall region" might vary appreciably. Again the high water content of this part of a hydrated cell results in a rather restricted range of the associated refractive index, probably between 1·40 and 1·44. Figure 21 illustrates the scattering variations possible as the cell wall

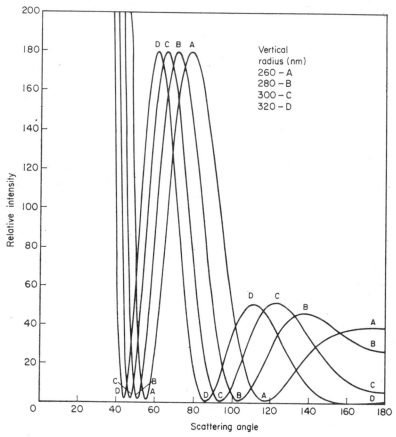

FIG. 13. Differential light scattering patterns for water suspended bacterial cells. Incident light vertically polarized at 514·5 nm. The model chosen consists of a concentric structure with a cell wall 80 nm thick. The refractive indices of cell wall and cytoplasm were 1·37 and 1·42, respectively, corresponding to fully hydrated cells. Cell radii from 260 nm to 320 nm.

refractive index varies from an unrealistic value of 1·35 (*less* than the refractive index of the cytoplasm) to 1·44. Note that within the range 1·42 (from Fig. 15) through 1·44, the angular positions of the extrema vary minimally.

(ii) *Suspension of cells.* Figs. 13, 15 and 17 present the salient scattering features of individual spherically symmetrical waterborne bacteria for vertically polarized incident light. Because such cells scatter weakly, the scattered light intensities from several thousand such cells must be simultaneously detected in any practical experiment. The recorded

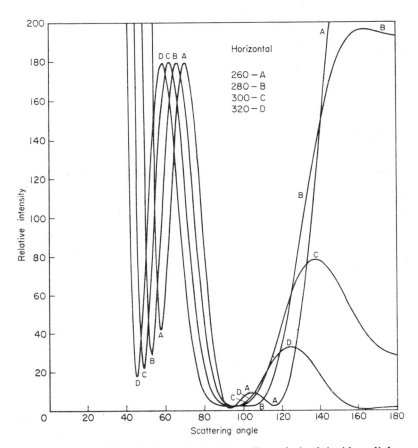

FIG. 14. Same as Fig. 13, but for horizontally polarized incident light.

pattern from such an ensemble will represent a linear superposition of the patterns of all the contributing members provided, however, that (1) the mean distance between cells is large compared to the wavelength of the illuminating radiation, (2) the mean-free-path is larger than the dimensions of the cuvette containing the suspension, (3) geometrical foreshortening effects are adequately compensated for, (4) internal reflections occurring within the cuvette are minimal, and (5) the liquid medium in which the cells are suspended is not too strongly absorbing at the wavelength of the illuminating radiation. Let us examine these conditions in greater detail.

Condition (1), the so-called coherence requirement, states that if scatterers are too close to one another they will not scatter light independently. If the number of scatterers per unit volume is N, the refractive index of the

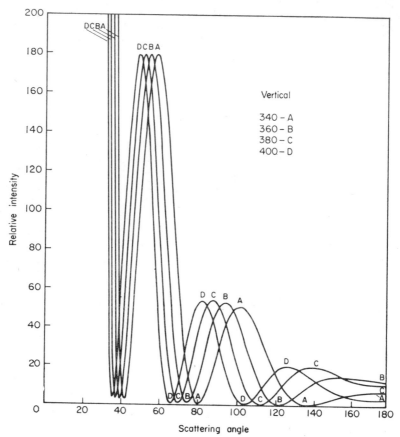

Fig. 15. Same as Fig. 13, but radii from 340 nm to 400 nm.

suspending medium n_0, and the illuminating wavelength λ_0, then condition (1) requires

$$1/N^{1/3} \gg \lambda_0/n_0 \tag{4}$$

At a wavelength of 514·5 nm in water this requires that the cell density must be considerably less than 10^{13} cells/ml, a condition always satisfied.

Condition (2) is the requirement that once a cell has scattered light, this scattered light will not be subject to further (multiple) scattering before it is recorded. Multiple scattering obviously tends to wash out the recorded light scattering pattern and must be avoided. If the dimension of the cuvette path is d and the effective scattering cross-section of an individual cell σ, then this condition becomes

$$1/(N\sigma) \gg d. \tag{5}$$

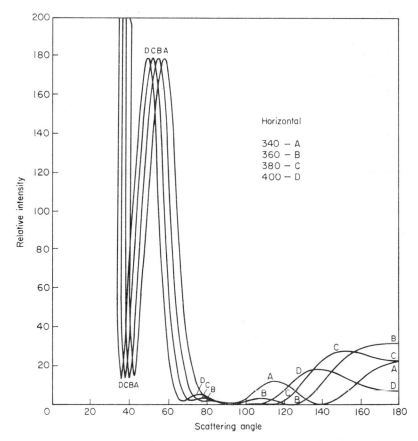

FIG. 16. Same as Fig. 15, but for horizontally polarized incident light.

Typical scattering cross-sections for water suspended cells are about 20% of their geometrical cross-section. (More realistically, this scattering cross-section fluctuates between 3% and 50% of the geometrical cross-section. This resonance fluctuation is responsible for various anomalies in traditional turbidity and nephelometric measurements and seems to be overlooked by most microbiologists.) If a standard cuvette has a mean diameter of about 2·5 cm and if the geometrical cross-section of a typical bacterium is 10^{-8} cm^2, then Eqn. (5) requires that the cell density N must be considerably less than 2×10^8 cells/ml. For smaller cuvettes this limit may be somewhat greater. We have found experimentally that multiple scattering effects are negligible when the cell density is less than 10^7 cells/ml.

Figure 22 represents an enlarged cross-section of an illuminated suspension of cells in a cuvette. The incident laser beam illuminates a narrow

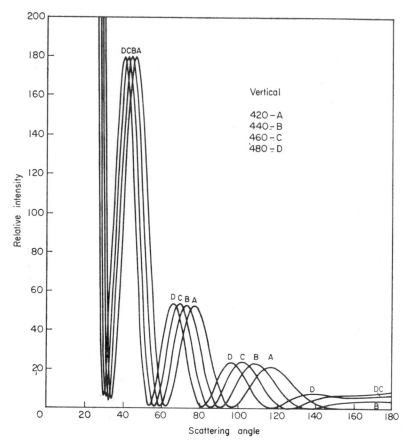

FIG. 17. Same as Fig. 13, but radii from 420 nm to 480 nm.

cylinder of cells as shown. The detector is collimated so as to accept any light scattered into the cone indicated. (This cone is usually about 2° wide.) Thus the only cells whose scattering characteristics are recorded (since no multiple scattering is assumed to occur) are those indicated in the cross-hatched volume V_0. Note, however, that the volume V_0 (and therefore the number of contributing cells) increases as the angle between the detector and the illuminated pencil decreases. To a first approximation

$$V_0 \propto 1/\sin \theta, \qquad (6)$$

where θ again is the scattering angle. The differential light scattering patterns recorded from such suspensions of cells should thus be *multiplied* by $\sin \theta$ to compensate for this effect, so that condition (3) be satisfied.

Although the detector only records the scattering patterns between 0°

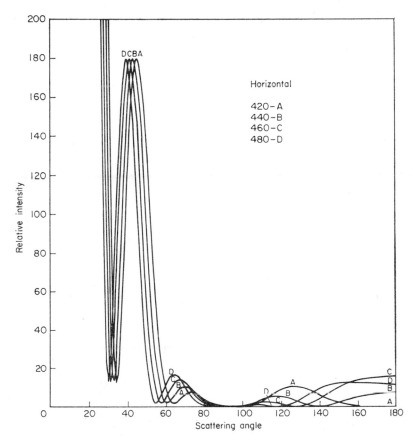

FIG. 18. Same as Fig. 17, but horizontally polarized incident light.

and 180° (the patterns from randomly oriented cells are symmetrical about 180°), the illuminated cells will of course also scatter light between 180° and 360°. If the cuvette is of circular cross-section or of the Witnauer–Scherr type (1952), a fraction of this light will be reflected back on to the scattering cells and reappear in the range 0° to 180°. At the cell exit window some of the incident light is reflected at the interface and re-illuminates the cells from the direction *opposite* the incident beam. These two types of reflections result in a modification of the recorded intensity, $I_R(\theta)$, at an angle θ (Kratohvil and Smart, 1965), viz.

$$I_R(\theta) \propto I(\theta) + 2f\,I\,(180° - \theta), \tag{7}$$

where $I(\theta)$ is the scattered intensity in the absence of extraneous incident beams and f is the fraction of incident light reflected at the air–cuvette

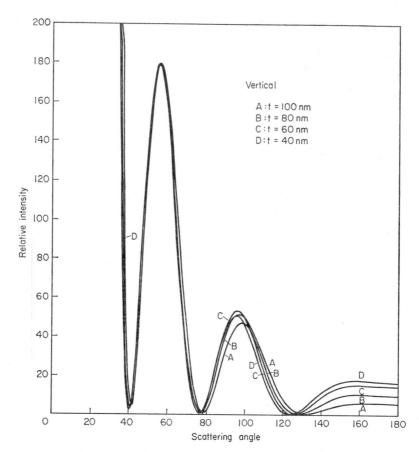

FIG. 19. Effects of cell wall thickness on the differential light scattering patterns for vertically polarized 514·5 nm light. Same model as Fig. 13, radius 350 nm, thickness 100, 80, 60, and 40 nm.

interface. These reflection effects are illustrated in greater detail in Section III. Other second order internal reflections further add to the recorded pattern. Using a cuvette with slightly pitched sides (Berkman and Schoefer, 1971) (a section of a cone), will eliminate many of these internal reflections and the scattering signature will be accordingly enhanced. If a standard test-tube cuvette is used, condition (4) warns us that quantitative inter-pretations, especially at larger scattering angles, may be difficult.

Many liquid media are pigmented and therefore absorb light at various wavelengths. Condition (5) points out that if the media are too strongly absorbing, the scattered light may not even reach the detector. As long as the absorption is not too great, the recorded signal will be proportional

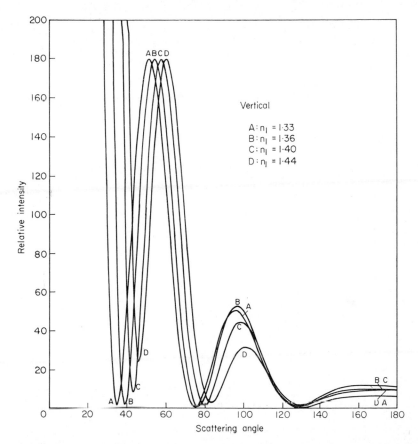

FIG. 20. Effects of cytoplasm refractive index variations on the differential light scattering patterns for vertically polarized 514·5 nm light. Same model as Fig. 13, radius 350 nm, for cytoplasm refractive indices 1·33, 1·36, 1·40, and 1·44. Cell wall 80 nm thick and refractive index 1·42.

to the superimposed scattering patterns of the ensemble of scatterers since the attenuation of the scattered signal is independent of direction. Nevertheless extreme care must be directed to the interpretation of any results involving absorbing media since (a) the intensity of illumination may vary over the spatial volume occupied by the scattering ensemble, and (b) the paths from different parts of the scattering volume V_0 to the surface of the cuvette (and thence into the detector) may be slightly different, thereby permitting absorption to distort the recorded patterns somewhat.

Although the five conditions discussed above are the most important ones to consider in the interpretation of differential light scattering patterns from suspensions of cells, several others are worthy of mention. Some

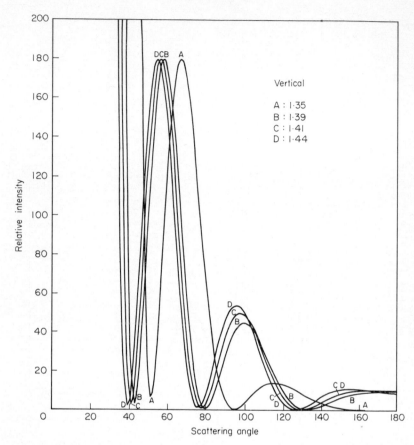

FIG. 21. Effects of cell wall refractive index variations on the differential light scattering patterns for vertically polarized 514·5 nm light. Same model as Fig. 13, radius 350 nm, for cell wall refractive indices 1·35, 1·39, 1·41, and 1·44. Cell wall 80 nm thick, cytoplasm refractive index 1·37.

geometrical aberrations will occur at the surface of the cuvette when scattered light from cells not at the centre of curvature of the cuvette is non-normally incident. Certain plastic cuvettes as well as some of untempered glass often depolarize both the incident and scattered light. This depolarization often varies with the scattering angle itself.

3. *Polydisperse systems*

The recorded differential light scattering patterns from suspensions of cells will not in general contain all the features that might be expected from the superposition of the patterns of the several thousand contributing cells because of variations of size and morphology in the scattering ensemble.

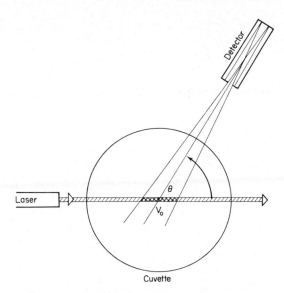

FIG. 22. Laser-illuminated suspension of bacteria (top view) showing the volume, V_0, whose cells' scattered flux is collected by the detector.

Neglecting the effects of non-spherical cells for the time being (we shall return to this facet shortly), any suspension of unsynchronized cells will have at least a 26% size spread. (The volume of a new "daughter" cell is V and division is assumed to occur when the cells reach a volume $2V$. Since the cell diameter D is proportional to the cube root of the volume, this parameter will vary between D and $1·26 D$.) Other factors tend to broaden this distribution even further. Figure 23 presents (Wyatt *et al.*, 1972) the relative scattered light intensities (differential light scattering patterns) for vertically polarized incident light ($\lambda = 632·8$ nm) from suspensions of cells of the same *average* size ($D = 900$ nm), but for different breadths of the size distribution. The cells are again assumed of a structure similar to that of water suspended *S. aureus*, except that the cell wall is not fixed in thickness, but rather is 18% of the cell radius (Wyatt, 1970). The size distribution chosen is quite similar to a Gaussian distribution, but given instead by

$$\rho(D) = \begin{cases} 0, & Z < -1 \\ (1 - Z^2)^4, & -1 \leq Z \leq 1. \\ 0, & Z > 1 \end{cases} \qquad (8)$$

where $Z = 1·082328 \ (D - D_0)/(\Delta D)$. The average cell diameter of the distribution is D_0. The full width of the distribution at half maximum

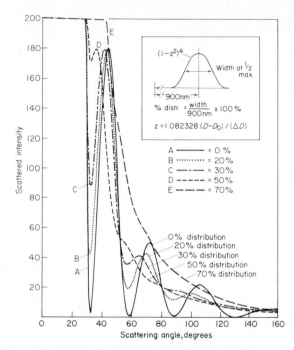

FIG. 23. Effects of size distribution on the differential light scattering patterns for vertically polarized 632·8 nm incident light. Cell wall thickness is 0·18 D. Mean diameter of cells in 900 nm. Refractive indices of cytoplasm and cell wall are 1·37 and 1·42, respectively.

is ΔD. The differential light scattering patterns of Fig. 23 are presented in terms of ΔD expressed as a percent of D_0. Figures 24 and 25 present similar scattering patterns for cells of smaller average size ($D_0 = 600$ nm) at 30% and 50% breadths, respectively.

Figures 26 and 27 present plots (on a relative logarithmic scale) of differential scattered light intensity distributions of bacterial cells about a mean radius of 400 nm. The cells were assumed to be uniformly distributed within the size distribution indicated. The cell wall thickness was again fixed at 80 nm and the refractive indices of cytoplasm and cell wall were chosen as 1·37 and 1·42, respectively. The uniform distributions are unrealistic but of interest as they show clearly the damping of the scattering patterns with increasing distribution breadth. The sharp minima are no longer present in such a plot, although the extrema are still very easy to locate. Again note that the major effect associated with the presence of a distribution of sizes is the smoothing out of the scattering pattern that would be associated with cells of identical sizes.

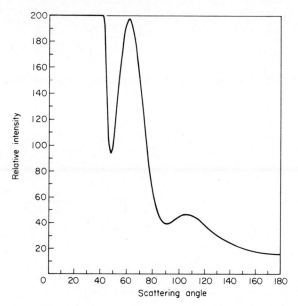

FIG. 24. Same as Fig. 23, but for cells of diameter 600 nm; size distribution 30%.

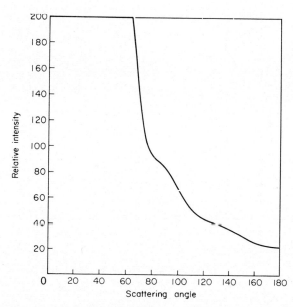

FIG. 25. Same as Fig. 24 but for size distribution of 50%.

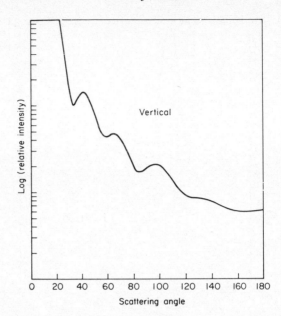

FIG. 26. Logarithmic plot of differential light scattering pattern from a homogeneous size distribution of bacterial cells of average radius 400 nm. Cells assumed uniformly distributed between 350 and 450 nm.

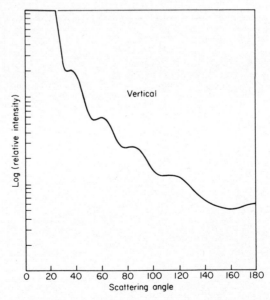

FIG. 27. Same as Fig. 26, but for cells uniformly distributed between 250 and 550 nm.

Another important type of size distribution (for which, unfortunately, no calculations have as yet been completed) is the multimodal type that would be expected to arise because of the presence of agglomerates among typical cellular suspensions. Thus a particular bacterial suspension will always have a certain proportion of single cells, doublets, triplets, etc. Each of these multiplet sub-groups will have a characteristic size distribution, perhaps of the type given by Eqn. (8). If $f_1, f_2, f_3, \ldots$ refer to the fraction of singlets, doublets, triplets, ... present in a particular suspension, where

$$f_1 + f_2 + f_3 + \ldots = 1,$$

then a multimodal distribution based on Eqn. (8) would be of the form

$$f_1 \rho(V_0) + f_2 \rho(2V_0) + f_3 \rho(3V_0) + \ldots \ .$$

Irrespective of the particular form of the individual distributions, the presence of relatively small numbers of cellular agglomerates will often produce a dramatic smoothing of the differential scattering pattern. Thus even if the individual cells have a very narrow size distribution, the presence of a few doubles and larger agglomerates will cause a scattering pattern degradation similar to that produced by broadening the size distribution of a single cell ensemble. Degraded scattering patterns may therefore correspond to an increase in the relative numbers of agglomerated cells, a general broadening of each size distribution present, or a lysis and disintegration of the cells. (See also Note added in proof, p. 257.)

4. Effect of cell density on logarithmic plots

The differential light scattering patterns from suspensions of cells are often most conveniently recorded on a logarithmic scale. This tends to compress the vertical excursions of the recorded patterns while at the same time compensating for modest changes in cell numbers. This latter fact is clearly evident from the following brief discussion.

In order to predict the differential scattered light intensity that would be recorded from an ensemble of scatttering cells we must integrate over the distribution present. If $\rho(D)$, as before, represents the number of cells with diameters between D and $D + dD$ and if there are N_0 cells per unit volume, then

$$N_0 = \int_0^\infty \rho(D)\, dD$$

$$= N_0 \int_0^\infty g(D)\, dD \tag{9}$$

where $\rho(D) = N_0 g(D)$ and $g(D)$ is a normalized distribution function such that

$$\int_0^\infty g(D)\, \mathrm{d}D = 1. \tag{10}$$

Consider now the differential light scattering pattern that the ensemble of N_0 cells/ml would produce. If a cell of diameter D yields the pattern $I(\theta, D)$, the superimposed pattern would be simply

$$I(\theta) = \int_0^\infty \rho(D)I(\theta, D)\, \mathrm{d}D$$

$$= N_0 \int_0^\infty g(D)I(\theta, D)\, \mathrm{d}D. \tag{11}$$

If we now plot $\log [I(\theta)]$ vs θ, we obtain the important result

$$\log [I(\theta)] = \log [N_0 \xi(\theta)]$$

$$= \log N_0 + \log \xi(\theta), \tag{12}$$

where

$$\xi(\theta) = \int_0^\infty g(D)I(\theta, D)\, \mathrm{d}D.$$

Equation (12) shows that if we plot the logarithm of the differential scattering pattern, *the shape of the scattering pattern will be independent of the number of cells/ml*, N_0, since the only effect of number density variation is the vertical *displacement* (proportional to $\log N_0$) of the scattering pattern. This independence of shape upon the number of cells present is not true for linear plots. In addition, even in the logarithmic plotting mode it will remain true, only if multiple scattering is not present at any of the concentrations, N_0, being studied. Implicit also is the assumption that the *distribution* itself does not vary with concentration. Evidence exists which shows that the distribution does indeed change as cells pass from their "lag" phase, through exponential phase, into stationary phase. This change, though, is usually not so great as to invalidate Eqn. (12).

5. *Non-spherical bacteria and agglomerates*

We now direct our attention to a consideration of the scattering characteristics of non-spherically symmetric cells. These include rods, chains, packets, and diplococci, as well as pleomorphic forms. No exact calculations have as yet been performed to predict (let alone interpret) the

differential light scattering patterns of inhomogeneous aspherical structures. Some procedures initiated by Waterman (1965) for perfect conductors and more recently Waterman (1969) and Erma (1969) for dielectrics
have resulted in methods (Barber, 1973) by which one may calculate the
exact differential light scattering patterns of homogeneous prolate spheroids or rods whose ends are capped with hemispheres. Although such
results represent a somewhat crude approximation to any actual cell
structure, especially since the effects of the cell wall are completely missing,
they provide an excellent quantitative starting point. The appropriate
scattering codes are quite time consuming to construct and not generally
available.

Because of the weak scattering qualities of liquid suspended cells, the
Rayleigh–Debye approximation (see Appendix) may be used to predict
their light scattering characteristics, taking their more complex structure
into account, with reasonable accuracy if the cells are not too large. This
means that for many bacterial ensembles suspended in water, we can
predict to at least first order the expected differential light scattering
patterns. The approximation is not without its shortcomings, however,
and principal among them are the extremely deep minima and slight
displacements of angular positions. Furthermore, if the cells are too large
or contain inclusions (such as spores) whose refractive index differs appreciably from that of the suspending medium, the results will be again in
error, though many of the correct qualitative features of the scattering
patterns will remain. Since we are dealing with aspherical inhomogeneous
objects, the scattering will also depend upon the orientation of the cell
with respect to the direction of the incident light.

Early experimental measurements of the differential light scattering
patterns from some suspensions of rod-like bacteria (Wyatt, unpublished;
Wyatt, 1969, 1972b) yielded scattering patterns equally crisp and sharp
as from suspensions of cells known to be spherically symmetric. (Examples
are shown in the next Section.) This result is surprising since one would
think that the tumbling motion of the rods would tend to wash out the
associated scattering patterns considerably. An explanation of the similarity between the scattering characteristics of prolate spheroidal cells and
spherical cells is readily seen by examining the Rayleigh–Debye approximation for both (Wyatt, 1968). The mathematical form of the scattering
patterns is identical except that for the spheroidal case the angular dependence is a further function of the orientation of the cell. If we simply
replace the orientation functional dependences by their *average* values,
then the predicted differential light scattering patterns are identical in all
respects to spherical cells if the equivalent "radius" of the ellipsoid is
replaced by its root mean square semi-axis. Thus a suspension of ellipsoids

of semi-major and minor axes a and b, respectively, will scatter light in virtually the same manner as a suspension of spherically symmetric cells of radius ξ, where

$$\xi = \sqrt{(a^2 + b^2)/2}. \tag{13}$$

Equation (13) is a considerable over-simplification that, nevertheless, seems to correlate quite well with the recorded data. In any event, it forms a qualitative basis for estimating the relative average "size" of liquid-suspended short rods.

Since suspensions of larger cells produce light scattering characteristics suggestive in most regards of larger spherically symmetric cells, the effective equivalent radius deduced from such measurements should be interpreted as representing an approximation to a mean size such as implied by Eqn. (13). Until more detailed analyses of aspherical cells are accomplished, there is very little we can use to interpret the light scattering patterns except by means of such an admittedly crude equivalent sphere description.

Cross and Latimer (1972) have recently performed measurements of the differential light scattering patterns from suspensions of *Escherichia coli*. They interpreted these results with the Rayleigh–Debye approximation assuming that the cells were prolate spheroids of uniform density and diameter, but of varying lengths. (Size distributions were obtained from Coulter counter measurements.) They also tried to fit the data with the addition of a cell wall whose thickness was proportional to the length of the radius vector from the centre of the spheroid. The random orientations of the cells and their size distribution were taken into account using an unpublished scheme of B. Tully. Despite the inaccuracies of the Rayleigh–Debye approximation, the somewhat unrealistic shape chosen to characterize the cells (the cells are really short rods, not spheroids), and the unrealistic cell wall structure and thickness, their results were in fair agreement with the experimental data. (At larger scattering angles the data differed from the theoretical results by a factor of 2–5.) Equally good fits (or perhaps slightly better) could have been achieved using a spherically symmetric model whose average radius could have been associated with a root mean square average for the ellipsoids chosen.

From the Rayleigh–Debye approximation (see Appendix), which produces qualitative agreement with many experimental measurements of bacterial cells, we find that the total amount of light scattered by a cell is directly proportional to the *square* of the cellular volume. Thus we would expect double cells to scatter twice the *total* light that the two individual cells alone would scatter. A triplet scatters nine times the light of a single cell, or *three* times the total light scattered by the three individual cells. In addition to the increased amount of light scattered by cellular agglomerates, they also produce more complex scattering patterns, as is evident from examining the effects of increasing size in Figs. 13–18. Thus the presence of a relatively small number of cellular agglomerates in a bacterial suspension could easily wash out the scattering pattern characteristic of the average cellular unit. Pleomorphism tends to create similar effects.

Most bacterial suspensions produce differential light scattering patterns which show some features. Means for preparing such suspensions are adequately described in Section III. Certain suspensions will produce curves virtually devoid of either extrema or even inflection points. Such featureless curves will arise (1) if the suspension contains a very broad size distribution caused either by agglomerates, age, significant physiological damage to the cells, or broad pleomorphism; (2) if the average cell size is very large, since large structures differing only slightly in size will produce differential light scattering patterns that are significantly dissimilar and thereby tend to cancel one another; (3) if highly refractile inclusions such as spores are present in appreciable numbers (a single spore will scatter three to ten times the total amount of light as a vegetative cell of equivalent size), (4) if multiple scattering is present.

6. *Complex structures and agglomerates in air*

The differential light scattering patterns from individual airborne cells and spores can be interpreted exactly only for spherically symmetric structures. For more complex inhomogeneous structures virtually no approximations such as the Rayleigh–Debye theory exist to permit even qualitative interpretations. Pijper (1919), as mentioned earlier, proposed that the patterns from rod-like bacteria be interpreted via diffraction theory treating the cells as two dimensional slits, but such a treatment ignores all internal features and yields quantitatively erroneous results as well. Homogeneous structures such as spheroids and sphere capped cylinders have already been discussed in the last Section. Erma (1969) and Barber (unpublished, 1972) have developed codes to treat these homogeneous structures. Most rod-like organisms may be closely approximated by forms such as these and, as more theoretical results become available in the next few years, the quantitative interpretation of many recent measurements will eventually be achieved. The effects of inhomogeneity, however, can only be estimated by reference to the equivalent spherical cases.

Individual cells and spores suspended in air for light scattering measurements by means of quasi-static electric fields (Wyatt and Phillips, 1972) will tend to align in the field direction thereby producing light scattering patterns characteristic of that orientation to the field. The apparent noise of the recorded patterns arises because of the tumbling of the individual cell or agglomerate. If the cell is of regular structure (both internally and externally) the noise component will be small. On the other hand, the light scattering patterns from irregular particles invariably exhibit noise components, though the correlation between the noise fraction and degree of irregularity has not yet been examined in detail.

Diplococci, packets, and other irregular structures (e.g. cells containing terminal spores) are the most difficult to approximate for analytical purposes. If their scattering patterns can be measured, then it has been found that the basic features of such patterns can be reproduced using an equivalent *spherical* model. The similarity of the scattering patterns from such spherically symmetric structures to the experimental data from irregularly shaped cells is remarkable. Indeed, even the scattering patterns of rods seem to be readily reproduced by a spherical model. An analysis of the relationship between the best-fit spherical structure and the data measured from aspherical cells has not as yet been completed. Hopefully, this will be done soon, though relatively few laboratories are currently making such light scattering measurements on individual cells.

III. EXPERIMENTAL PROCEDURES, DATA, AND INTERPRETATIONS

The experimental data presented in this Section were produced primarily at the Science Spectrum, Inc. laboratories using commercially available laser light scattering photometers (Phillips, 1971; Wyatt and Phillips, 1972a). Although a great amount of other information concerning light scattering measurements on bacterial systems may be found in the literature, the vast majority of that material relates to conventional turbidimetric (cf. Bateman, 1968) and nephelometric measurements and is not, therefore, of particular interest for this Chapter. The major purpose of this Section, of course, is to familiarize the reader with the preparation techniques and measurements currently found to be the most representative.

A. Bacterial suspensions

1. *Instruments*

Having become familiar with the general types of results expected on theoretical grounds as outlined in Section II, we now turn our attention to the specific measurements and their interpretations. We begin first with the simplest types of measurements, namely those involving suspensions of bacterial cells. For this purpose, a laser light scattering photometer of the *Differential I* type (Phillips, 1971) is most easily used. Other photo-

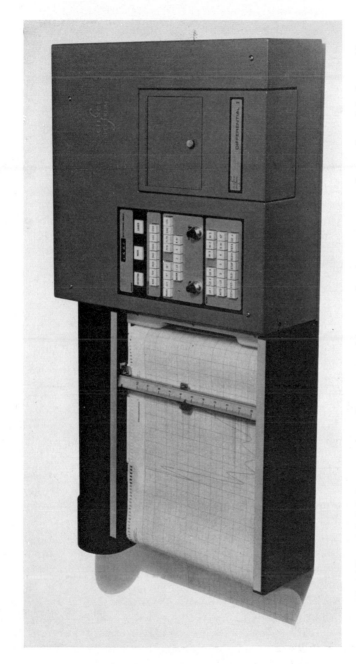

FIG. 28. *Differential I* light scattering photometer with argon-ion laser, x–y recorder, and module for making measurements on bacterial suspensions.

meters, such as the Brice–Phoenix (Brice *et al.*, 1950), may be modified for making these measurements by including some type of automatic scanning circuit and a means for graphical display.

Figure 28 shows a *Differential I* equipped with an x–y recorder and a low power (1 mW) tunable argon-ion laser. (The rear end of the laser is clearly visible as a black cylinder behind the recorder.) Included in the rear housing of the laser is a prism adjustment which permits the laser to be tuned to any of the characteristic lines of A^+. The relative intensities of the lines available are quite varied; the strongest are 514·5 nm (1·0 mW), 496·5 nm (0·34 mW), 488·0 nm (0·6 mW), 476·5 nm (0·36 mW), and 457·9 nm (0·08 mW). The laser beam (diameter approximately 1 mm) is reflected internally and passes diagonally through the scattering module shown to the right of the control panel. Cuvettes are introduced through the hinged door at the top of the module and rest securely in a holder which aligns the cuvette at the centre of the laser beam. The various functions of the control panel are indicated in Fig. 29. Included among them are buttons for $\sin \theta$ correction, log amplifier, variable scan speeds and ranges, photomultiplier detector voltage adjust (gain), electrical filters and recorder controls. A "stationary position" control permits the instrument to be used as a turbidimeter and nephelometer. Within the restricted range of wavelengths available, the instrument can also function as a spectrophotometer if the spectral response of the photomultiplier detector is known. Various digital interfacing options permit direct computer processing from punched cards or tapes.

2. *Cuvettes*

Optical grade cuvettes (diameter approximately 25 mm) of cylindrical form, perhaps of the Witnauer–Scherr (1952) type which have a flat entrance and exit surface normal to the illuminating beam, are readily available from most spectrometer manufacturers, though they are relatively expensive. In addition, any type of a test-tube may be used that can fit into the instrument, though such containers often require small modifications for holding purposes. In addition, of course, their optical quality is rather poor and the scattering curves may exhibit effects associated with optical distortion as the test-tube is rotated. The effects of optical distortions on the recorded patterns decrease as the test-tube diameter increases.

From much of our work we have found a cuvette of the Berkman–Schoefer type (1972) to be most suitable. This consists of a conical section and is most often available in the form of disposable plastic cups manufactured by several vendors. These cups are of clear polystyrene, have a wedge angle of about 7°, hold 25 ml of solution, and have a base diameter of 25 mm. They are also available with caps and are easily destroyed by

MAIN CONTROL PANEL

SCATTERING ANGLE
Indicates the angular position of the detector (0° = looking into the laser beam)

POWER (three push-on, push-off switches, illuminated when ON)

MAIN	Controls power to the whole unit.
DETECTOR	Controls high voltage to the detector photomultiplier (and levitator photomultipliers in the Differential II module).
LASER	Turns laser on and off.

DETECTOR

Selects the voltage applied to the photomultipliers (500V if no pushbutton is depressed). The higher the voltage, the more sensitive the photomultipliers are for weakly scattering particles.

RECORDER

MARK	Makes a mark on the recorder chart when pressed.
OFF	Turns recorder off.
9", 18"	Turns recorder on and spreads chart pattern over 9 inches or 18 inches per 180 degrees (20 degrees per inch or 10 degrees per inch).*
PEN	Lowers pen onto chart paper.
FLTR	Passes the detector output through the active filter; time constant is 0.1 second if FLTR switch is not depressed.
SINE	Multiplies the detector output by the sine of the scattering angle. Normally used with Differential I module; do not use with Differential II module.
LOG	Passes the detector output through a logarithmic amplifier so that signal amplitude is shown on a five-decade logarithmic scale instead of a linear one.
NORM	Automatically selects time constant equal to the time needed to cover 0.05 degrees of scan.
1LO,2,3,4HI	Select fixed time constants of 0.10, 0.12, 0.25, and 0.4 seconds respectively.
ZERO	Ten-turn potentiometer with lock. Suppresses detector dark current to set recorder pen on zero. Normally set near 5.0.
SIGNAL LEVEL	Ten-turn potentiometer with lock. Varies signal level to expand or contract vertical extent of pattern on recorder. Should be set at not less than 1.0 (1 volt full scale) to use the full height of the chart; may be set at any higher level without damage to the recorder.

SCAN

LO1,....,HI3	The LO pushbuttons select the lower limit, and the HI pushbuttons the upper limit, of the scan angle. A LO switch must be selected to scan in the - direction and a HI switch to scan in the + direction. The LO and HI limits may be set at any desired angles between about 8° and 172°.
AUTO	Reverses the scan when the selected limit is reached. If not depressed, scan stops at the limit. Both a HI and a LO limit must be selected for AUTO to work.
1LO,....,5HI	Scan speed selectors: 11.3, 22.5, 45, 90, and 180 degrees per minute (360 degrees per minute if no speed selected).
SP	When this Stationary Position switch is depressed, the recorder will move but the detector will not, for studies of the time variation of scattering at a fixed angle.**
GO-,GO+	Start the scan in the direction indicated, at the selected speed.
FST,SLO	Override the selected scan speed to move the detector in the direction indicated: FST, for quick reset, or SLO, for precise setting. Maximum override speed (720 degrees per minute) is obtained when no scan speed is selected.
STOP	Stops scan (unless AUTO pushbutton is depressed).

*When none of OFF, 9", 18" is depressed, pen will move (Y motion) but there is no X motion.

**Recorder speed and detector time constant are still controlled by the RECORDER and SCAN controls. When the 18" button is depressed, recorder speed is 1-1/8, 2-1/4, 4-1/2, 9 or 18 inches per minute for 1LO, 2, 3, 4, or 5HI scan speed; half those speeds if 9" button is depressed.

FIG. 29. Control functions of an automatic light scattering photometer (*Differential I*) providing versatility for measurements on bacterial suspensions.

autoclaving. Their conical shape virtually eliminates all internal reflection difficulties, though some other distortions are evident. Clear polystyrene pill boxes or pill containers available from most supply houses (base diameter approximately 25 mm) are also adequate for most purposes, though the internal reflections can be bothersome and will tend to mask some of the larger angle scattering characteristics. In addition, most polystyrene vessels (because of strains introduced during manufacture) depolarize the incident and scattered light somewhat. For the most part, these effects are not of particular importance though they should be considered if precise quantitative interpretations are to be made. By rotating the cuvette containing a bacterial suspension and recording the scattering pattern for different orientations of the cell, one can immediately obtain a realistic estimate of the severity of depolarization, if indeed it is to be a problem.

3. *Concentration*

We have already noted in Section II that the required range of bacterial concentration is between 10^5 and 10^7 cells/ml—with a density of approximately 10^6 cells/ml as optimum. (The cuvette diameter is assumed to be approximately 25 mm.) If the exact number density is not important for a particular measurement, then the appropriate concentration is readily obtained by adjusting the suspension until it is just barely turbid to the eye. By *just barely turbid* we mean that another dilution by a factor of five would render the solution indistinguishable (to the naked eye) from a clear solution.

4. *Suspending media*

Bacteria can be examined directly in broth provided that the broth does not appreciably absorb the incident or scattered light (see Section II. C, 2(ii)). If broths are too pigmented, then it is recommended that they be diluted with water or isotonic solution so that unattenuated differential light scattering patterns may be recorded. After dilution, if the cellular concentration falls below about 5×10^5/ml, it may have to be increased slightly to obtain a good scattering pattern. An ideal preparation procedure consists of adding a few tenths of an ml of a turbid broth culture to 15 to 20 ml of pure distilled water. If the distilled water contains particulate contaminants, it should first be filtered through 0·2 μm Nuclepore filters. These filters (manufacturered by General Electric Co. and distributed by most laboratory supply houses) are recommended for light scattering studies since they are considerably stronger than conventional cellulose filters, have well-defined cylindrical holes in a tough substrate, and do not discharge filter debris into solutions passing through them.

5. *Cells from plates*

Bacterial cells growing on plates are readily examined by resuspending them in distilled water and diluting until the appropriate turbidity has been achieved. A small loop of cells is adequate for most purposes and provides enough cells for a suspension of about 50 ml. It is extremely important that cells removed from plates and resuspended be well agitated so as to break up any agglomerates that may be present. Debris from the agar media should not be introduced into the cuvette. If large quantities of debris and agglomerates are present, the recorded scattering patterns will in general exhibit noise. For certain species, cellular agglomerates are unavoidable and cannot be broken up by agitation. Recourse to selective filtration may be necessary. For example, in the case of mycobacteria, it is often necessary to prefilter even broth suspensions through a 5 μm filter prior to scanning. Reich (1973) is currently developing new broth media and techniques for measuring differential light scattering patterns from the mycobacteria. Bacterial laden urine, cerebrospinal fluid, and serums often require prefiltering to remove the large non-bacterial contaminants.

A suspension is ideal, of course, if it produces the characteristic differential light scattering patterns discussed in detail in the previous Section. Depending upon conditions of growth, it often occurs that differential light scattering patterns do not approach the ideal. This is also often due to the particular strains and/or growth conditions used. Wolfe and Amsterdam (1972), for example, recently found that different strains of *Staphylococcus epidermidis* (distinguished by certain agglutination properties) produced distinctively different curves, some of which are virtually featureless. The relative absence of features in such scattering patterns is usually an indication of the presence of multicellular agglomerates. Occasionally certain strains or species cannot be removed from plates and resuspended in distilled water. Accordingly, different types of media may have to be used or the bacteria grown directly in liquid media.

6. *Interactions with biochemicals*

For many types of measurements, a suspension of young cells will produce the most suitable differential light scattering patterns. Broths are heavily inoculated and then incubated for approximately 60 min (in the case of rapidly growing cells) or a few hours for the more fastidious organisms. (The mycobacteria may require several days growth in broth before suitable for examination by light scattering techniques.)

Although isotonic solutions may be used, most of our own work has made use of pure distilled or demineralized water with a neutral pH. For most species such distilled water suspensions produce good scattering characteristics for many hours. Nevertheless, even the more fragile species

10

including anaerobes are easily examined in distilled water since the measurement requires only a few seconds; a period quite short compared to typical survival times. Anaerobic organisms are readily examined by removing directly from anaerobic conditions and resuspending in distilled water for immediate measurement.

The effects of antibiotics and biochemicals upon cells may be seen in various ways. Sometimes their differential light scattering patterns are observed periodically while they grow in a broth medium in the presence of the biochemical of interest. Alternatively, young broth cultures may be immediately transferred to distilled water solutions containing the biochemical. In the latter case, the bacterial suspension is kept at incubation temperatures for a period of approximately 60 min before measurement. The effects of the biochemical on the cells is evident via the changes in the differential light scattering pattern. (See Section III.C, "Data representations".) Whenever such changes are being measured, a control specimen (suspension without the biochemical) is prepared at the same time from an aliquot of the initial culture.

In summary, therefore, the preparation procedures required for the examination of bacterial suspensions are relatively simple. The investigator may often wish to introduce his own special techniques and by and large there are very few that will not produce adequate differential light scattering patterns.

7. Plotting modes, angular range, signal processing, cuvette effects

As indicated earlier in Section II the differential light scattering patterns are usually recorded with an x–y recorder in one of two modes. Either the relative scattered intensity or its logarithm may be plotted as a function of angle. This latter mode presents the scattering curves in a more compressed form (approximately one order of magnitude for each three inches of scale is usual) and generally eliminates the effects of concentration (provided, however, that the initial inoculum is less than 10^7 cells/ml). Some instruments are equipped with a sin θ correction setting that multiplies the recorded pattern by this foreshortening factor (see Section II. C, 2(ii)).

The most important features of the differential scattering patterns of bacteria are usually found in the 20° to 160° scanning range. Instruments capable of scanning within this range are most suitable. Various scanning speeds may be used with equal success, though a total scan time of approximately 10 sec is adequate for most purposes. If the suspensions are particularly noisy, some types of electrical filtering may result in better quality scattering curves.

A variety of light sources are available, though for the most part vertically polarized laser sources are preferable. These highly collimated and monochromatic sources simplify considerably much of the interpretation associated with the recorded curves. If a vertically polarized light source is not available, an unpolarized one will provide essentially equivalent curves since the horizontally polarized component affects the recorded signal negligibly.

For the types of 25 mm cuvettes mentioned earlier, the light beam should have a diameter no greater than 2 mm. In general, this can be obtained from non-laser sources by suitable masking and collimation. For laser sources a beam diameter of less than 1 mm is not unusual and permits the use of cuvettes that do not have flat entrance and exit faces without fear of distortion of the incident beam. (In other words, the diameter of the incident light beam should be very small compared to the radius of curvature of the cuvette being used. If this condition cannot be met then the cuvette should have flat faces for both entrance and exit apertures.) If cylindrical cuvettes rather than the conical type are used, improved scattering results will be obtained if black absorbing paint is applied to the back side of the cuvette, i.e. the side farthest from the detector scan. The effects of internal reflections upon the light scattering patterns are readily noted if the cuvette is painted. Most of the internal reflections contribute signals at the larger scattering angles, i.e. greater than about 110° for cuvettes of conventional design.

Figure 30 shows the effects of internal reflection in a standard Witnauer–Scherr (1952) cylindrical glass cuvette. The flat entrance and exit apertures of the cell are clearly indicated. The back surface is frosted to reduce internal reflections. Such reflections arise from two sources as indicated in B and C of this figure. Since part of the incident light is reflected at the exit window, this reflected beam then acts as a source from the right and produces a scattering pattern that is the complement of the primary pattern recorded per Fig. 30A. In Fig. 30C we see the effects of the cell back surface that refocuses scattered light, thereby producing another contribution that is complementary to the primary recorded pattern.

Figure 31 shows a differential light scattering pattern from a suspension of 1·2 μm-diam. polystyrene latex spheres. The effect of painting the back of the cell in reducing the scattering pattern in the backward direction is clearly indicated. Note however that within the range from 40° to approximately 120° the curve is quite similar to that of the unpainted cell. Figure 32 shows the effect of scattering cell misalignment; namely, when the front entrance window of the cell is not aligned perpendicular to the incident beam the scattering pattern will be displaced in angle. This misalignment problem is never found when cells of conical or cylindrical cross-section are used provided that the incident beam is not of too great a cross-section.

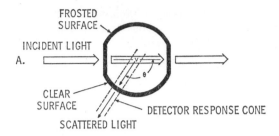

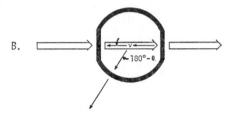

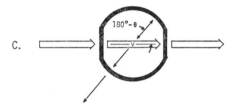

FIG. 30. Contributions of internally reflected rays to the scattered intensity recorded at θ for Witnauer–Scherr cell.

8. *Speciation*

One of the earliest motivations for obtaining differential light scattering patterns from bacterial cells (Wyatt, 1968, 1969) was the hope that the patterns for different species would be significantly distinct to provide a means for identification. Figure 33 shows an example of one of these earlier measurements upon suspensions of *Streptococcus lactis* and *Serratia marcescens*. Nutrient agar plates were inoculated with these cultures and incubated at 37°C for approximately 36 h. An inoculum was then removed from a region of confluent growth, suspended in distilled water, and examined in the modified Brice–Phoenix (Brice *et al.*, 1950) light scattering photometer. Part of the light scattering patterns are shown. The noisy appearance of the curves is a consequence of the cellular and agar plate

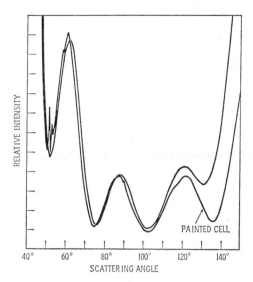

FIG. 31. Effect of painting Witnauer–Scherr scattering cell upon the differential light scattering pattern from 600 nm-radius polystyrene latex spheres. $\lambda = 632{\cdot}8$ nm, vertical polarization.

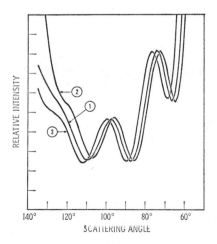

FIG. 32. Effects of scattering cell (with flat entrance and exit faces) misalignment. Curves labelled 1, 2 and 3 correspond respectively to properly aligned, rotated 8 degrees clockwise, and rotated 8 degrees counter-clockwise. Latex suspension, $\lambda = 632{\cdot}8$ nm, vertical polarization.

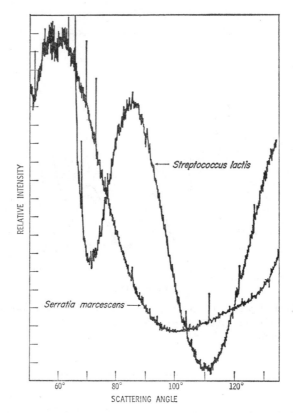

FIG. 33. Differential light scattering patterns for vertically polarized 632·8 nm light from *Streptococcus lactis* and *Serratia marcescens*. The distilled water suspensions were prepared from 36-h nutrient agar colonies.

debris present in the suspension. Relative to the broad differential scattering peaks, the noise contributions are usually negligible. Note that the scanning range for these earliest runs was quite restricted and the first peaks ($\theta \sim 30°$) are not even shown. The illumination source was a vertically polarized He-Ne laser producing a 1 mW beam at 632·8 nm.

Figure 34 presents the differential light scattering pattern for vertically polarized light from a mercury arc lamp for the species *Proteus morganii*. Two recordings were made from this suspension—one at 546 nm and the other at 436 nm (two of the stronger lines of mercury). The cells were removed from 12-h heart infusion agar plates incubated at 37°C. These scattering curves were obtained at three different amplifier gains. In this manner the larger angle scattering data may be emphasized, since the intensity of light decreases rapidly with increasing scattering angles. The

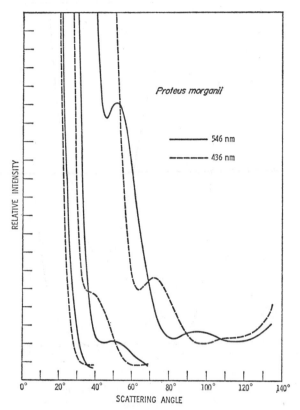

FIG. 34. Differential light scattering patterns for vertically polarized 546 nm and 436 nm Hg arc light from *Proteus morganii*. The distilled water suspensions were prepared from 12-h heart infusion agar colonies incubated at 37°C.

relative change in gain is readily determined by comparing each curve with the curve below it produced at a lower gain setting. All curves were traced from the recorded data and do not, therefore, exhibit the superimposed noise shown earlier. Note also that the curve produced at the shorter wavelength has been displaced to the left, i.e. towards smaller scattering angles. Since the scattering characteristics of bacterial cells (and indeed most small particles) are primarily a function of the ratio of the size of the cell to the wavelength of the incident light, we see that the effect of decreasing the wavelength is equivalent to increasing the size of the cell, since in either case the ratio of size to wavelength would have increased. A manifestation of an increasing size is a corresponding shift of the scattering pattern towards the smaller scattering angles as discussed in Section II.

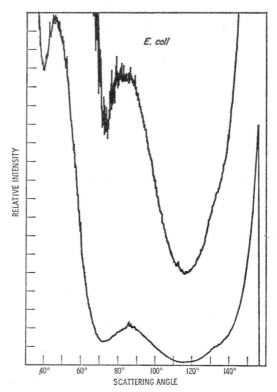

Fig. 35. Differential light scattering pattern for vertically polarized 632·8 nm light from *Escherichia coli*. The colonies were incubated for 6 h at 37°C and at room temperature for an additional 18 h. These heart infusion agar-grown colonies were then suspended in doubly distilled water.

Figure 35 presents the differential scattered light intensity for vertically polarized helium-neon laser light incident upon a suspension of *E. coli* cells. These cells were grown on heart infusion agar incubated at 37°C for 6 h and then allowed to grow at room temperature for 18 h. The higher curve again represents an amplification of the lower one achieved by increasing the photomultiplier gain. Unless otherwise stated none of the figures in this Chapter have been corrected for geometrical foreshortening, i.e. the sin θ correction discussed earlier.

Figures 36 and 37 present the light scattering patterns (with signal amplification as previously described) for the same strain of *Klebsiella* grown under two different conditions. In both cases the cells were removed from agar plates that were heavily inoculated initially and then incubated at 37°C for several hours. Note in particular the difference in the scattering pattern produced by *Klebsiella* grown for 24 h on heart infusion agar

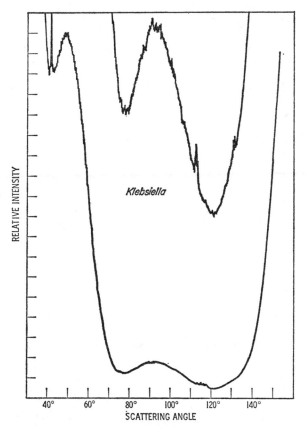

FIG. 36. Differential light scattering pattern from cells of *Klebsiella* prepared per Fig. 35.

(Fig. 36) (and then resuspended in water) with that produced from cells grown in HIA broth for 3 h (Fig. 37). Cells from the young broth culture produced a scattering pattern showing three distinct peaks at approximately 40°, 70° and 110°. The older agar-grown cells produced only two peaks at about 50° and 90°. From these curves we can immediately deduce that the younger broth-grown cells were of larger average size. Since the average size of the cell suspension is inversely proportional to $\sin \theta/2$ where θ is the angle of the first maximum, the relative change in size of the two suspensions is readily calculated (see Section II.C, 2(i)).

The approximate root-mean-square average size of the two *Klebsiella* suspensions that produced Figs. 36 and 37 may be deduced from Figs. 15 and 17 by comparing the angular positions of the maxima of the scattering patterns. Note, however, that the theoretical curves (Figs. 13 through 17)

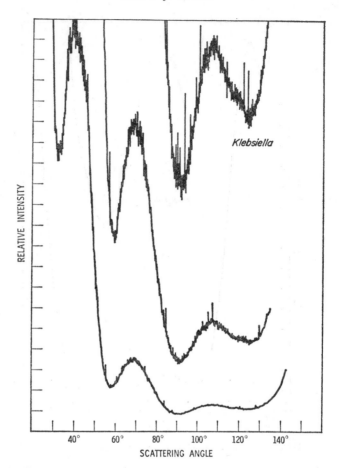

FIG. 37. Differential light scattering patterns from cells of *Klebsiella* from heavily inoculated 3-h heart infusion broth culture incubated at 37°C, centrifuged and then resuspended in distilled water. $\lambda = 632\cdot8$ nm.

for monodisperse suspensions of bacteria in water are presented in terms of an illuminating light source at a wavelength of 514·5 nm. Figures 31 through 37, on the other hand, were produced using a He-Ne laser operating at 632·8 nm. Neglecting slight variations of cell refractive index with wavelength, a particular scattering curve corresponds to a particular $kR = \text{const.}$, i.e. $R \propto 1/k = \lambda_0/(2\pi n_0)$. Thus the "radii" of the cells producing these latter experimental curves may be interpreted in terms of the theoretical curves by multiplying the deduced theoretical values by the factor $632\cdot8/514\cdot5\cdot5 =$ 1·23. This type of calculation is discussed in greater detail in Section II. C, 2(i). (Measurements made with the argon-ion laser wavelength of 514·5 nm, however, may be interpreted directly.) We should also point out that the

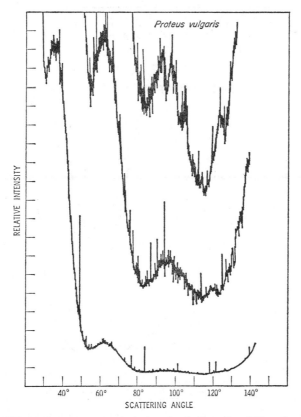

FIG. 38. Differential light scattering pattern from cells of *P. vulgaris* incubated 4 h at 37°C in heart infusion broth. $\lambda = 632 \cdot 8$ nm.

Wittnauer–Scherr cuvettes used in most of the He–Ne measurements produced a large background signal due to distortions at the larger scattering angles thereby masking out the third peak that would have been present from the cells producing Fig. 36. (Note also that the 632·8 nm curves were not usually corrected for the $\sin \theta$ foreshortening effect discussed earlier.) Applying the peak positions of Fig. 15 to the data of Fig. 36 shows an effective rms radius between 360 nm and 380 nm which must be multiplied by the wavelength change factor 1·23 to yield a value between 443 nm and 468 nm. The cells producing Fig. 37 may similarly be compared with the curves of Fig. 17 to yield an approximate rms average radius between 566 nm and 590 nm. Only the first two peaks were used to deduce the above values which are only approximate. In addition, the theoretical curves correspond to spherical Gram-positive cocci which are

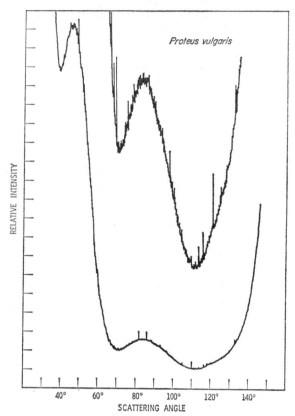

FIG. 39. Same culture as in Fig. 38, but for $7\frac{1}{2}$ h incubation.

expected to have cell wall structures distinctively different from the Gram-
negative rods of the current example. See Section II.C, 2(i) for other effects.

Although it was found in practice that some speciation of agar-plate-
grown cells could be achieved by examining their light scattering characteristics, it was soon realized that the scattering patterns depended critically
upon the particular growth media and incubation conditions. Later methods
relied more heavily upon broth suspensions (cf. Fig. 37) and greater
uniformity within a species was obtained. Nevertheless, the identification
of cells from their differential light scattering patterns produced from
suspensions was at best a marginal approach and required as much
attention to growth conditions as some of the more common biochemical
procedures. Figs. 38 and 39, for example, show differences in cultures of
Proteus vulgaris that were grown in broth for 4 and $7\frac{1}{2}$ h respectively.
(Again note how the older cultures invariably yield curves characteristic
of *smaller* cells.)

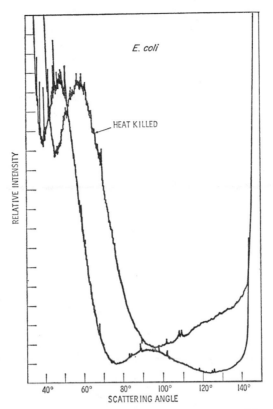

FIG. 40. Differential light scattering patterns from live and heat-killed cells of *E. coli*. Cells were grown on heart infusion agar at 37°C for 6 h before heat treatment. $\lambda = 632 \cdot 8$ nm.

9. *Heat*

As already mentioned and discussed in some detail in the last Section, the effects of changing size on the light scattering patterns is to shift the pattern either towards smaller angles if the cells are increasing in size or towards larger angles if the cells on the average are decreasing in size. Figure 40 presents an interesting example of the effects of heat on a suspension of *E. coli* cells. These cells were grown for 6 h on heart infusion agar at 37°C and then suspended in distilled water. The suspension was divided into two parts, one of which was heated to 85°C for 5 min. The displacement of the heat-killed cells' first peak (from approximately 50° to 60°) relative to that of the live cells shows quite clearly that the heat treated cells decreased in size. Further analyses of the effects of heat on cellular suspensions by Berkman and Wyatt (1970) showed that the effect of heat

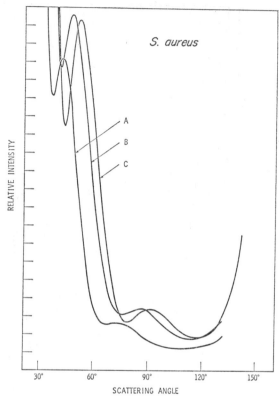

Fig. 41. Differential light scattering patterns from same strain of *Staph. aureus* grown under three different growth conditions. $\lambda = 632 \cdot 8$ nm.

is primarily to shrink the cells yet leave the cell wall thickness for the most part unaffected.

10. *Growth conditions*

The differential light scattering patterns of growing bacteria are affected both as regards the relative intensity of the peaks as well as the angular position of the extrema. Figure 41 shows three different light scattering curves (vertically polarized incident He–Ne laser radiation of $632 \cdot 8$ nm) obtained for *Staphylococcus aureus* cultures treated as follows: for Curve A the cells were grown on brain heart infusion agar overnight at 37°C followed by incubation in BHI broth for 20 min at 37°C; for Curve B, they were grown at 37°C in Mueller–Hinton broth diluted 25% its normal concentration in distilled water (25% MH broth), followed by incubation for 1 h at 37°C in 5% nutrient broth; for Curve C, the cells were grown on BHI agar overnight followed by incubation for 8 h in 2% BHI broth.

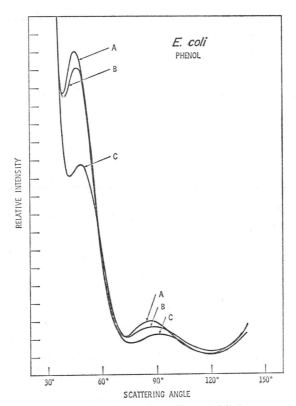

FIG. 42. Effects of 0·25% phenol on the differential light scattering patterns of 20-h cultures of *E. coli* grown on nutrient agar. (A) untreated, (B) treated cells after 3 min, (C) treated cells after 21 h. $\lambda = 632.8$ nm.

The three curves shown in Fig. 41 were displaced right or left depending upon these growth conditions. Curve A is characterized by a shift to smaller angles suggesting that mean cell size is larger than those producing the other curves shown. This result confirms the expected relation between cell growth and size. Furthermore, cells grown under starvation conditions (Curve C) tended to be smaller since the peaks are shifted towards larger angles. The sharper peaks of Curve C relative to Curve A suggest a rather narrow size distribution of the former. Such conclusions are confirmed in the literature and also by theoretical analyses. One obvious implication of these results is that differential light scattering curves can be enhanced by growing the test organisms under controlled conditions. Such refinements often improve resolution and facilitate species differentiation.

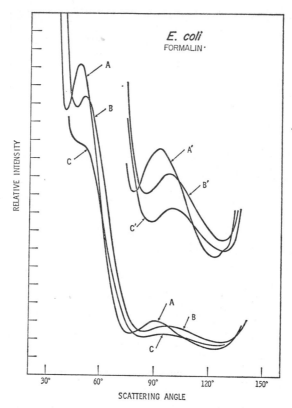

Fig. 43. Effects of 2% formalin on the differential light scattering patterns of 20-h cultures of *E. coli* grown on nutrient agar. (A) untreated, (B) treated cells after 10 min, (C) treated cells after 12 h. $\lambda = 632{\cdot}8$ nm.

11. *Phenol and formaldehyde*

The effects of phenol and formaldehyde on differential light scattering patterns (vertical polarization, 632·8 nm) were studied on a culture of *E. coli*. Figure 42 reveals the effects of phenol (0·25%) on *E. coli* cultures grown on nutrient agar for 20 h at 37°C. Curve *A* of this figure represents the untreated control, Curve *B* shows the effect of phenol after only 3 min, and Curve *C* after 21 h at room temperature. (Not shown is a 40-min curve which appeared to be similar to Curve *B*.) The effects of phenol were minimal, consisting mainly of a moderate shift of the scattering patterns to higher scattering angles, indicative that some cell shrinkage had occurred.

The effect of formaldehyde, a so-called gentle fixative, on cultures of *E. coli* is shown in Fig. 43. The light scattering characteristics of untreated cells is indicated by Curve A, while Curve B and C show the light scattering characteristics of cultures after 10 min and 12 h in 2% formalin, respectively. Curves A', B' and C' are amplifications of the secondary peaks of the initial curves to show the extrema more clearly. In some respects the effect of formalin is similar to that of phenol, since the scattering peaks were shifted to higher angles as the length of treatment increased. A 12-h treatment, however, resulted in a markedly distorted primary peak (Curve C), in contrast to the more uniform effects of phenol. Again, the data agree well with the known fact that formalin fixation is gentle if restricted to relatively short periods. The marked degradation of the differential scattering patterns for the longer treated cells is characteristic of a broadening of their size distribution and probably a modification of their cell walls.

12. *Antibiotic susceptibilities*

One of the most interesting recent developments with differential light scattering has been the realization that these techniques provide a means for rapidly determining the antibiotic susceptibility of challenged specimens. Two to 3 ml of broth are inoculated with several colonies removed from an isolation plate and the broth culture is then incubated for about 30 min. Several tenths ml of the broth are then added to prewarmed distilled water–antibiotic mixtures and allowed to incubate for an additional 60 min. The light scattering characteristics of such antibiotic-treated specimens are then compared with their untreated counterparts; i.e. a control made from suspending an equal aliquot of the broth inoculum in distilled water. Figure 44 shows a typical result for penicillin-susceptible cells of *S. aureus*. The shift to smaller angles of the penicillin-treated bacteria is characteristic of the cells having become larger as a consequence of the weakening of their cell wall in the presence of high osmotic stress. Untreated or resistant cells can withstand the added osmotic stress of the distilled water and show little or no shift of their scattering patterns during the measurement period. Vertically polarized 514·5 nm light from an argon-ion laser was used. Such experiments are often performed in a 30% broth medium.

A typical result for the aminoglycoside gentamicin is shown in Fig. 45. Broth cultures of *Pseudomonas aeruginosa* were added respectively to a control cuvette containing distilled water and a test cuvette containing, in addition, 25 μg/ml of gentamicin. Within 15 min the effects indicated in Fig. 45 were obtained. The susceptibility of this particular *Pseudomonas* strain, clearly evident by the dramatic degradation of the differential scattering pattern, is typical of an increased breadth of the size distribution that must have occurred because of a condition of unbalanced metabolism;

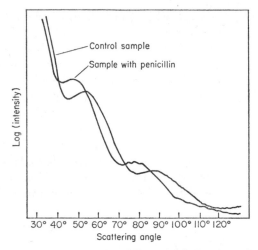

FIG. 44. Effect of penicillin on the differential light scattering pattern of susceptible cells of *S. aureus*. $\lambda = 514.5$ nm.

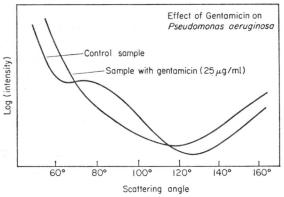

FIG. 45. Effect of gentamicin on the differential light scattering pattern of susceptible cells of *Pseudomonas aeruginosa*. $\lambda = 514.5$ nm.

i.e. the treated cells produced a light scattering pattern characteristic of the size distribution having been broadened. (Recent evidence points to the secondary action of most antibiotics at the cell wall since cell wall metabolism is not necessarily affected immediately by protein synthesis blockers (Rohatgi and Krawiec, 1972).) The curves from *Pseudomonas* were obtained using an argon-ion laser source operating at a wavelength of 514.5 nm.

A similar effect is shown in Fig. 46 when a susceptible strain of *S. aureus* was challenged with streptomycin. The streptomycin concentration used was 100 μg/ml and the distinctive change in the scattering curve shows

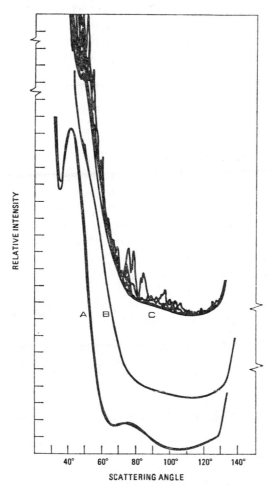

FIG. 46. Effect of streptomycin of the differential light scattering pattern of susceptible cells of *S. aureus*. $\lambda = 632 \cdot 8$ nm. (A) Initial, (B) 10 min, (C) 15 min.

not only the presence of possible cell lysis, but again we see the pattern smoothing characteristic of a broadening of the size distribution. Measurements on slower growing cells (Wyatt *et al.*, 1972) showed clearly that a major effect of streptomycin on susceptible cells is the weakening of the cell membrane thereby permitting leakage of the cytoplasmic contents. The light scattering patterns showed substantial shifts to larger angles after streptomycin treatment, i.e. the cells shrank. In an isotonic solution, however, no such shift was observed.

When cells are challenged by antibiotics to which they are resistant, the differential light scattering patterns for both the control and challenged cells are similar. An interesting effect is often observed with penicillinase-producing cells that are able to metabolize penicillin even in distilled water after several hours. The scattering curves change in a manner indicative of the cells having again started to grow. The features sharpen up considerably and the patterns shift to larger angles suggestive of the cells becoming smaller.

13. Detection of bacteria in fluids

Once a bacterial concentration in solution exceeds about 5×10^5 cells/ml, the characteristic light scattering patterns discussed earlier and illustrated in many of the Figures are readily observed. It remains a relatively simple task, therefore, to inoculate a broth solution with a suspect contaminated solution, incubate, and examine the inoculated broth at 30 min intervals until the characteristic scattering pattern is observed. Other workers (Khan et al., 1972) have been able to detect the presence of bacteria in urines, cerebrospinal fluid, and blood cultures using this procedure within periods of less than 3 h. Naturally care must be taken to eliminate any larger particles whose presence would tend to mask out the characteristic bacterial signatures. Inocula are therefore often prefiltered through a 5 μm Nuclepore filter (General Electric Co., Pleasanton, Calif.) to remove any large debris prior to incubation and subsequent light scattering observations.

14. Determination of minimum inhibitory concentrations and serum levels of antibiotics

An important application of differential light scattering to antibiotic susceptibilities relates to the rapid determination of minimum inhibitory concentrations (MIC's). By definition the MIC is the lowest concentration that will inhibit bacterial growth. The translation of traditional in vitro determined MIC's to realistic therapeutic in vivo values is often ambiguous, especially for those drug/bacteria combinations that prevent cell division yet permit an increase in biomass via filament formation ("snaking"). Two procedures have currently been developed by which MIC's may be determined using differential light scattering. Both seem equally applicable to aerobic and anaerobic species as well as the more fastidious myco-bacteria. It should be pointed out, however, that no "conventional" procedures are at this time fully developed for the anaerobes with which the differential light scattering methods could be compared. In addition, the differential light scattering methods do not seem to yield ambiguous results, whereas such results are often present in conventional tube dilution procedures.

Both procedures are based on the hypothesis that the light scattering pattern of affected cells will differ from that of a control suspension containing no antibiotics. The first method consists simply of adding small equal aliquots of an exponential phase broth culture into cuvettes containing distilled water and varying concentrations of the antibiotic whose MIC is to be determined. An example of this procedure is shown in Fig. 47.

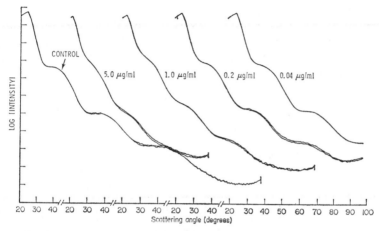

FIG. 47. Change of differential light scattering patterns with changes in concentration of nafcillin for a susceptible strain of *S. aureus*. $\lambda = 632 \cdot 8$ nm.

Several tenths of a ml of exponential phase *S. aureus* broth (cellular concentration approximately 10^7/ml) were added to 15 ml preheated distilled water containing the indicated concentrations of nafcillin (Wyeth). The control cuvette contained no nafcillin. The cuvettes were incubated at 37°C for 1 h and the differential light scattering patterns were recorded on a three decade logarithmic scale. Note that the scattering curve for a concentration of 0·04 μg/ml is almost identical to that of the control, thereby establishing an MIC between 0·2 μg/ml and 0·04 μg/ml. (See Section III.C for a further discussion of data representation.)

Khan *et al.* (1972) combined a detection procedure with an MIC determination and have thereby developed a different differential light scattering technique. To ten cuvettes of broth containing varying concentrations of gentamicin (plus one control consisting of broth alone), they added a small inoculum of spinal fluid directly from the tapped specimen. The cuvettes were then incubated at 37°C and their light scattering curves recorded at

30 min intervals. By 2½ h, characteristic curves had begun to evolve from some of the cuvettes and the control (showing the presence of bacteria in the initial inoculum). Comparing the drug treated cuvette curves with those of the control permitted an immediate identification of the MIC level that was confirmed 20 h later by conventional tube dilution determinations.

Serum levels of unbound antibiotics may be easily determined in a reciprocal manner. The serum is filtered through 0·2 μm Nuclepore filters and then added in various dilutions to cuvettes containing prewarmed distilled water (a control with no serum is also prepared). An exponential phase broth culture of a species whose susceptibility (to the antibiotic in the serum) is known is prepared and equal aliquots added to the cuvettes. These are then incubated and after about 30–60 min, their differential light scattering patterns recorded. Comparing the patterns of the control cuvette with those containing the serum immediately identifies the serum dilution corresponding to the MIC of the species being used (see Section III.C).

B. Single bacteria and spores

1. *Sample preparation and measurement*

Bacterial cells and spores, prior to measurement in a single particle light scattering photometer (Wyatt and Phillips, 1972a), are usually cleaned by washing in distilled water. Spores are often subjected to more extensive cleaning procedures in order to remove the exosporium. Once cleaned the cells, or spores, are resuspended in distilled water and placed in a nebulizer by which means they may be aerosolized and, in the process, electrostatically charged.

Figure 48 presents an exploded view of the *Differential II* scattering cell in which the measurements are made. Because of the charge acquired during their aerosolization, the cells are electrostatically suspended in a "Millikan oildrop" apparatus, the upper plate of which is the settling chamber with the base forming the lower plate. An insulated pin electrode located at the centre of the upper plate provides an inward directed radial field that keeps the particle centred. The transparent scattering cell is shown beneath the upper O-ring and provides a light trap, entrance mask (through which the laser beam enters), and side port for viewing the scattering particle through a low powered microscope (not shown). Part of the scattered signal observed through the side port provides a measure of the particle's position which is then used by a servo system to automatically maintain the particle position at the centre of the cell. Further details may be found in the paper by Wyatt and Phillips (1972a).

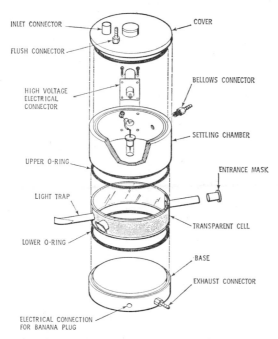

INLET CONNECTOR

COVER

FLUSH CONNECTOR

HIGH VOLTAGE
ELECTRICAL
CONNECTOR

BELLOWS CONNECTOR

SETTLING CHAMBER

UPPER O-RING

ENTRANCE MASK

LIGHT TRAP

TRANSPARENT CELL

LOWER O-RING

BASE

EXHAUST CONNECTOR

ELECTRICAL CONNECTION
FOR BANANA PLUG

FIG. 48. Exploded view of the single particle light scattering chamber with electrodes used in the *Differential II* to make differential light scattering measurements on individual bacteria or spores.

2. Some typical measurements and interpretations

Figure 49 presents the differential light scattering patterns from a single cell of *S. epidermidis* (Wyatt and Phillips, 1972b). The lack of any depolarized signal was indicative of a spherically symmetric cell and permitted an immediate application of the appropriate scattering theory summarized in the Appendix (Wyatt, 1962).

For this "simple" geometry, a least square fit of the theory to selected experimental points yields essentially unique values of cell radius, cell wall thickness, and average refractive indices of cytoplasm and cell wall. The results of this analysis are summarized in Section II.C,1.

Figures 50 and 51 present the differential light scattering patterns (vertical and horizontal polarized incident light) for a single spore of *Bacillus sphaericus*. Again we have a spherically symmetric scatterer though producing considerably noisier scattering curves than the *S. epidermidis* cell, probably because of the presence of exosporium remains. Least squares analysis of these curves (Wyatt, 1972a) yielded a spore radius of 483 ± 5 nm, coat thickness of 80 ± 10 nm, and cortex and coat refractive indices of 1.56 ± 0.02 and 1.48 ± 0.03, respectively. Note that the spore coat

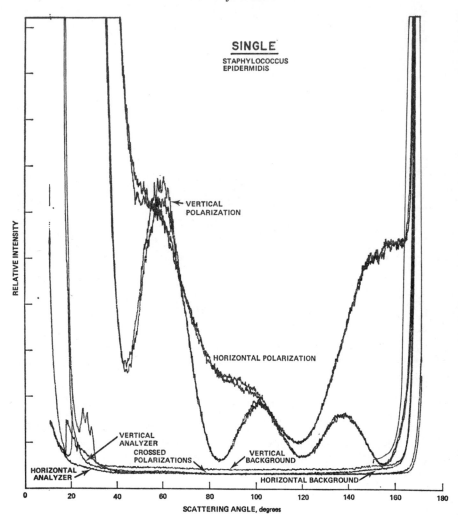

FIG. 49. The differential light scattering patterns from a single cell of *S. epidermidis*. Two successive traces each for vertical and horizontal polarized light of wavelength 514·5 nm are shown together with the associated background curves. Also shown are the so-called depolarization curves obtained by fitting the detector with a polarizer crossed with respect to the polarization of the incident light.

has a refractive index even less than the index of the cell wall of dehydrated *S. epidermidis*.

Although spherically symmetric cells are relatively simple to analyse, bacteria of more complex structure may be only approximated. This subject has been discussed in considerable detail in Section II. Suffice it to

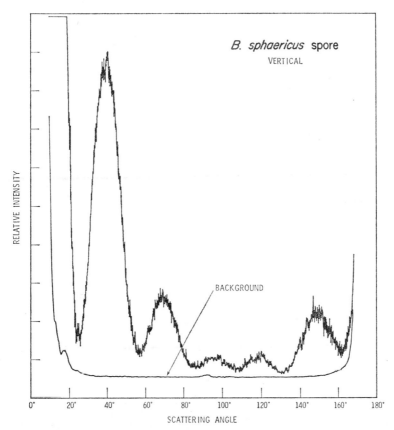

FIG. 50. Differential light scattering patterns from a single spore of *Bacillus sphaericus*. Incident light vertically polarized at 514·5 nm.

remark that much additional analytical work will probably be undertaken at such a time as the information derivable from single cell measurements takes on added importance. The author believes (Wyatt, 1968) that these measurements and procedures will play an important role in epidemiology where the rapid identification of bacteria is often desirable. Some preliminary and as yet unpublished data and analyses seem to indicate that speciation based upon the examination of the differential light scattering characteristics of a few hundred individual cells is possible.

Single cell measurements may be very useful for an accurate determination of size distributions. As already mentioned in Section II, the cells dehydrate almost immediately upon removal from their liquid environment (Wyatt and Phillips, 1972b). Thus any size distribution deduced (Stull, 1972) will correspond to a distribution of dried cells. However, the

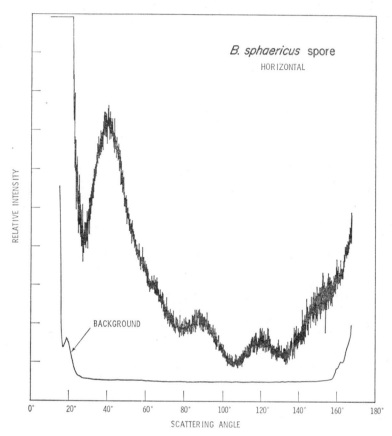

FIG. 51. Same spore as used Fig. 50, but for horizontally polarized incident light.

potential resolution obtainable from light scattering is so much greater (perhaps by more than an order of magnitude) than that obtainable via electron microscopy (Cooke and Kerker, 1972), that there is good justification for making these measurements—at least for the case of cells exhibiting spherical symmetry. Besides, measurements of the size distribution of dehydrated cells will yield a better understanding of the total biomass distributions, which are probably of more importance than a determination of the volume distribution occupied by cells in solution. Although equivalent "spherical" size distributions may be obtained from light scattering measurements of aspherical cells by the analyses discussed in Section II, the correlation between such derived distributions and the actual distributions has still not been attempted at the present time.

C. Data representations

V. R. Stull (unpublished) has recently examined in some detail the problem of extracting meaningful information from recorded differential light scattering curves. Although he directed his primary attention to measurements made on particulate suspensions, most of his analyses apply equally well to single cell measurements. This Section summarizes some of his work concerned primarily with the comparison of a pair of recorded light scattering patterns. Such a pair of curves may correspond to treated and untreated bacterial suspensions, the same suspensions measured at different times, etc.

1. *Data generation*

Only after the light scattering photometer has been carefully aligned and checked should measurements be initiated. During this check-out phase it is often useful to make a measurement using a suspension of monodisperse latex particles of a diameter of about 1000 nm. Such calibrated particles are available through the Dow Chemical Company and other manufacturers. This recorded pattern should then be compared with a satisfactory pattern produced during earlier measurement programmes, or with the test pattern supplied by the photometer manufacturer for calibration purposes. For bacterial suspensions, it is most useful to record the light scattering patterns on a logarithmic scale (see Section III.A, 7).

Suppose now that we want to compare the light scattering patterns of cuvette A and cuvette B. Record the scattering pattern of cuvette A, noting the starting angle and ending angle of the scan. As a rule, the former should be as small as possible and the latter as large as possible within the restraints of distortions or abberations that may be present in the equipment being used. It is wise to start with this angular interval quite wide. It can be narrowed later; but it is often useful to see the full scattering curve initially.

Avoid signal saturation if at all possible. This merely puts a meaningless straight line (or false feature, if the $\sin \theta$ correction is used) at the top of the chart paper for small scattering angles. If too much saturation is present, the photomultiplier gain should be reduced or the suspension diluted further. Now record the scattering characteristics of B *superimposed on A!* (A different colour pen is helpful for this purpose.) The usefulness of overlaying the curves cannot be overemphasized. Displaced curves can be of interest in some rare cases, but not very often. If you have a second (or third, etc.) cuvette to compare with A in the experiment, record A again on a new section of chart paper. It only takes a minute.

2. *Reading the data*

(i) *Angular shifts.* A possible resultant pair of curves A and B is shown in Fig. 52. We note that in this example there are three maxima in curves A and B. The angular differences, $\Delta\theta$, between corresponding "peaks" may be read from the superimposed plots. These shifts, individually or added together, can be recorded as the "observable" of the measurement and plotted against, for example, the difference in drug concentration of cuvettes A and B if the effects of a particular drug were being investigated. The angular displacement of the minima could equally well have been used as the observables.

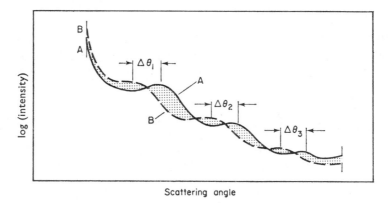

Fig. 52. Superimposed differential light scattering characteristics from two different measurements A and B which illustrate the angular displacements of the extrema. The scattering angle and logarithmic intensity scales are omitted.

There are also inflection points in the curves which can be used, particularly when there are no maxima and minima. Recall an inflection point occurs where the slope of the curve goes from increasing (decreasing) to decreasing (increasing), or in other words the curvature changes from convex (concave) to concave (convex). (You should be pleasantly surprised at how readily inflection points can be located with a little practice.)

It is important to note that the angular shift observable should be used *only when curves A and B are qualitatively similar*. That is, they must have the same number of maxima and minima and/or the same number of inflection points. There must be assurance of a true correspondence between the points whose angular displacement is recorded.

(ii) *Slope differences.* Another possible resultant pair of curves A and B is shown in Fig. 53. The inflection points have been marked A_1, A_2, A_3, A_4, A_5, and B_1, B_2, B_3, B_4 and B_5. A straight line drawn tangentially through

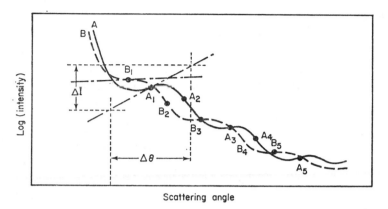

FIG. 53. Superimposed differential light scattering characteristics from two different measurements A and B which illustrate changes in slope at various corresponding regions of the curves.

each inflection point (as shown for A_1 and B_1) can be used to determine the corresponding slope; i.e. a straight line defines a vertical distance ΔI for a given horizontal distance $\Delta\theta$, permitting the calculation of the slope $\Delta I/\Delta\theta$. If we always use the same $\Delta\theta$, this quantity is redundant and may be dropped. Thus it is only necessary to record ΔI for each tangent at each inflection point.

The slope difference observables to record for the pair of curves A and B are $[\Delta I (A_1) - \Delta I (B_1)]$, $[\Delta I(A_2) - \Delta I(B_2)]$, etc.

(iii) *"Area" between curves.* Whenever there is a difference in particle abundance between cuvettes A and B (not caused inadvertently, but as a "real" effect of the difference between these samples), this will manifest itself by a greater overall intensity in one or the other of A or B (i.e. these curves will be displaced vertically). Also there may be cases where the angular shifts and slope differences are obscured by gross shape differences. For such situations we need a more general observable. A readily measured quantity which fulfills this requirement is the *area* between the curves as illustrated by the *total* shaded area in Fig. 52. This is *not* an arbitrarily selected quantity, for it represents a well-known measurement of the *correlation* between two curves. When the curves are defined by the sets of angles $\theta_{A1}, \theta_{A2}, \ldots, \theta_{An}$ and $\theta_{B1}, \theta_{B2}, \ldots, \theta_{Bn}$, then their correlation

$$Q = \sum_{i=1}^{n} |\theta_{Ai} - \theta_{Bi}| \bigg/ \sum_{i=1}^{n} \theta_{Ai}$$

is essentially the area between the curves.

3. *Data processing*

Once the comparison of curves A and B has been quantified by one or several or a combination of the foregoing observables, the rest is up to the individual performing the experiment. Presumably, he has "designed" a known difference between A and B (drug concentration, time, etc.). The light scattering observables can be plotted as a function of this designed difference. Several such plots can be compared and meaningful conclusions drawn.

Figure 54 presents two examples of such plots. It shows the results of a

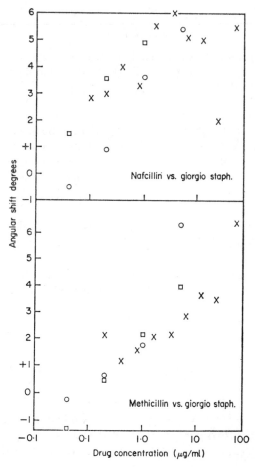

Fig. 54. Plots of the effects of varying methicillin and nafcillin on concentrations on the angular shifts of the differential light scattering patterns from suspensions of *Staph. aureus* (*Giorgio*). The minimum inhibitory concentrations may be derived from an extrapolation of the data to zero angular shift.

large series of light scattering observable measurements *vs* the corresponding drug concentrations for two drugs. A measure of the difference in effectiveness and minimum detectable concentration for the drugs may be readily obtained from these plots.

Although the graphical recording of the differential light scattering curves forms an excellent basis for making subsequent plots and thereby interpreting the data, many subtle features of the curves and sets of potential observables are overlooked because of the time consuming nature of most such types of data reduction. These problems can often be alleviated by use of digital computers many of whose variants now fall within the budgets of even the most modest of laboratories. All that is required is that the data be recorded digitally on magnetic or punched paper tape or on cards by means of an analogue-to-digital converter interfaced between the light scattering photometer and the digital output device. These units are readily available and may even be used to interface the photometer with a computer directly. Once the data is in digital form they may be subjected to a myriad of different calculations and algorithms in extremely short periods of time. The modern microbiology laboratory would do well to familiarize itself with the enormous analytical capabilities of computers, if it has not already done so.

IV. FURTHER APPLICATIONS OF DIFFERENTIAL LIGHT SCATTERING

Differential light scattering techniques clearly offer considerable experimental opportunities for microbiology. Many new applications are currently under investigation at various laboratories and other applications will certainly be developed in the years to come. Unlike turbidimetric and nephelometric measurements which have traditionally been used to measure morphological changes in suspensions of microparticles, differential light scattering measurements provide a more sensitive and far less ambiguous means for monitoring the fine structural details associated with such changes.

Among the many types of further applications that have been considered to be of significant importance are those that relate to studies of bacterial sporulation and germination. No measurements of this type are known as yet to have been attempted, though some rather straightforward experiments do seem obvious. Because of their high relative refractive index and pleomorphism, bacterial spore suspensions should yield essentially featureless scattering patterns. Upon germination, however, such suspensions would revert to vegetative cells which would be expected to produce the characteristic light scattering patterns discussed in this Chapter. Thus the *degree* of germination should be monitorable by measuring the evolution of the light scattering pattern features. Conversely, we would expect the presence of appreciable spores in a suspension of vegetative cells to result in a *degradation* of the corresponding light scattering pattern. This latter effect could therefore be used to monitor sporulation phenomena.

An interesting series of experiments of an ecological nature is currently in progress at the Rensselaer Polytechnic Institute (Troy, New York) laboratory of L. S. Clesceri. She is performing studies (using differential light scattering techniques) of the interactions between micro-organisms by exposing pure cultures to the metabolic products of controlled mixed populations. As in the case of antibiotics and other biochemicals, the effects of such metabolic products could be expected to result in marked changes in the differential light scattering patterns of the interacting micro-organisms.

A number of interesting serological applications should also be mentioned. In an unpublished series of measurements, R. M. Berkman examined the light scattering characteristics of a *Salmonella typhi* suspension interacting with its specific antiserum. He found that the light scattering pattern suggested that the average cell size had decreased after the addition of the antiserum, even though the measurement was performed under hypotonic conditions. A large number of additional possibilities suggest themselves in this same regard since the experimental results may be obtained within a matter of minutes after the addition of specific antisera.

Historically, one of the most important applications of light scattering techniques is related to the determination of molecular weights (cf. Kerker, 1969) using so-called Zimm-plots and measurements at relatively small scattering angles. Monitoring *changes* in molecular weights, i.e. molecular interactions, should, therefore, be a rather obvious extension of these earlier-developed procedures. Some preliminary and unpublished measurements have been performed to detect the presence of the Australia antigen (HAA) by measuring changes in differential light scattering patterns at very small angles subsequent to the addition of antibody-containing serum. Such a procedure *may* prove particularly sensitive at very low antigen levels, i.e. one to two orders of magnitude below those levels required to yield a visible precipitate. More work in this general area is certainly required.

An important guideline when considering the possible application of differential light scattering techniques is an answer to the question: are the phenomena that I wish to monitor associated in any way with structural changes? An affirmative answer generally suggests that the method is worth considering. However, it should be stressed that the method works best when the size distribution of the suspended particles is relatively narrow and the average particle size is comparable to the wavelength of visible light, i.e. that the particles are within the resonance region. Note that the overall size of the suspended particles should be comparable to the wavelength of visible light even though we may wish to monitor structural changes occurring in constituents much smaller than the cells themselves. These small secondary changes are often sufficient to affect the resonance scattering characteristics in a clearly discernable manner.

It seems judicious to close this Section by presenting a few questions asked by the Editors of this book during the final stages of preparing this manuscript. They all relate to other potential areas of application that have not been discussed in much detail. Nevertheless, they are suggestive of areas which could perhaps be of considerable importance for further research using differential light scattering techniques. Among the important questions/suggestions presented, the following are particularly interesting: Might the techniques be applied to studying changes in macromolecular constituents of cells that occur during lag phases and stationary phases, such as ribosome synthesis or polymer deposition or subsequent utilization? Are there applications connected with the synthesis of organelles within eucaryots, such as yeast or the development of membrane systems in photosynthetic organisms? Can the techniques be applied to studying virus or phage replication? All of these questions can be answered affirmatively, though to varying degrees. The most important feature of any particular measurement, however, is the means by which the available tools (light scattering in this case) are adequately exploited in the design and strategy of an experiment.

Note added in proof

A rather unusual effect upon the differential light scattering patterns has recently been found by M. Goldschmidt of the University of Texas (to be published). While investigating the effects of certain disinfectants upon suspensions of viable bacteria, she noted that the scattering curves tended to wash out with increased disinfectant concentration. In addition, the associated scattering curves became significantly displaced upwards. The source of these unusual degradation phenomena (which resulted in curves resembling those produced by too high a bacterial concentration) was not a change of the size distribution, but rather arose from the fact that many cells had collapsed into highly refractile spore-like bodies. These added polydisperse features caused a considerable degradation of the scattering patterns.

APPENDIX

MATHEMATICAL FORMULATION

With the exception of spherically symmetric structures (cf. Wyatt, 1962; Kerker, 1969), no explicit mathematical procedures have been formulated by which the scattering characteristics of inhomogeneous particles may be calculated. Non-spherical homogeneous particles of regular shape (spheroids and hemi-spherically capped rods, for example) may be treated exactly by methods developed by Barber (1973), Waterman (1969), and Erma (1968); however, the calculational procedures are difficult and time consuming. We expect within a few years that computer programs will be more readily available to the interested investigator with access to the required large scale digital computers. In this Appendix only two types of particles will be explicitly discussed: those that are spherically symmetric and those that scatter light so weakly that their light scattering characteristics may be approximated by the so-called Rayleigh–Debye theory. It is a relatively simple matter to construct or borrow computer programs that will permit the rapid calculation of light scattering patterns from bacteria and spores satisfying either one of these criteria.

A. Spherically symmetric particles

The refractive index of a spherically symmetric particle is a function only of the distance from the centre of the particle, r. If the particle is absorbing then the refractive index $n(r)$, will be complex, i.e. contain an imaginary part. To calculate the differential light scattering pattern of such a particle we must in general find appropriate solutions of the following two differential equations (Wyatt, 1965) for all values of the integer l greater than zero

$$\frac{d^2W_l}{d\rho^2} - \frac{1}{\epsilon}\frac{d\epsilon}{d\rho}\frac{dW_l}{d\rho} + \left[\epsilon - \frac{l(l+1)}{\rho^2}\right]W_l = 0 \tag{14}$$

and

$$\frac{d^2G_l}{d\rho^2} + \left[\epsilon - \frac{l(l+1)}{\rho^2}\right]G_l = 0, \tag{15}$$

where $\rho = kr = 2\pi n_0 r/\lambda_0$, and $\epsilon(r) = n(r)^2$

The solutions we seek must have no singularities at $\rho = 0$. For homogeneous particles these become

$$W_l(\rho) = G_l(\rho) = \rho n j_l(n\rho) = \psi_l(n\rho), \tag{16}$$

where j_l is the spherical Bessel function of order l. In the general case $\epsilon(r)$ is given and Eqns. (14) and (15) must be integrated from $\rho = 0$ to $\rho = ka$, where a is outermost radius of the scatterer.

The intensity of light scattered by the particle in the direction θ with respect to an incident plane polarized wave is given by

$$I_\parallel(\theta) = \frac{I_0}{(kR)^2}\left|\sum_{l=1}^{\infty}\frac{(2l+1)}{l(l+1)}[{}^eB_l\pi_l(\cos\theta) + {}^mB_l\tau_l(\cos\theta)]\right|^2 \tag{17}$$

or

$$I_\perp(\theta) = \frac{I_0}{(kR)^2}\left|\sum_{l=1}^{\infty}\frac{(2l+1)}{l(l+1)}[{}^eB_l\tau_l(\cos\theta) + {}^mB_l\pi_l(\cos\theta)]\right|^2 \tag{18}$$

according as to whether the incident light is polarized parallel ($\parallel$) or perpendicular ($\perp$) to the plane of scattering. Parallel and perpendicular polarizations are frequently referred to as horizontal and vertical polarizations, respectively (see Section II.A). The incident intensity is I_0, the distance from the particle to the detector R, and π_l and τ_l are functions of the scattering angle θ, viz.

$$\pi_l = P_l^1(\cos\theta)/\sin\theta \qquad (19)$$

and

$$\tau_l = (d/d\theta)P_l^1(\cos\theta) = l(l+1)P_l(\cos\theta) - \pi_l\cos\theta. \qquad (20)$$

The "electric" and "magnetic" scattering coefficients are given by

$$^eB_l = \frac{\psi_l(x)}{\zeta_l^{(1)}(x)}\,\frac{\epsilon W_l(x)_l D - W_l'(x)}{W_l'(x) - \epsilon W_l(x)\Gamma_l} \qquad (21)$$

$$^mB_l = \frac{\psi_l(x)}{\zeta_l^{(1)}(x)}\,\frac{G_l'(x) - G_l D_l}{G_l(x)\Gamma_l - G_l'(x)}. \qquad (22)$$

where $x = ka$, and D_l and Γ_l are the logarithmic derivatives of ψ_l and $\zeta_l^{(1)}$, viz

$$D_l = \psi_l'(x)/\psi_l(x),$$

$$\Gamma_l = \zeta_l^{(1)'}(x)/\zeta_l^{(1)}(x), \qquad (23)$$

The function $\zeta_l^{(1)}(x) = xh_l^{(1)}(x)$, where $h_l^{(1)}(x)$ is the spherical Hankel function of the first type.

As $l \to \infty$, the coefficients of Eqns. (21) and (22) tend to zero, so that the sums of Eqns. (17) and (18) can be truncated for l slightly greater than about $x+5$. In general, a computer program that calculates the differential light scattering characteristics of the particle [via (17) and (18)] will truncate the summations as soon as a particular term yields a contribution less than, say, 10^{-6} of the sum collected by that time.

Spherically symmetric bacteria are readily treated by this formalism by assuming that there is a smooth, yet rapid, transition from the homogeneous cytoplasm to the homogeneous cell wall, thereby permitting direct integrations of Eqns. (14) and (15). An alternative procedure would consist of using the method of Aden and Kerker (1951) for treating structures of concentric shells. This latter procedure requires extensive calculations of additional Bessel functions and, although not requiring the explicit integration of differential equations, does not save appreciable computer time. Specific details of the computer formalism for the general inhomogeneous case may be found in Wyatt (1962).

B. The Rayleigh–Debye approximation

The Rayleigh–Debye (or often called the Rayleigh–Gans) approximation is most useful for obtaining semi-quantitative results for liquid surrounded cells of arbitrary shape and structure. The approximation has two stringent requirements, however, that limit its usefulness considerably. They are:

$$|1 - n/n_0| \ll 1 \qquad (24)$$

and

$$2ka|1 - n/n_0| \ll 1 \qquad (25)$$

where n is the average refractive index of the scatterer of average radius a. Equation (24) states that the refractive index difference between the cell and its surrounding medium is very small, whereas Eqn. (25) is the requirement that the total phase shift of a wave passing through the cell is also very small. Reasonably small bacterial cells in water satisfy these conditions fairly well.

If the cells are in a medium of refractive index n_0, then the intensity of light scattered in the polar direction (θ, ϕ) is given by

$$I_{||}(\theta,\phi) = \frac{I_0}{(kR)^2} \left| S_{11}(\theta,\phi) \right|^2 = \frac{I_0}{(kR)^2} \left| S(\theta,\phi) \right|^2 \cos^2 \theta \tag{26}$$

$$I_{\perp}(\theta,\phi) = \frac{I_0}{(kR)^2} \left| S\ (\theta,\phi) \right|^2 = \frac{I_0}{(kR)^2} \left| S(\theta,\phi) \right|^2 \tag{27}$$

according as whether the incident light is polarized parallel ($||$) or perpendicular ($\perp$) to a reference plane of scattering. The scattering amplitude

$$S(\theta, \phi) = \frac{ik^3}{2\pi} R(\theta, \phi), \tag{28}$$

where

$$R(\theta, \phi) = \frac{3}{2} \int \frac{n^2 - n_0^2}{n^2 + 2n_0^2} e^{i\delta} dV \approx \int \frac{[n(r,\theta,\phi) - n_0]}{n_0} e^{i\delta} dV; \tag{29}$$

the integration of Eqn. (29) being performed over the entire particle volume V and δ is the phase difference measured with respect to an arbitrary (fixed) origin. The latter explanation of Eqn. (29) is valid whenever Eqn. (24) is valid.

For the case of homogeneous spheres. Eqn. (29) may be shown (Wyatt, 1968; Kerker, 1969) to reduce to

$$R(\theta, \phi) = R(\theta) = V G(u) \tag{30}$$

where $V = 4/3 \pi a^3$, $u = 2ka \sin(\theta/2)$, and

$$G(u) = (3/u^3) (\sin u - u \cos u). \tag{31}$$

The function $G(u)$ may also be expressed in terms of the Bessel function of order 3/2, viz

$$G(u) = (9\pi/2u^3)^{\frac{1}{2}} J_{3/2}(u). \tag{33}$$

For a spherical cell of radius a and cell wall thickness t, the scattering amplitude $S(\theta, \phi) = S(\theta)$ may be shown to be (Wyatt, 1968; 1969)

$$S(\theta) = \frac{ik^3}{2\pi} \left[(m_1 - 1)R_1(\theta) + (m_2 - m_1)R_2(\theta) \right] \tag{34}$$

where the refractive index of the cell wall is n_1, the cytoplasm is n_2 and $m_1 = n_1/n_0$, $m_2 = n_2/n_0$. The functions $R_1(\theta)$ and $R_2(\theta)$ may be simply expressed in terms of the function, G, viz

$$R_1(\theta) = \frac{4}{3} \pi a^3 G(u) \tag{35}$$

$$R_2(\theta) = \frac{4}{3} \pi (a - t)^3 G(u - tu/a). \tag{35}$$

Setting

$f = 1 - t/a$, $\eta = (m_2 - m_1)/(m_1 - 1)$, and $V = 4/3 \pi a^3$ yields the simpler form (Wyatt, 1970)

$$S(\theta) = \frac{ik^3}{2\pi} V(m_1 - 1) \ [G(u) + \eta f^3 G(fu)]. \tag{36}$$

For a prolate spheroid of semi-major and minor axes a and b respectively, and cell wall thickness t, a remarkably similar form to Eqn. (36) may be obtained, viz.

$$S(\theta, \phi) = \frac{ik^3}{2\pi} V(m_1 - 1) \ [G(z) + \eta f^3 G(fz)] \tag{37}$$

where $V = 4/3 \pi ab^2$,

$$z = 2k[a^2 \cos^2 \beta + b^2 \sin^2 \beta]^{\frac{1}{2}} \sin (\theta/2), \tag{38}$$

and β is the angle between the bisectrix and the major axis of the spheroid. The bisectrix is the vector that bisects the angle between the incident plane wave and the direction of observation (θ, ϕ). If α is the angle between the incident beam and the major axis of the spheroid, then

$$\cos \beta = - \cos \alpha \sin (\theta/2) + \sin \alpha \cos \phi \cos (\theta/2). \tag{39}$$

Equation (39) shows that the scattering pattern will in general be a function of the orientation of the spheroidal cell.

Inserting Eqn. (36) or (37) into Eqns. (26) and (27) will yield the appropriate differential scattering patterns for spherical (36) or spheroidal (37) bacteria having a cell wall of thickness t. The maxima and minima of the scattering patterns are thus seen to correspond to the roots of the derivatives of the resultant expression, i.e. $u = $ const. or $z = $ const., respectively. This is the basis for the interpretation of the shifts of the scattering patterns as described in Eqns (1) and (2) in Section II. C, 2(i).

The scattering characteristics for more complex structures may be generated beginning with Eqn. (29) and modifications thereof (Kerker, 1969). Since most measurements of liquid suspended cells involve averaging over the scattering characteristics of thousands of cells, approximations more elaborate than the foregoing seem somewhat superfluous. Indeed most scattering characteristics of bacterial suspensions are probably adequately described, at least qualitatively, using a simple spherically symmetric model. As mentioned in Section III, the differential light scattering characteristics of bacterial suspensions manifest certain general features that seem virtually independent of shape or detailed structural considerations. The differential light scattering patterns from most bacterial suspensions thus seem adequately characterized in terms of an equivalent spherical model. Even in their airborne state, bacterial cells seem to yield scattering patterns quite similar to particles of spherical symmetry.

ACKNOWLEDGMENTS

The author would like to acknowledge the major roles played by Dr. Richard M. Berkman and Dr. David T. Phillips in the formulation and execution of many of the experiments described herein and the development of most of the specialized hardware that permitted the suitable execution of these experiments. Many other individuals contributed to the experimental programmes and the development of the techniques described in this Chapter. Foremost among them were Thomas K. Waitzfelder, Keith A. Montgomery, David G. Gorbet, Dr. C. R. Weston, Joseph B. Estrada, and Joel West. Col. Dan Crozier through the U.S. Army Medical Research and Development Command (Office of the Surgeon General) supported many of the early measurement programmes, especially those associated with speciation and measurements on single cells. His early encouragement and support of these projects are gratefully acknowledged. In addition to the unique instrumentation developments of Dr. Phillips, the engineering accomplishments (i.e. the work that moved us from crude prototypes to reliable laboratory instruments) of Herman Brooks, Donald Dyne and Jack Buckley were, of course, invaluable. They were assisted on many occasions by Peter B. Schoefer who made significant contributions in the optical design of the instruments. Critical reviews of the theoretical bases and interpretations of the measurements by Dr. V. R. Stull were appreciated.

REFERENCES

Aden, A. L., and Kerker, M. (1951). *J. appl. Physics*, **22**, 1242.
"Atlas of Light Scattering Curves" (1971, 1972). Science Spectrum, Inc., Santa Barbara. P. J. Wyatt and V. R. Stuill, *eds*.
Barber, P. (1973). Unpublished thesis, University of California at Los Angeles.
Barer, R. (1952). *Nature, Lond.*, **169**, 366–367.
Barer, R. (1953). *Nature, Lond.*, **172**, 1097–1098.
Barer, R., Ross, K. F. A., and Tkaczyk, S. (1953). *Nature, Lond.*, **171**, 720–724.
Bateman, J. B. (1968). *J. Colloid & interface Sci.*, **27**, 458–474.
Berkman, R. M., and Schoefer, P. B. (1972). United States Patent No. 3701620.
Berkman, R. M., and Wyatt, P. J. (1970). *Appl. Microbiol.*, 510–512.
Berkman, R. M., Wyatt, P. J., and Phillips, D. T. (1970). *Nature, Lond.*, **228**, 458–460.
Blau, H. H., Jr., McCleese, D. J., and Watson, D. (1970). *Appl. Optics*, **9**, 2522–2528.
Brice, B. A., Halwer, M., and Speiser, R. (1950). *J. opt. Soc. Am.*, **40**, 768–778.
Cooke, D., and Kerker, M. (1973). *J. Colloid & interface Sci.*, **42**, 150–155.
Cox, R. T., and Ponder, E. (1941). *J. gen. Physiol.*, **24**, 619–624.
Cross, D. A., and Latimer, P. (1972). *Appl. Optics*, **11**, 1225–1228.
Davies, H. G., Wilkins, M. H. F., Cahyen, J., and La Cour, L. F. (1954). *Q. Jl. microsc. Sci.*, **95**, 271–304.
Dilley, R. A., and Vernon, L. P. (1964). *Biochem.*, **3**, 817–824.
Erma, V. A. (1969). *Phys. Rev.*, **179**, 1238–1246.
Fikhman, B. A. (1959). *Dokl. Akad. Nauk SSSR*, **124**, 1141–1143.
Fikhman, B. A. (1963). *Biofizika*, **8**, 441–447.
Gotterer, G. S., Thompson, T. E., and Lehninger, A. L. (1961). *J. Biophys. Biochem. Cytol.*, **10**, 15–21.
Hind, G., and Jagendorf, A. T. (1965). *J. biol. Chem.*, **240**, 3195–3201; *Ibid.*, **240**, 3202–3209.
Kerker, M. (1969). "The Scattering of Light and other Electro-magnetic Radiation." Academic Press, New York.
Khan, W., Controni, G., Wyatt, P. J., and Ross, S. (1972). *Bact. Proc.* (abstract).

Knaysi, G. (1951). "Elements of Bacterial Cytology", 2nd ed. Cornell Univ. Press, Ithaca, New York.

Koch, A. (1961). *Biochim. biophys. Acta*, **51**, 429–441.

Koch, A. (1968a). *J. theor. Biol.*, **18**, 133–156.

Koch, A. (1968b). *Biochim. biophys. Acta*, **165**, 262–275.

Koch, A. (1970). *Analyt. Biochem.*, **38**, 252–259.

Koga, S., and Fujita, T. (1961). *J. gen. appl. Microbiol.*, **7**, 253–261.

Kratohvil, J. P. (1964). *Analyt. Chem.*, **36**, 458R–472R.

Kratohvil, J. P. (1966). *Analyt. Chem.*, **38**, 517–R526R.

Kratohvil, J. P., and Smart, C. (1965). *J. Colloid Sci.*, **20**, 875–892.

Lewis, P. C., and Lothian, G. F. (1954). *Br. J. appl. Phys.*, *Suppl.* 3, S71–S75.

Lorenz, L. V. (1890). *Videnski Selsk. Skrifter*, **6**, 1–62 (Danish). Translated into French in 1896. "Oeuvres scientifiques de L. Lorenz". Librairc Lehmann, Copenhagen. Reprinted 1964. Johnson, New York, 405–502.

Mie, G. (1908). *Ann. Phys.*, **25**, 377–445.

Oster, G. (1955). *In* "Physical Techniques in Biological Research", Vol. 1, "Optical Techniques". Chap. 2, pp. 51–71 (Eds. G. Oster and A. W. Pollister). Academic Press, New York.

Packer, L. (1963). *Biochim. biophys. Acta*, **75**, 12–22.

Packer, L., Marchant, R. H., and Mukohata, Y. (1963). *Biochim. biophys. Acta*, **75**, 23–30.

Packer, L., and Perry, M. (1961). *Archs Biochem. Biophys.*, **95**, 379–388.

Phillips, D. T. (1971). *Bio Science*, **21**, 864–867.

Pijper, A. (1919). *Med. J. South Africa*, **14**, 211.

Pijper, A. (1931). *J. Path Bact.*, **34**, 771–777.

Ponder, E. (1934). *J. exp. Biol.*, **11**, 54–57.

Ponder, E. (1944). *In* "Medical Physics", pp. 301–308 (Ed. O. Glasser). Year Book Publications, Chicago.

Reich, C. (1973). Proc. International Leprosy Assn., Bergen, Norway (August).

Rohatgi, K., and Krawiec, S. (1972). *Bact. Proc.* (abstract).

Ross, K. F. A., and Billing, E. (1957). *Gen. Microbiol.*, **16**, 418–425.

Stull, V. R. (1972). *J. Bact.*, **109**, 1301–1303.

Van de Hulst, H. C. (1957). "Light Scattering by Small Particles". John Wiley and Sons, Inc., New York.

Waterman, P. C. (1965). *Proc. IEEE*, **53**, 805–812.

Waterman, P. C. (1969). *Alta Frequenza*, **38**, (*Speciale*), 348–352.

Witnauer, L. P., and Scherr, H. J. (1952). *Rev. scient. Instrum.*, **23**, 99–100.

Wolfe, M. W., and Amsterdam, D. (1972). *Bact. Proc.* (abstracts of annual ASM meeting).

Wyatt, P. J. (1962). *Phys. Rev.*, **127**, 1837–1843; *Ibid*, *errata* (1964). **134**, ABI.

Wyatt, P. J. (1965). *J. appl. Physics*, **36**, 3875–3881.

Wyatt, P. J. (1968). *Appl. Optics*, **7**, 1879–1896; *Ibid.*, *erratum* (1969). **8**, 485.

Wyatt, P. J. (1969). *Nature, Lond.*, **221**, 1257–1258.

Wyatt, P. J. (1970). *Nature, Lond.*, **226**, 277–279.

Wyatt, P. J. (1972a). *Spores X*, 61–67.

Wyatt, P. J. (1972b). *J. Colloid & interface Sci.*, **39**, 479–491.

Wyatt, P. J., Berkman, R. M., and Phillips, D. T. (1972). *J. Bact.*, **110**, 523–528.

Wyatt, P. J., and Phillips, D. T. (1972a). *J. Colloid & interface Sci.*, **39**, 125–135.

Wyatt, P. J., and Phillips, D. T. (1972b). *J. theor. Biol.* **37**, 493–501.

Author Index

Numbers in *italics* refer to the pages on which references are listed at the end of each Chapter.

A

Abelson, J., 160, *181*
Abraham, E. P., 113, *180*
Achey, P. M., 156, *174*
Ackermann, E., 58, *59*
Adelberg, E. A., 109, *173*
Aden, A. L., 259, *262*
Adler, R. J., 40, *59*
Alcino, J. F., 114, *173*
Aldous, E., 105, *180*
Alexander, P., 159, 161, *175*
Al-Hilly, J. N. A., 89, *94*
Allinne, M., 82, *94*
Allison, M. J., 118, *176*
Allwood, M. C., 99, 103, 119, 124, 125, 126, 134, 137, *173*
Alper, T., 105, *173*
Amsterdam, D., 225, *263*
Anand, N., 168, *173*
Anderson, E. S., 117, *173*
Anderson, J. S., 167, *173*
Anderson, Thomas, F., 14, *31*
Andrews, J. F., 42, *58*
Annear, D. I., 112, *173*
Aoki, S., 152, 155, *173*
Araki, Y., *174*
Aris, R., 38, *59*
Asscher, A. W., 108, *182*
"Atlas of Light Scattering Curves", 188, 190, *262*
Avi-Dor, Y., 125, *178*
Axel, R., *175*

B

Baarda, J. R., 133, 134, *176*
Baird-Parker, A. C., 103, 105, *174*
Barbaro, A. M., 110, *174*
Barber, M., 112, *174*

Barber, P., 217, 257, *262*
Barer, R., 184, *262*
Barnes, G., 18, *31*
Bateman, J. B., 220, *262*
Bauer, W., 147, 149, *174*
Bayde, A., 125, *174*
Beckmann, H., 168, *179*
Beerens, H., 103, *178*
Bentley, M., 133, 139, *174*
Benveniste, R., 116, *179*
Berger, R., 101, *177*
Berkman, R. M., 125, *174*, 186, 208, 211, 222, 237, 243, *262, 263*
Bernheim, F., 125, *174*
Best, G. K., 108, *174*
Biagi, G. L., 110, *174*
Bibby, W. R., 136, *174*
Bier, M., 123, *174*
Billen, D., 105, 156, *174, 176*
Billing, E., 184, 189, *263*
Birdsell, D. C., 137, *174*
Bischoff, K. B., 38, 40, 41, *58*
Bisiach, M., 18, *32*
Blau, H. H., Jr., 188, *262*
Boddy, A., 58, *58*
Boling, M. E., 155, *180*
Borek, E., 138, *181*
Bosch, L., 171, *181*
Bourgain, M., 87, *94*
Boyce, R. P., 152, 155, 158, *173, 174, 176*
Boyde, A., 15, 18, *31*
Boyle, J. M., 155, 156, 159, *179*
Brenner, S., 135, *174*
Breznak, J. A., 61, 62, 66, 71, *73*
Brice, B. A., 222, 228, *262*
Bridges, B. A., 105, *174, 175*
"British Pharmacopoeia", 98, *174*
Brock, M. L., *174*
Brock, T. D., 172, *174, 177*

Brown, M. R. W., 104, *174*
Bulba, E., 18, *31*
Bulla, L. A., 14, 18, 20, 25, *31, 32*
Burrell, A. D., 162, 163, *174*
Burton, K., *174*
Busta, F. F., 119, *180*

C

Cahyen, J., 184, *262*
Clam, C. T., 43, *58*
Caldwell, I., 161, *177*
Campbell, L. L., 18, 19, *32*
Canale-Parola, E., 61, 62, 63, 64, 66, 68, 69, 70, 71, 73, *73*
Cannefax, G. R., 87, *94*
Carleton, J., 137, 138, *175, 182*
Chabaud, A., 85, *94*
Chan, L. M., 146, *174*
Charlebois, M., 113, *175*
Chatterjee, A. N., 126, *174*
Chen, G. C. C., 109, *173*
Chen, K. C., 85, *94*
Ciak, J., 138, *174*
Ciferro, O., 164, *174*
Citri, N., 114, *174*
Clarke, P. H., 58, *58*
Clive, D., 135, *174*
Cocklin, E., *178*
Coe, A. W., 112, *176*
Coffey, E. M., 83, *94*
Cole, A., 163, *174*
Coles, A. C., *94*
Controni, G., 244, 245, *262*
Cook, A. M., 104, *174*
Cooke, D., 250, *262*
Cordone, L., 100, 153, *180*
Corry, P. M., 163, *174*
Cota-Robles, E. H., 137, *174*
Cox, E. C., 169, 171, *174, 175*
Cox, R. T., 184, *262*
Crawford, L. V., 147, 150, *174*
Crewe, A. V., 13, 28, *31*
Cross, D. A., 218, *262*
Crothers, D. M., 149, *177*
Crumpton, J. E., 102, *180*
Cundliffe, E., 167, *174*
Curds, C. R., 42, *58*
Curran, H. R., 104, *174*

D

Dalton, H. P., 118, *176*
Danckwerts, P. V., 40, *58*
Dark, F. A., 99, 135, *174, 181*
Datta, N., 117, *173, 174, 178*
Davenport, E., 103, 105, *174*
Davies, A., 133, 139, *174*
Davies, B. D., 168, 170, *173, 174*
Davies, H. G., 184, *262*
Davies, J., 116, *174, 179, 182*
Davies, J. E., 168, 170, 171, *174, 175*
Dean, C. J., 159, 161, 162, 163, *174, 175*
Deenen, L. L. M., van, 136, *179*
Degn, H., 58, *58*
De Lamater, E. D., 80, 85, 89, *94*
Denbigh, K. G., 41, *58*
Depieds, R., 90, *94*
Dienes, L., 138, *175*
Dilley, R. A., 184, *262*
Dittmer, J. C., 110, *175*
Donbrow, M., 143, *175*
Donnellan, J. E., 152, 153, *175, 181*
Dorfler, G., 28, *31*
Dressler, I., 85, *94*
Driedger, A. A., 162, *175*
Dronzek, B., 15, *31*
Duma, R. J., 114, *175*
Dunmore, R. T., 113, *175*
Dunnick, J. E., 110, *175*
Durham, N. N., 108, *174*
Dyke, K. G. H., 112, *175*

E

Eakman, J. M., 38, *58*
Eberle, H., 155, *175*
Echlin, P., 15, 29, *31*
Eggertson, G., 167, *177*
Ehrenstein, G., van, 166, *179*
Eisenstadt, J., 167, *177*
Ellis, J. J., 20, *31*
Ellis, S. H., 43, *58*
Elson, L. A., 127, *175*
Englesberg, E., *176*
Epstein, R. L., 136, 137, *178*
Erickson, L. E., 40, *59*
Erma, V. A., 217, 219, 257, *262*
Ernst, R. R., 104, *175*
Errera, M., 100, 153, *180*

Evans, F. R., 104, *174*
Eveland, W. C., 83, *94*

F

Fan, L. T., 40, *59*
Faulkner, R. R., 81, *94*
Faure, A., 90, *94*
Feingold, D. S., 109, *181*
Feldschrieber, P., 162, 163, *174*
Felsenfeld, G., 144, 146, 148, *175*
Felsenfeld, O., 80, 90, 91, *94*
Fennell, D. I., 20, *32*
Few, A. V., 136, *175*
Field, B. S., 133, 139, *174*
Fikhman, B. A., 184, *262*
Finland, M., 112, *180*
Fitz-James, P. C., *175*
Flaks, J. G., 169, 171, *174, 175*
Fleming, P. C., 113, *175*
Fleming, R., 46, *59*
Folch, J., 110, *175*
Forage, A. J., *175*
Forman, A., 135, *177*
Foster, J. W., 98, *180*
Fraenkel-Conrat, H., 129, *175*
Fraser, D., *178*
Fredrickson, A. G., 38, *58, 59*
Freeman, B. M., 105, *175*
Freimer, F. H., 136, *175*
Friedman, S. M., *175*
Friefelder, D., 149, 162, *175*
Fujita, T., 184, *262*

G

Galinas, R., 104, *177*
Gamba, M. F., 110, *174*
Gardner, J. F., 97, *180*
Garett, H., 149, *179*
Garrett, A. J., 127, 129, *175*
Garrod, L. P., 108, *175*
Gear, J. H. S., 90, *94*
Geigy, R., 93, *94*
Gellert, M., 144, 146, 148, *175*
Gerhardt, P., 135, *174*
Gerstein, D. A., 112, *180*
Ghosh, B. R., 136, *175*
Gilbert, W., 167, *175*
Gillies, N. E., 105, *173, 175*

Ginsberg, V., 130, *179*
Ginsburgh, D. M., 161, *175*
Gittelson, B. L., 148, *175*
Gledhill, W. E., 127, *175*
Godtfredsen, W. O., 107, *175*
Goldbergh, I. H., 141, 145, *182*
Goldberg, L. M., 137, 138, *182*
Gooday, M. A., 18, *31*
Gooder, H., 136, 138, *175, 177*
Gordon, M. P., 155, *180*
Gorini, L., 169, 170, 171, *174, 176, 179*
Gotterer, G. S., 184, *262*
Gould, G. W., 98, 99, 111, 112, *175, 176, 177*
Grant, D. W., *178*
Gray, G. W., 104, 106, 109, 137, *175, 180*
Grayston, M. J., 162, *175*
Grijm-Vos, M., 171, *181*
Gross, J. D., 100, 153, 158, *178*
Guerra, M. C., 110, *174*
Gunne, I., 126, *177*
Gustafson, L., 107, *178*

H

de lu Haba, 167
Hagan, 160
Hahn, F. E., 138, 143, 144, *174, 179*
Haight, R. D., 164, *175*
Hales, H. B., 158, *176*
Halvorson, Harlyn O., 18, 25, *32*
Halwer, M., 222, 228, *262*
Hamburger, M., 137, 138, *175, 182*
Hamelin, H., 90, *94*
Hamilton-Miller, J. M. T., 113, 114, 117, *176*
Hamkalo, B. A., 155, *176*
Hanawalt, P. C., 100, 101, *181*
Hancock, R., 127, *179*
Hanson, A. W., 87, *94*
Harold, F. M., 133, 134, *176*
Harris, E. J., *180*
Harris, I. I., 129, *175*
Harris, N. D., 102, *176*
Harrison, D. E. F., 58, *58*
Harrison, J. S., 133, *181*
Harvey, R. J., 126, *176*
Haskin, M. A., 167, *173*
Hatton, M. P., 127, *176*

Hawker, Lillian, 18, *31*
Hayes, T. L., 11, *31*
Hazatsu, H., 170, *179*
Henry, R. J. 115, *176*
Heppel, A. L., 106, *176*
Herczog, D., 115, *181*
Hespell, R. B., 61, 62, 63, 64, 68, 69, 70, 73, *73*
Hesseltine, C. W., 14, 18, 20, 25, *31*, *32*
Hewitt, J. H., 112, 113, *176*, *179*
Hewitt, R. R., 156, *174*
Heywood, V. H., 18, *32*
Hillier, J., 2, *33*
Himmelblau, D. M., 38, 40, *58*
Hindi, G., 184, *262*
Hinshaw, V., 118, *176*
Hirokawa, H., 138, *176*
Hitchins, A. D., 98, 104, *176*, *180*
Hoffee, P., *176*
Hollander, A., 105, *176*, *181*
Holt, R., 113, 116, *176*
Holt, S. C., 61, 63, 68, *73*
Hopwood, D. A., 106, *176*
Hosokawa, K., 166, *181*
Hosszu, J. L., 157, *180*
Houldsworth, M. A., 58, *58*
Housewright, R. D., 115, *176*
Howard-Flanders, P., 101, 151, 152, 153, 155, 156, *173*, *176*, *180*
Hugo, W. B., 96, 110, 134, 138, *176*
Humphrey, A. E., 58, *59*
Hunter, E. H., 83, *94*
Hunter, J. R., 43, 44, *59*, 98, 100, 102, 104, *180*
Hurst, A., 98, *176*
Hutchinson, F., 158, *176*
Hutchinson, W. G., *178*
Hwang, M., 56, *59*
Hyatt, M. T., 98, *177*

I

I.B.M., 58, *58*
Igarashi, K., 167, *176*
Irie, R. N., 153, *176*
Ishitsuka, H., 167, *176*
Iterson, W., van, 136, *179*
Ito, E., *174*
Iyer, V. N., 146, *176*
Izaki, K., *176*

J

Jacherts, D., 149, *177*
Jack, G. W., 114, *176*
Jacob, T. M., 170, *179*
Jacoby, G. A., 169, *176*
Jagendorf, A. T., 184, *262*
Jagger, J., 101, 152, 153, 154, *176*
Jagger, W. S., *180*
James, A. M., 110, *176*
Jevons, M. P., 112, *175*
Jeynes, M. H., 135, 138, *174*, *177*
Jezeski, J. J., 119, *180*
Johnson, J. H., *180*
Jones, D. S., 170, *175*, *177*, *179*
Joseph, R., 61, 70, *73*

K

Kabat, E. A., *177*
Kaji, A., 167, *176*, *177*
Kaji, H., 167, 168, 172, *177*
Kallings, L. O., 126, *177*
Kandler, O., 135, *174*
Kaplan, H. S., 101, *181*
Kattan, A., 40, *59*
Katz, W., *177*
Kellenberger, F., 135, *174*
Kelly, T. K., 29, *32*
Kelton, W. H., *177*
Kembo, H., 153, *176*
Kerker, M., 184, 188, 199, 250, 256, 257, 259, 260, 261, *262*
Kersten, H., 147, *177*
Kersten, W., 147, *177*
Khan, S. R., 97, *177*
Khan, W., 244, 245, *262*
Khorana, H. G., 170, *175*, *177*, *179*
Kilgore, W. W., 166, *181*
King, J. R., 136, *177*
King, W. L., 111, 112, *175*, *177*
Kirby, S. M., 103, 115, 117, 133, *179*
Kittrell, J. R., 47, *59*
Klainer, A. S., 18, *32*
Kleinschmidt, A. K., 149, *177*
Klieneberger-Nobel, E., 135, *174*, *177*
Knaysi, G., 194, *262*
Knights, D., 29, *31*
Knox, R., 113, 114, *176*, *181*
Koch, A. L., 125, *177*, 184, *262*

Koga, S., 58, *59*, 184, *262*
Kogut, M., *177*
Kollin, V., 107, *177*
Kondo, M., 167, *177*
Krajan, A. A., 81, *94*
Kratohvil, J. P., 184, 207, *262*
Krawiec, S., 242, *263*
Kronish, D. P., 136, 137, *178*
Krsmanovic-Simic, D., 100, 153, *180*
Kuczynski, M., 125, *178*
Kunz, L. J., 114, *175*
Kupfer, D. G., 66, 68, *73*
Kurland, C. G., 166, *177*
Kushner, D. J., 97, *177*
Kynaston, D., 29, *31*

L

Lacey, B. W., 108, *177*
La Cour, L. F., 184, *262*
Lamy, F., *176*
Landman, O. E., 135, *174*, *177*
Lang, D., 149, *177*
Lantorpe, K., 126, *177*
Lapidus, L., 56, *59*
Lapthisophon, T., 156, *174*
Lark, C., 126, *177*
Lark, K. G., 126, 155, *175*, *177*
Latarjet, R., 101, *177*
Latimer, P., 218, *262*
Leaf, C. D., 112, *180*
Leben, Curt, 18, *32*
Leder, P., *179*
Lederberg, J., 109, 138, *177*
Lee, P. A., 118, *177*
Lees, M., 110, *175*
Lehmann, A. R., 161, 162, *177*, *179*
Lehninger, A. L., 184, *262*
Leive, L., 97, 106, 107, 163, *177*, *181*
Leloir, L. F., 127, 128, *180*
Lengyell, P., 166, *177*
Leon, S. A., 172, *177*
Le Pecq, J. B., 146, 147, *177*
Lerman, L. S., 148, *177*
Lester, R. L., 110, *175*
Lett, J. T., 161, *177*
Leutgeb, W., 127, *177*
Levaditi, C., 90, *94*
Levinson, H. S., 98, *177*
Levy, A. L., 129, *175*

Lewis, M. J., 117, *173*
Lewis, P. C., 184, *262*
Li, H. J., 149, *177*
Likeover, T. E., 166, *177*
Lillie, R. D., 81, *94*
Lilly, M. D., 58, *58*
Lindqvist, W. F., 29, *32*
Lipmann, F., 166, *179*
Little, J. G., 161, *177*
Locci, R., 18, 20, *32*
Longworth, A. R., 134, *176*
Loosemore, M., 98, *177*
Lorenz, L. V., 184, *262*
Lothian, G. F., 184, *262*
Lovett, S., 125, *177*
Lowry, C. V., 167, *179*
Lund, B. M., 98, *177*

M

Maass, D., 127, *177*
McCann, M. J., 43, *58*
McCleese, D. J., 188, *262*
MacDonald, N. C., *32*
McGrath, R. A., 154, 159, 160, *178*
Mach, B., *177*
MacLeod, R. A., 104, *177*
McQuillen, K., 135, 136, 137, 138, 167, *174*, *178*
Maestrone, G., 83, *94*
Mager, J., 125, *178*
Mahler, H. R., *178*
Mandel, M., 61, 62, 63, 68, *73*, 109, *173*
Mandelstam, J., 127, *178*
Manteufel, P., 85, *94*
Marchant, R. H., 184, *263*
Markham, R., 147, *178*
Marr, A. G., 126, *176*
Marshall, R., 169, *179*
Marszalek, D. S., 15, *32*
Martin, H. H., 135, *177*, *178*
Marx, R., 82, *94*
Matsuhashi, M., 109, 167, *173*, *176*, *181*
Matthei, H., 166, *179*
Mattingly, A., 157, 155, *178180,*
Maxwell, H., 168, *178*
Mazur, P., 100, *178*
Medhill-Brown, M., *178*
Megee, R. D., 47, 58, *59*
Mejbaum, W., 133, *178*

Merworth, W. R., 17, *32*
Meselson, M., 172, *181*
Meyer, P. E., 83, *94*
Meynell, E., 100, 117, *178*
Meynell, G. G., 100, 117, *178*
Mie, G., 184, *262*
Mitchell, P., 125, *178*
Moats, W. A., 43, *59*
Mohan, R. R., 136, 137, *178*
Monk, M., 101, 153, 158, *178*
Monod, J., 39, *59*
Monro, R., 166, *179*
Monro, R. E., 167, *181*
Moore, S., 133, *178*
Mooser, H., 87, *94*
Morenne, P., 101, *177*
Morgan, W. T. J., 127, *175, 180*
Morichi, T., 153, *176*
Morris, A., 133, 141, *178, 179*
Morrison, E. W., 104, *178*
Moseley, B. E. B., 151, 152, 156, 157, *178*
Moss, C. W., 100, 104, 105, *178*
Mossel, D. A. A., 103, *178*
Moyle, J., *178*
Muggleton, P. W., *179*
Muhammed, A., 154, *178*
Muir, M. D., 29, *32*
Mukohata, Y., 184, *263*
Munton, T. J., 97, 103, *178*
Murphy, Judith, A., 18, 19, *32*
Murray, R. G. E., 106, 136, *175, 178*
Murrell, W. G., 99, 104, *178*
Muschel, L. H., 107, 137, *178*

N

Nakamura, M., 105, *178*
Nakayama, H., 159, *178, 179*
Nathans, D., 166, 167, *178, 179*
Nelson, F. E., 103, 133, *179*
Neu, H. C., 107, 108, *179*
Neufeld, E. G., 130, *179*
Neve, N. F. B., 18, *31*
Neville, D., 144, 146, 148, *175*
Nirenberg, M., 169, *179*
Nirenberg, M. W., 166, 167, *179*
Nishimura, S., 170, *179, 179*
Nixon, W. C., 2, *32*
Nomura, H., 166, *181*

Nomura, M., 166, 167, 168, *179, 181*
Novick, R. P., 114, *179*

O

Oatley, C. W., 2, *32*
O'Brien, R. L., 143, 144, *179*
O'Callaghan, C. H., 103, 115, 117, 133, *179*
Ochoa, S., 166, *177*
Ogilvie, Robert E., 11, *32*
Ohtsuka, E., 170, *179*
Okumata, T., 167, *179*
Okubo, S., 159, *178, 179*
Old, D., 171, *179*
O'Leary, W. M., 110, *175*
Olenick, J. G., 143, 144, *179*
Olsen, A. M., 104, *179*
Op Den Kamp, J. A. F., 136, *179*
Ordal, Z. J., 119, 164, *181*
Ormerod, M. G., 159, 161, 162, *175, 177, 179*
Oster, G., 184, *262*
Owen, C. J., 17, *32*
Ozanne, B., 116, *179*

P

Packer, L., 184, *263*
Paden, D., 15, *31*
Pampana, E. J., 87, *94*
Panos, C., *179*
Paoletti, C., 146, 147, *177*
Parisi, B., 164, *174*
Park, J. T., 127, *179*
Parker, M. S., 98, 99, *179*
Parker, M. T., 112, 113, *175, 176, 179*
Paterson, M. C., 155, 156, 159, *179*
Peacey, M., 101, 153, 158, *178*
Peacock, A. R., 142, 143, 148, *179*
Pease, Daniel, C., 14, *32*
Pease, R. F. W., 2, 11, *31, 32*
Perkins, H. R., 126, *180*
Perkins, R. L., 18, *32*
Perret, C. J., 114, *179*
Perry, M., 184, *263*
Pestka, S., 167, 169, *179*
Pethica, B. A., *179*
Petris, S. de, 106, *179*

Pfennig, N., 64, *73*
Phillips, D. T., 186, 189, 211, 219, 220, 243, 246, 247, 249, *262, 263*
Pianotti, R. S., 136, 137, *178*
Pietsch, P., 149, *179*
Pijper, A., 183, 219, *263*
Pitzurra, M., 138, *179*
Pollard, E. C., 101, 165, *179*
Pollock, M. R., 116, *179*
Ponder, E., 184, *262, 263*
Postgate, J. R., 43, 44, *59*, 99, 100, 102, 104, *180, 181*
Powell, E. O., 98, *180*
Powell, J. F., 98, *179*
Powell, J. R., 98, *180*
Pressman, B. C., *180*
Price, G., 155, *180*
Punch, J., 118, *176*

Q

Quaroni, S., 20, *32*

R

Radman, M., 100, 153, *180*
Rahn, R. O., 157, *180*
Ramage, C. M., 105, *178*
Ramareddy, G., *180*
Ramkrishna, D., 39, *59*
Randolph, M. L., 155, *180*
Ranganathan, V. S., 18, *32*
Ranque, J., 90, *94*
Raper, K. B., 20, *32*
Ravenswaay Claasen, J. C., van, 171, *181*
Ray, B., 119, *180*
Razin, S., *180*
Reich, C., 186, 225, *263*
Reich, E., 141, 145, *182*
Reissig, J. L., 127, 128, *180*
Reiter, H., 155, *180*
Repaske, R., 137, *180*
Rettger, L. F., 104, *178*
Rhodes, R. A., 14, 18, *31*
Richmond, M. H., 114, 118, *176, 177, 181*
Roberts, N. A., 104, 106, 100, *180*
Roberts, R. B., 105, *180*
Roberts, T. A., 102, 104, *180*

Rode, L. J., 98, *180*
Rogers, H. J., 126, 127, *180*
Rohatgi, K., 242, *263*
Rondle, C. J. M., *180*
Rosenbrock, H. H., 47, 56, *59*
Rosenthal, S. L., 66, 68, *73*
Ross, K. F. A., 184, 189, *262, 263*
Ross, S., 244, 245, *262*
Roth, I. L., 16, 18, 20, *32*
Rousseau, Paul, 18, 25, *32*
Rubbo, R. B., 97, *180*
Rubio-Huertos, M., 135, *174*
Rupp, W. D., 156, *180*
Russ, J. C., 18, 28, *31, 33*
Russell, A. D., 97, 98, 99, 102, 103, 104, 106, 109, 113, 114, 119, 124, 125, 126, 133, 138, 141, *173, 176, 177, 178, 180*
Rye, R. M., 126, *180*

S

Sabath, L. D., 112, 113, *180*
Sacks, L. E., 14, *32*
Salt, W. G., *180*
Salton, M. R. J., 135, *174*
Sato, M., 100, *180*
Sato, T., 109, *181*
Sbarra, A. J., 105, *181*
St. Clair, J., *177*
St. Julian, G., 14, 18, 20, 25, *31, 32*
Saunders, L., 46, *59*
Saurino, V. D., 80, 85, 89, *94*
Scharzberg, M., 125, *178*
Scherr, H. J., 207, 222, 227, *263*
Schmidt, J. J., 100, *178*
Schmueli, U., 148, *181*
Schoefer, P. B., 208, 222, *262*
Schuhardt, V. T., 90, 91, *94*
Schulman, J. H., *175, 179*
Schwartz, B. S., 136, 137, *178*
Scott, S. S., 109, *181*
Scott, W. J., 104, *179*
Seinfeld, J. H., 56, *59*
Selzer, G. B., 115, *180*
Serianni, R. W., 159, 161, *175*
Setlow, J. K., 153, 154, 156, 157, *178, 180*
Setlow, R. B., 155, 156, 159, *174, 179*
Sharp, J. T., 138, *175*

Shaw, W. V., 115, *181*
Shimada, A., *174*
Shingler, A. H., 133, *179*
Sikorski, J., 17, *32*
Silva, M. T., 124, *181*
Sinclair, C. G., 42, *59*
Sinclair, N. A., *178*
Skerret, J. N. H., 142, 143, 148, *179*
Sloane-Stanley, G. H., 110, *175*
Small, E. B., 15, 18, *32*
Smart, C., 207, *262*
Smith, C. A. B., 46, *59*
Smith, C. E., 144, 146, 148, *175*
Smith, H. W., 117, *181*
Smith, J. L., 134, *181*
Smith, J. T., 113, 114, *176, 181*
Smith, K. C., 100, 101, *181*
Smith, L. D. H., 104, *177*
Snow, J. M., 23, 154, *176*
Snyder, R. L., 2, *33*
Sompolinsky, D., 115, *181*
Speck, M. L., 100, 104, 105, *178*
Speiser, R., 222, 228, *262*
Speyer, J. F., 166, *177*
Sprenkman, W., 17, *32*
Staehelin, T., 172, *181*
Stafford, R. B., 152, 153, *175*
Stafford, R. S., 152, 153, 154, *176, 181*
Stapleton, G. E., 105, *176, 181*
Stay, J. H., 152, *181*
Stein, G. J., 89, *94*
Stein, W. H., 133, *178*
Stewart, G. T., 113, *176*
Stintzing, H., 1, *32*
Stokes, J. L., 104, *181*
Storey, C., 47, 56, *59*
Straka, R. P., 104, *181*
Strange, R. E., 98, 99, 135, *174, 180, 181*
Straugnh, W. R., 136, *174*
Stretton, R. J., 110, *176*
Strickland, E. H., 58, *59*
Strominger, J. L., 109, 126, 127, 128, 167, *173, 176, 180, 181*
Stubbs, J. M., 111, 112, *175*
Studier, F. W., 160, *181*
Stull, V. R., 191, 249, *263*
Subirana, J. A., 148, *181*
Sud, I. J., 109, *181*
Suwalsky, M., 148, *181*

Suzuka, I., 167, *177*
Suzuki, H., 166, *181*
Swenson, P. A., 155, *176*
Sykes, G., 111, *181*
Sykes, R. B., *181*
Szybalski, W., 138, 146, 147, *176, 177, 179*

T

Taber, H., 126, *174*
Tabor, C. W., 138, *181*
Takagi, Y., 159, *178, 179*
Takahashi, H., 100, *180*
Takanami, M., 167, *179, 181*
Tal, M., 164, *181*
Tamaki, S., 109, *181*
Tanaka, Y., 168, 172, *177*
Tatum, E. L., *177*
Thacore, H., 138, *182*
Theriot, L., 101, 155, 156, *176*
Thomas, C. A., 160, *181*
Thompson, T. E., 184, *262*
Thornton, P. R., 2, 4, 6, *32,*
Threnn, R. H., 109, *181*
Thurston, E. L., 18, *33*
Tipper, D., 116, *179*
Tkaczyk, S., 184, *262*
Tomasz, A., 138, *181*
Tomcsik, J., 135, *174*
Tomlins, R. I., 119, *181*
Topiwala, H. H., 42, *59*
Town, C. D., 101, *181*
Trabu, W., 148, *181*
Trant, R. R., 167, *181*
Traub, P., 166, 168, *179, 181*
Trevelyan, W. E., 133, *181*
Tsai, B. I., 40, *59*
Tsuchiya, H. M., 38, *58, 59*
Turner, J. C. R., 41, *58*
Twigg, G. H., 115, *182*

U

Udris, Z., 61, 62, 63, 68, *73*

V

Vaisman, A., 90, *94*
Van de Hulst, H. C., 188, *263*

Van Iterson, W., 136, *181*
Van Knippenberg, P. H., 171, *181*
Vasquez, D., 168, *181*
Vedstron, H., 171, *181*
Veldkamp, H., 61, 70, *73*
Vernon, L. P., 184, *262*
Vinograd, J., 147, 149, *174*
Vinter, V., 99, *181*
Vole, M. J., 97, *181*
Von Ardenne, M., 2, *33*
Voss, J. G., 106, *182*

W

Walker, I. O., 141, 142, 143, 144, 146, 148, *175, 182*
Walker, J. R., 155, 156, 158, *182*
Walton, J. R., 117, *182*
Ward, D. C., 141, 145, *182*
Waring, M. J., 143, 144, 145, 147, 149, 150, *174, 182*
Warth, A. D., 99, *178*
Watanabe, T., 117, *182*
Watarakunakorn, C., 137, 138, *182*
Waterman, P. C., 217, 257, *263*
Waterworth, P. M., 108, *175*
Watson, D., 188, *262*
Wayte, R., 15, *31*
Weatherwax, R. S., 105, *182*
Webb, M., 108, *182*
Webb, R. L., 97, *180*
Webster, H. K., 161, *176*
Weibull, C., 135, 136, *174, 182*
Weidel, W., 127, *177*
Weinberg, E. D., 134, *181*
Weinstein, I., *176*
Weisblum, B., 168, *182*
Weiser, R., 108, *182*
Weller, P. K., 101, 165, *179*
Weyer, F., 87, *94*
White, J. R., 169, 171, *174, 175*

Wilkins, M. H. F., 184, *262*
Wilkinson, S. G., 104, 106, 109, 137, *175, 180*
Willett, H. P., 138, *182*
Williams, R. A. D., 18, *31*, 125, *174*
Williams, R. W., 154, 159, 160, *178*
Wimpenny, J., 108, *182*
Winkle, Q., van, 146, *174*
Winshell, E. B., 108, *179*
Wise, W. S., 115, *182*
Wiseman, D., 126, *180*
Wishart, D. R., 103, 115, 117, *179*
Witkin, E., 151, *182*
Witnauer, L. P., 207, 222, 227, *263*
Witting, M. L., 169, *176*
Woese, C. R., 105, *182*
Wolfe, M. W., 225, *263*
Wolfe, R. S., 73, *73*
Wolman, B., 84, *94*
Wolman, M., 84, *94*
Wolstenhome, B., 90, *94*
Wood, C., 15, *31*
Wright, W. W., 115, *180*
Wyatt, P. J., 125, *174*, 184, 186, 189, 194, 195, 211, 217, 219, 220, 228, 237, 243, 244, 245, 246, 247, 249, 257, 260, *262, 263*

Y

Yano, N., 153, *176*
Young, F. E., 126, *174*
Young, H., 84, *94*

Z

Zahn, R. K., 149, *177*
Ziegler-Schlomowitz, R., 115, *181*
Zwietering, Th. N., 40, *59*
Zworykin, V. K., 2, *33*

Subject Index

A

N-acetylamino sugars,
  cell wall, in 127–128
Acridines,
  DNA interaction with, 141
Acriflavine,
  membrane permeability of, 134
Actinomycin,
  bacterial resistance to, 97
  DNA interaction with, 148, 150
  RNA polymerase interaction with, 150
Adhesin test,
  Borrelia sp., for, 91–2
Aerobacter sp.,
  R-factor transfer in, 118
Aerobacter aerogenes,
  cold damage to, 99, 104
Agar stab cultures, 72–73
Agglutination test,
  Borrelia sp., for, 89
D-alanyl-D-alanine,
  synthesis of, 129
Allantoic membrane cultures, 85
Amino-acids,
  estimation of, 133
  leakage of, 132
  spheroplast preparation, for, 138
Amino group estimation, 129–130
Aminoacyl t-RNA, 167
p-amino benzoic acid, 103
Aminoglycoside antibiotics,
  inactivation of, 116
Analogue computers,
  mathematical models and, 56
Aniline dyes,
  Borrelia sp. staining, for, 78–81
Aniline-α-napthyl-amino-β-sulphonic acid, (ANS), 134
Antibacterial agents,
  adsorption of, 119–123
  cell permeability and, 106–112

chelating agents and, 106–110
DNA interaction with, 141–150
inactivation of, 102–103, 113–117
L-form sensitivity to, 139–140
membrane damage by, 131–135
mucopeptide synthesis and, 131
mutagenic effects of, 150
mycoplasma sensitivity to, 140
protoplast sensitivity to, 138–139
resistance to, 106–118
spheroplast preparation, in, 137–138
spheroplast sensitivity to, 139
viability, effect on, 102–103
Antibiotic susceptibility tests, 186, 241–246
Antibody formation,
  Borrelia sp., to, 88
Apurinic acid, 144
Arsenicals,
  inactivating agents for, 103
Aspergillus sp.,
  morphology of, 20, 22
Aspergillus cremeous, 22
Aspergillus rugulosus, 20, 22
Aspergillus stramenius, 20, 22
Aspergillus variecolor var *astellus*, 20, 22
Astigmatism,
  electron microscope, in, 12
Astigmator, 4, 6

B

Bacillus cereus,
  benzylpencillin and, 117
  colony morphology of, 20–21
  β-lactamase in, 116
B. lentimorbus,
  spore morphology of, 19
B. megaterium,
  protoplast preparation from, 136
B. mycoides,
  colony morphology of, 20, 21

B. polymyxa,
spore morphology of, 19
B. popilliae,
spore morphology of, 19
B. sphericus,
light scattering pattern from, 247–250
B. stearothermophilus,
heat treatment of, 104
protein synthesis in, 164–165
B. subtilis,
antibiotic assay, in, 115
colony morphology of, 20–21
mucopeptide from, 127
protoplast preparation from, 136
B. thuringiensis,
spore germination in, 24–26
spore morphology of, 19, 29
Bacitracin, 138
Bacteria,
cold shock to, 99–100
enzyme induction in, 116
fixation of, 124
genetic transformation in, 156–157
heat treatment of, 99, 103–104
injury repair in, 118–119
ionizing irradiation of, 101
L-form preparation from, 138
light scattering techniques for, 183–262
morphological changes in, 124–126
Bacterial cell walls,
damage to, 126–131
light scattering by, 200–202, 208, 210
lipids in, 110–111
permeability of, 106–112
synthesis of, 126–131
Bacterial colonies,
morphology of, 20–21
Bacterial damage,
assessment of, 96–173
chemical agents by, 97–99, 102–103
126–150, 163–173
membranes and, 131–140
morphological changes in, 124–126
physical processes, by, 99–101, 103–106, 150–159
recovery from, 105–106
repair of, 150–159
Bacterial mucopeptide, (*see under* mucopeptide)

Bacterial permeability, 106–112
Bacterial protoplasts,
drug sensitivity of, 135, 138–139
preparation of, 136–137
Bacterial size,
measurement of, 125–126, 184, 195–215, 233, 237–239
Bacterial spheroplasts,
drug sensitivity of, 135, 139
preparation of, 107, 137–138
Bacterial spores,
drug resistance of, 111–112
drug sensitivity of, 97–99
freezing and thawing of, 100
germination of, 25–28, 98
heat treatment of, 103–104
light scattering by, 246–250
morphology of, 18–19, 24
outgrowth of, 24–26, 98–99
preparation of, 97–98
u.v. sensitivity of, 151
Bacterial sporulation,
drug inhibition of, 99
Bacterial u.v. irradiation, 150–159
Bacterial viability,
antibacterial agents and, 102–106
Berkman-Schoefer cuvette, 222–224
Borrelia sp., 76–94
animal inoculation with, 92–93
concentration of, 80–81
culture methods for, 84–86
diagnosis of, 92–93
diseases caused by, 76–77
distribution of, 77–78
morphology of, 77–78
preservation of, 86–88
serological tests for, 76, 88–92
staining of, 78–84
taxonomy of, 76
vectors for, 76–7
Borrelia anserina,
animal inoculation with, 92
avian disease and, 77–78
concentration of, 81
culture of, 85
distribution of, 77
serological tests for, 89
vectors for, 77
B. crocidurae, 77, 92
B. duttonii, 77, 86, 92

B. hermsii, 77
B. hispanica, 77, 86, 87, 92
B. latyshevyi, 77
B. parkerii, 77
B. persica, 77, 86, 87, 92
B. recurrentis, 76, 77, 86, 92
B. theileri, 76, 77
B. turicatae, 77
B. venezolensis, 77
B. vincentii, 77, 86
Borreliolysin test, 91
Borreliosis, 93
Botryodiploidia theobromae, 27, 28
Bromouracil, 158

C

Carboxypeptidation, 130
Cathode ray tubes,
    electron microscope, in, 11–12
Cathodoluminescence, 11
Cephaloridine,
    E. coli resistance to, 113
    hydrolysis of, 115
Cephalosporins, 103, 113–115
Chalaropsis B,
    protoplast preparation by, 137
Chick embryo,
    Borrelia sp., culture in, 85–86
Chloramphenicol, 115
Chopping coils, 6–7
Chromatic aberration, 12
Chloroplasts,
    light scattering by, 184
Clostridium botulinum spores,
    heat treatment of, 104
Clostridium perfringens spores,
    heat treatment of, 104
Coherance, 203–204
Cold shock, 99–100
Complement fixation test, 89–90
Computer programme, 57
Continuous culture systems,
    mathematical models of, 42–43, 45, 58
Continuous flow stirred tank reactor,
    (CFSTR), 41
Critical point drying, 14
Crystal violet, 80
7-cyanoacetylaminocephalosporanic
    acid, 113

Cycloserine,
    mucopeptide synthesis and, 131
    spheroplast preparation by, 138
Cytoplasmic membrane,
    damage to, 131–135
    function of, 132–135
    isolation of, 132
    permeability of, 132–135
    synthesis of, 132

D

Deoxyribonucleic acid, DNA,
    acid-denaturation of, 144
    bromouracil in, 158
    damage to, 140–163
        measurement of, 140–163
        repair of, 152–156
    drug interaction with, 141–150
    endonuclease action on, 159
    equilibrium dialysis of, 148
    genetic transformation by, 156–157
    melting profile of, 145
    molecular weight of, 160–163
    photoreactivation of, 152–154
    PS formation in, 151–153
    renaturation of, 146
    sedimentation coefficient of, 147
    strand breaks in, 154, 159–163
    sucrose density centrifugation of,
        159–163
    supercoiled, 149–150
    synthesis of, 140–141
    thermal denaturation of, 145–146
    u.v. degradation of, 151–159
    viscosity of, 147–148
"Depression" culture, 73
Dibromohydroxymercurifluoroscein,
        (*see under* mercurochrome)
Difference spectroscopy, 122
Differential light scattering photo-
        meters, 221–223, 246–247
Differential light scattering patterns,
    cell suspensions, from 202–210, 220–
        246
    comparison of, 251–255
    single cells, from, 192–201, 247–250
    small spherical particles, from 189–
        190
    spores, from, 247–250

Differential light scattering techniques, 183–262
  antibiotic susceptibility testing, for, 186, 241–246
  bacterial detection by, 244
  bacterial speciation by, 228–236
  bacterial suspensions, for 194–246
  cell size measurement by, 184
  cellular agglomerates, for, 215, 218–220
  chloroplast measurement by, 184
  coherence requirement in, 203–204
  cuvettes for, 222–224, 226–229
  data representation in, 251–255
  digital computors in, 185
  geometrical foreshortening in, 203, 205–206
  large particles, for, 188
  light sources in, 185, 226–227
  mathematical formulation in, 257, 261
  media pigmentation in, 203, 208–210
  mitochondrial measurement by, 184
  multiple scattering in, 204–205
  non-spherically symmetrical cells, for, 215, 218–220
  photometers for, 220–223, 246–247
  photo-phosphorylation studes, for, 184
  plotting modes in, 226
  polydisperse systems, for, 210–215
  refractive index measurement by, 184
  resonance region particles, for, 188–226
  sample preparation for, 225–226, 246
  scanning range in, 226
  single cells, for, 188–201, 246–250
  small particles, for, 188–190
  spherically symmetrical particles, for, 258–259
  spores, for, 246–250
  suspending media for, 224
Diffraction, 12
Digital computers,
  languages for, 58
  light scattering techniques, in, 185
  mathematical models and, 56–58
  programme for, 56–57
Dihydrostreptomycin (DHSM), 169, 171–173
Dipicolinic acid, (DPA), 98–99

Drugs,
  bacterial adsorption of, 119–123
  bacterial damage by, 97–99, 102–103 106–150
  bacterial permeability to, 106–112
  bacterial resistance to, 106–119
  bacterial viability and, 102–103
  DNA interaction with, 141–150
  L-form sensitivity to, 139–140
  membrane damage by, 131–135
  mucopeptide synthesis and, 131
  mutagenic effects of, 150
  mycoplasma sensitivity to, 140
  protoplast sensitivity to, 138–139
  spheroplast preparation by, 137–138
  spheroplast sensitivity to, 139

E

Electron detector system, 9
Electron gun, 4, 6
Electron lenses, 4, 6
Electron microscope,
  cell size measurement by, 124–125
  imaging systems in, 2–4
  scanning type (*see under* scanning electron microscope)
  transmission type, 3
Electron source, 6, 7
Electron particle counter, 126
Electrophoresis,
  bacteria, of, 121, 123
Empirical curve fitting, 47–49
Endonuclease, 159
Enterobacteriaceae,
  R-factor transfer in, 117
Escherichia coli,
  cold damage in, 99, 104–105
  drug resistance in, 107–109, 113, 115, 116
  ionizing irradiation of, 105–106, 158
  protoplast preparation from, 136–137
  R-factor transfer in, 117–118
  spheroplast preparation from, 136–137
Ethidium, 145
Ethidium bromide, 149
Ethylenediamine tetra-acetic acid, 106–106–9, 137

Excision repair, 152, 154–156
Exponential growth, 49–52

F

Faulkner and Lillie staining method 81–82
Fluorescent antibody technique, 82–83
5-fluorouracil,
spheroplast preparation, for, 138
Fucidin, 107

G

γ-modulation, 29
γ-irradiation,
bacterial damage by, 101
Gallochrome (see under Mercuro-chrome)
Genetic transformation, 156–157
Gentamycin, 245–246
Geometrical foreshortening, 203, 205–206
Giemsa stain, 79, 80
Glutaraldehyde, 97
Gram-negative bacteria,
drug resistance of, 106–110
mucopeptide from, 127
permeability of, 106–110
protoplast preparation from, 136–137
spheroplast preparation from, 107, 137–138
Gram-positive bacteria,
drug resistance of, 110–111
protoplast preparation from, 136
spheroplast preparation from, 137–138
wall lipids in, 110–111
Gram-stain,
membrane permeability to, 134
Graphical methods,
microbiological models, in, 46–55
Griseofulvin synthesis, 43
GTY broth, 67, 71
GYP medium, 67
GYPT medium, 67–69

H

Haemophilus influenzae,
transforming DNA in, 157

HE medium, 67
High vacuum evaporator, 17
Host cell reactivation, 156
Human body louse (see under Pediculus humanus)
Human relapsing fever, 76, 77, 93

I

Immobilizine test, 90–91
Ion etching, 29–30
Ionizing radiation,
bacterial damage by, 101, 105–106

J

Jenner-Romanowski stains, 79

K

Klebsiella sp.,
light scattering patterns from, 232–236
R-factor transfer in, 118
Krajan staining method, 81

L

L-forms,
drug sensitivity of, 135, 139–140
preparation of, 136, 138
β-lactam drugs, 114–115, 138
β-lactamase, 112–116
Laser light scattering photometers, 185, 220–223
Least-square fit method, 53–55
Leishman's stain, 79
Lens aberrations,
electron microscope, in, 12
Leucozyme C,
spheroplast preparation by, 137
Levaditi staining method, 81
Linear graph paper, 49
Lysin test, 91
Lithium chloride,
spheroplast preparation by, 138
Listeria monocytogenes,
protoplast preparation from, 136
Logarithmic death rate, 50
Logarithmic graph paper, 52–53
Ludvig Lorenz scattering theory, 184

Lysostaphin,
  L-form preparation by, 138
  protoplast preparation by, 137
Lysozyme,
  L-form preparation, by, 138
  protoplast preparation by, 136
  spheroplast preparation by, 137

M

Mass balances,
  microbiological models, in, 39–42
Mathematical models, 35–58
  antibiotic production, of, 43
  classification of, 37–39
  computer analysis of, 56–58
  construction of, 36
  continuous culture systems, of, 42–43, 45
  formulation of, 39–41
  graphical methods in, 46–55
  mass balances in, 39–42
  microbiological systems, of, 35–58
  rate expression in, 39–40
  thermal death rate, of, 43–44
  waste treatment plants, of, 42
May-Grünwald stain, 80
Merbromin, (*see under* mercurochrome)
Mercurochrome, 83–84
Methicillin, 99, 112
Methyl violet, 84
Methylene blue, 79
Michaelis-Menten equation, 47, 54–55
Microbiological system models,
  (*see under* mathematical models)
Mie scattering theory, 184
Minimum inhibitory concentration
      (MIC) determination, 244–246
Micrococcus lysodeikticus,
  endonuclease from, 159
  mucopeptide from, 127
  protoplast preparation from, 136
M. radiodurans,
  DNA damage in, 162–163
  genetic transformation in, 156–157
  spheroplast preparation from, 159, 162
Mitochondria,
  light scattering estimation of, 184

Mitomycin C, 141, 144
Mucopeptide,
  cross linking in, 129
  estimation of, 126
  precursors of, 127–128
  synthesis of, 127–131
Muralytic enzymes, 136–138
Mycoplasma sp.,
  drug sensitivity of, 140

N

Nafcillan, 245
Nichols medium, 86
o-nitrophenyl-β-D-galactoside,
      (ONPG), 134–135
Nucleic acids, (*see under* DNA and RNA)

O

Optimization techniques,
  mathematical models, in, 47
Ornithodorus sp.,
  Borrelia sp. vectors, as, 76–77, 86–87, 93

P

Panoptic staining, 80
Pediculus humanus,
  Borrelia sp. vector, as, 76, 77
Penicillin,
  inactivation of, 103, 113–115
  mucopeptide synthesis and, 131
  sporogenisis and, 99
Penicillinase, (*see under* β-lactamase)
PEP medium, 67
Phleomycin, 149
Photoproduct (PS) formation, 150–151, 153
Photoreactivation, (PR), 152–154
Physarum polycephalum,
  morphology of, 23–24
Polymyxins, 135
Polypeptide synthesis,
  drug effect on, 170–172
Polyribonucleotides,
  drug effect on, 144–145
Porfiromycin, 141

Proflavin,
  apurinic acid and, 144
  DNA interaction with, 142, 146, 149
  resistance to, 97
Protein,
  biosynthesis of, 168–173
  damage to, 166–173
  drug binding by, 168
  estimation of, 132
Proteus mirabilis,
  drug resistance of, 109–110
P. morganii,
  light scattering patterns from, 230–231
P. vulgaris,
  light scattering patterns from, 235–236
Protoplasts, (*see under* bacterial proto-plasts)
Pseudomonas sp.,
  cold damage to, 99, 104
Pseudomonas aeruginosa,
  drug resistance in, 108–109, 113
  light scattering patterns from, 241–242
  spheroplast from, 137
Purines,
  leakage of, 132
Puromycin reaction, 167–168
Pyrimidines,
  leakage of, 132

R

Rate expressions,
  mathematical models, in, 39–41
Rayleigh-Gans-Debye approximation, 184, 217–218, 259–261
Recombinational repair, 152–153, 156
Refractive index, 184
Reiter's spirochaete, 82–83
Relapsing fever, 76, 77, 93
Resistance (R) factors, 117–118
Resonance region particles, 188–220
Rhizopus sp.,
  taxonomy of, 20
Rhizopus stolonifer,
  spore germination in, 26, 28
Ribonucleic acid, RNA,
  damage to, 163–166

drug interaction with, 144–145, 164
protein synthesis and, 164–165, 167
synthesis of, 166
RNA polymerase,
  actinomycin D and, 150
Ribosomal sub-units,
  drug sensitivity of, 171–173
Ribosomes,
  damage to, 164–165, 172–173
  isolation of, 164
  protein synthesis in, 164–170
  reconstitution of, 167–168
Ristocetin, 131
Runge-Kutta methods, 56

S

Saccharomyces cerevisiae,
  morphology of, 25, 27–28
Salmonella anatum,
  damage repair in, 119
S. typhi,
  cold shock in, 99
  R-factor transfer in, 117–118
S. typhimurium,
  damage repair in, 119
Sarcina lutea,
  protoplast from, 136
Scanning electron microscope, 2–13
  apertures in, 3–4, 6
  astigmator in, 4, 6
  cathode ray tubes in, 11–12
  chopping coils in, 4, 6–7
  contrast formation in, 7–11
  depth of focus in, 13
  electron gun in, 4, 6
  electron lenses in, 4, 6
  electron optical column in, 4–7
  imaging system in, 2–4
  lens aberrations in, 12
  magnification in, 13
  primary electron beam in, 7, 8
  record display unit in, 11–12
  resolution in, 13
  scanning coils in, 4, 6
  secondary electron detector system in, 8, 9
  signal detection in, 7–11
  vacuum system for, 7

Scanning electron microscopy,
  ancillary techniques to, 28–30
  applications of, 18–28
  instruments for, (*see under* scanning electron microscope)
  microbial morphology and, 18–28
  specimen preparation for, 13–18
Scanning transmission electron microscopy, 28
Semilogarithmic graph paper, 49–52
Serratia marscesens,
  light scattering patterns from, 228, 230
Shigella sonnei,
  u.v. damage in, 105
Silver impregnation methods, 81–82
Simpson's rule, 56
Simulation languages, 58
Single particle light scattering photometer, 246–247
Specimen stubs,
  electron microscopy, for, 15–16
Spherical aberration, 12
Spermine, 148–149
Spheroplasts, (*see under* bacterial spheroplasts)
Spirillum gracile,
  growth veil in, 68
Spirochaeta sp.,
  classification of, 61–62
  colony growth of, 68, 71
  DNA content of, 62
  growth media for, 67–71
  isolation of, 61, 63–68
  metabolism of, 61–62, 69–71
  size of, 62
  storage of, 71–73
Spirochaeta aurantia, 61–62, 66–67, 71
S. litoralis, 62–65, 69–70, 73
S. plicatilis, 62
S. stenostrepta, 62–64, 67–69
S. zuelzerae, 61–62, 70
Spores, (*see under* bacterial spores)
Spray apertures, 3–4, 6
Staphylococci sp.,
  methicillin resistance in, 112
Staphylococcus aureus,
  light scattering patterns from, 194, 238–239, 241–243, 245
  mucopeptide estimation in, 127

Staph. epidermidis,
  light scattering patterns from, 189, 225, 247–248
"Stereoscan" scanning electron microscope, 5
Strand breaks,
  DNA, in, 159–163
Streptococcus faecalis,
  protoplast from, 136
S. faecium,
  protoplast from, 136
S. lactis,
  light scattering patterns from, 228, 230
Streptomyces griseus,
  muralytic enzyme from, 136
Streptomycin,
  inactivation of, 116
  ribosomal sensitivity to, 169–173
Sulphonamides, 103
Sulphones, 103
SZ medium, 67, 70

T

Tetrazolium dyes, 134
Thermal death,
  mathematical model of, 43–44
Three-dimensional analysis,
  electron microscope and, 28–29
Ticks, (*see under Ornithodorus* sp.)
N-tolyl-α-naphthyl-amino-β-sulphonic acid, (TNS), 134
Transforming DNA, 156–157
Transmission electron microscope, 3
Transpeptidation, 130
Trapezium rule, 56
Treponema zuelzerae, (*see under Spirochaeta zuelzerae*)
Triphenylmethane dyes, 141
2,3,5-triphenyl tetrazolium bromide, 134
2,3,5-triphenyl tetrazolium chloride, 134
Tris buffer, 137
Turbidimetric methods, 124–125

U

UDP—acetyl muramyl peptides, 131

U.V. irradiation,
  bacterial damage by, 100–101, 105, 150–159

V

Vancomycin,
  E. coli sensitivity to, 109
  L-form preparation for, 138
  mucopeptide synthesis and, 131
Vincent's angina, 77

W

Waste treatment plant,
  mathematical model of, 42

Witnauer-Sherr cuvette, 222, 227–229
Wolman and Wolman medium, 84, 86
Wright's stain, 79–80

X

Xenodiagnosis, 93
X-rays,
  bacterial damage by, 101
  electron microscope, in, 11

Z

Ziehl-Neelsen carbol fuchsin dye, 78–79